American Book Company's

PASSING THE

Georgia High School Graduation Test

in

Science

Written to GPS Standards

Liz Thompson
Michelle Gunter

American Book Company
PO Box 2638
Woodstock, GA 30188-1383
Toll Free: 1 (888) 264-5877   Phone: (770) 928-2834
Fax: (770) 928-7483 Toll Free Fax 1 (866) 827-3240
Web site: www.americanbookcompany.com

ACKNOWLEDGEMENTS

The authors would like to gratefully acknowledge the formatting and technical contributions of Becky Wright.

We also want to thank Mary Stoddard for her expertise in developing the graphics for this book.

A special thanks to Marsha Torrens for her editing assistance.

This product/publication includes images from CorelDRAW 9 and 11 which are protected by the copyright laws of the United States, Canada, and elsewhere. Used under license.

TABLE OF CONTENTS

Chapter 7: Nuclear Processes   155

Chapter 8: Structure, Properties and Bonding of Elements   167

Chapter 9: Matter and Energy   197

Preface

The Georgia High School Graduation Test in Science will help students who are learning or reviewing material for the Georgia test that is now required for earning a high school diploma. **The materials in this book are based on the Georgia Performance Standards as published by the Georgia Department of Education.**

This book contains several sections. These sections are as follows: 1) General information about the book; 2) A Diagnostic Test and Evaluation Chart; 3) Chapters that teach the concepts and skills that improve readiness for Georgia High School Graduation Test in Science; 4) Two Post Tests. Answers to the tests are in a separate manual. The answer manual also contains a Chart of Standards for teachers to make a more precise diagnosis of student needs and assignments.

We welcome comments and suggestions about the book. Please contact us a

American Book Company
PO Box 2638
Woodstock, GA 30188-1383

Toll Free: 1 (888) 264-5877
Phone: (770) 928-2834
Fax: (770) 928-7483
Web site: www.americanbookcompany.com

About the Authors

Liz A. Thompson holds a B.S. in Chemistry and an M.S. in Analytical Chemistry, both from the Georgia Institute of Technology. Research conducted as both an undergraduate and graduate student focused on the creation and fabrication of sensors based on conducting polymers and biomolecules. Post graduate experience includes work in radioanalytical chemistry. Her publications include several articles in respected scientific journals, as well as partial authorship of the textbook *Radioanalytical Chemistry* (2007). At every educational level, Mrs. Thompson has enjoyed teaching, tutoring and mentoring students in the study of science.

Michelle Gunter graduated from Kennesaw State University in Kennesaw, Georgia with a B.S. in Secondary Biology Education. She is a certified teacher in the field of Biology in the state of Georgia. She has three years experience in high school science classrooms. She has nine years experience in biology and biological systems. She has won awards for her research in the field of aquatic toxicology. Mrs. Gunter enjoys teaching students of all ages, the wonders of the natural world.

Preface

Diagnostic Test

Science Facts and Formulas

Some of the questions in this test require you to solve problems. This page contains all the basic facts and formulas you will need to solve those problems. Some questions may require information from the Periodic Table. You may refer to these pages as often as you wish while you take the test.

Basic Facts

Acceleration due to gravity = 9.8 meters/second/second (9.8m/s^2)

Weight = mass (m) $\times$ Acceleration due to gravity (g)   (W = mg)

Density = Mass/Volume

Volume of a Rectangular Solid = Length $\times$ Width $\times$ Height

1 newton = 1 kilogram·meter/second/second

1 joule = 1 newton·meter

1 watt = 1 newton·meter/second = 1 joule/second

Motion

Velocity = distance/time $v = \dfrac{d}{t}$

Acceleration = Change in Velocity/Time Elapsed $a = \dfrac{v_f - v_i}{t}$

Force, Mechanical Advantage, Power, Work

Force = Mass $\times$ Acceleration   (F = ma)

Mechanical Average

Actual Mechanical Advantage $\left(AMA = \dfrac{F_R}{F_E} \right),$

where F_R is Force due to resistance and F_E is Force due to effort.

Ideal Mechanical Advantage $\left(IMA = \dfrac{\text{Effort Length}}{\text{Resistance Length}} \right)$

Power = Work/Time $\left(P = \dfrac{w}{t} \right)$

Work = Force $\times$ Distance   (W = Fd)

Electricity

Voltage = Current $\times$ Resistance (V = IR)

Go On

PERIODIC TABLE

KEY

atomic number - 5
atomic symbol - **B**
name of element - Boron
atomic weight - 10.811
electron arrangement - 2,3

PERIOD	GROUP 1 (Ia)	2 (IIa)	3	4	5	6	7	8	9	10	11	12	13 (IIIa)	14 (IVa)	15 (Va)	16 (VIa)	17 (VIIa)	18 (VIIIa)
1	1 **H** Hydrogen 1.00797 1																	2 **He** Helium 4.0026 2
2	3 **Li** Lithium 6.941 2,1	4 **Be** Beryllium 9.0122 2,2											5 **B** Boron 10.811 2,3	6 **C** Carbon 12.011 2,4	7 **N** Nitrogen 14.0067 2,5	8 **O** Oxygen 15.9994 2,6	9 **F** Fluorine 18.998 2,7	10 **Ne** Neon 20.183 2,8
3	11 **Na** Sodium 22.9898 2,8,1	12 **Mg** Magnesium 24.312 2,8,2											13 **Al** Aluminum 26.9815 2,8,3	14 **Si** Silicon 28.086 2,8,4	15 **P** Phosphorus 30.9738 2,8,5	16 **S** Sulfur 32.064 2,8,6	17 **Cl** Chlorine 35.453 2,8,7	18 **Ar** Argon 39.948 2,8,8
4	19 **K** Potassium 39.102 2,8,8,1	20 **Ca** Calcium 40.08 2,8,8,2	21 **Sc** Scandium 44.956 2,8,9,2	22 **Ti** Titanium 47.90 2,8,10,2	23 **V** Vanadium 50.942 2,8,11,2	24 **Cr** Chromium 51.996 2,8,13,1	25 **Mn** Manganese 54.9380 2,8,13,2	26 **Fe** Iron 55.847 2,8,14,2	27 **Co** Cobalt 58.9332 2,8,15,2	28 **Ni** Nickel 58.71 2,8,16,2	29 **Cu** Copper 63.546 2,8,18,1	30 **Zn** Zinc 65.37 2,8,18,2	31 **Ga** Gallium 69.72 2,8,18,3	32 **Ge** Germanium 72.59 2,8,18,4	33 **As** Arsenic 74.9216 2,8,18,5	34 **Se** Selenium 78.96 2,8,18,6	35 **Br** Bromine 79.904 2,8,18,7	36 **Kr** Krypton 83.80 2,8,18,8
5	37 **Rb** Rubidium 85.47 2,8,18,8,1	38 **Sr** Strontium 88.905 2,8,18,8,2	39 **Y** Yttrium 88.905 2,8,18,9,2	40 **Zr** Zirconium 91.22 2,8,18,10,2	41 **Nb** Niobium 92.906 2,8,18,12,1	42 **Mo** Molybdenum 95.94 2,8,18,13,1	43 **Tc** Technetium (97) 2,8,18,13,2	44 **Ru** Ruthenium 101.07 2,8,18,15,1	45 **Rh** Rhodium 102.905 2,8,18,16,1	46 **Pd** Palladium 106.4 2,8,18,18,0	47 **Ag** Silver 107.868 2,8,18,18,1	48 **Cd** Cadmium 112.40 2,8,18,18,2	49 **In** Indium 114.82 2,8,18,18,3	50 **Sn** Tin 118.69 2,8,18,18,4	51 **Sb** Antimony 121.75 2,8,18,18,5	52 **Te** Tellurium 127.60 2,8,18,18,6	53 **I** Iodine 126.9045 2,8,18,18,7	54 **Xe** Xenon 131.30 2,8,18,18,8
6	55 **Cs** Cesium 132.905 2,8,18,18,8,1	56 **Ba** Barium 137.34 2,8,18,18,8,2	57 - 71 Lanthanide Series	72 **Hf** Hafnium 178.49 2,8,18,32,10,2	73 **Ta** Tantalum 180.9488 2,8,18,32,11,2	74 **W** Tungsten 183.85 2,8,18,32,12,2	75 **Re** Rhenium 186.2 2,8,18,32,13,2	76 **Os** Osmium 190.2 2,8,18,32,14,2	77 **Ir** Iridium 192.2 2,8,18,32,15,2	78 **Pt** Platinum 195.09 2,8,18,32,16,2	79 **Au** Gold 196.967 2,8,18,32,18,1	80 **Hg** Mercury 200.59 2,8,18,32,18,2	81 **Tl** Thallium 204.37 2,8,18,32,18,3	82 **Pb** Lead 207.19 2,8,18,32,18,4	83 **Bi** Bismuth 208.9806 2,8,18,32,18,5	84 **Po** Polonium (209) 2,8,18,32,18,6	85 **At** Astatine (210) 2,8,18,32,18,7	86 **Rn** Radon (222) 2,8,18,32,18,8
7	87 **Fr** Francium (223) 2,8,18,32,18,8,1	88 **Ra** Radium (226) 2,8,18,32,18,8,2	89 - 103 Actinide Series	104	105													

Go On

Diagnostic Test

Refer to the formula sheet and Periodic Table on pages 1 and 2 as you take this test.

Use the graphic below to answer the following question.

	G	g
G	GG	Gg
g	Gg	gg

1 In this hybrid cross of two pea plants, G represents a gene for green peas, and g represents a gene for yellow peas. What percent of the phenotype of the offspring could be yellow? SB2c

A 25% **B** 50% **C** 75% **D** 100%

2 A normal DNA base sequence is shown below. Identify the DNA sequence that has undergone an inversion mutation. SB2d

AAT TCG GGT CGA ATT

A AAT GGT CGA ATT **C** AAT TCG TGG CGA ATT

B AAT TCG TCG GGT CGA ATT **D** TTA AGC ACC GCT TAA

3 Pollen grains produced by a particular pine tree contain 25 chromosomes. When the pollen grain comes into contact with a female embryo, the resulting seed contains 50 chromosomes. What type of reproduction is this? SB2e

A sexual **B** asexual **C** haploid **D** abiotic

4 Which of the following situations would require the most force? SPS8b

A sliding a 50 pound box initially at rest over a distance of 5 feet

B sliding a 50 pound box already in motion over a distance of 5 feet

C rolling a 50 pound box over a distance of 5 feet

D All the above would require equal force.

Go On

5 At standard temperature and pressure, a 5 gram sample of powdered iron will react more quickly with dilute hydrochloric acid than a 5 gram sheet of hammered iron. Why is this?   SPS6a, 6b

   A Because the iron sheet is denser than the iron powder.

   B Because the iron powder has more surface area exposed to the acid than the iron sheet.

   C Because the iron sheet has more surface area exposed to the acid than the iron powder.

   D Because the iron sheet is less dense than the iron powder.

6 Which of the following illustrates active transport?   SB1a

W.
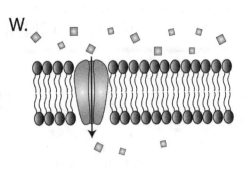

X.
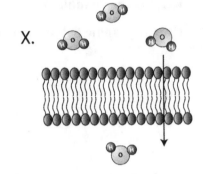

Y.
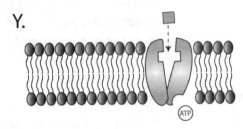

Z.
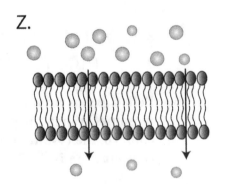

   A Image W

   B Image X

   C Image Y

   D Image Z

Go On

7 What process does the following description refer to: "a wet sidewalk begins to steam in the Sun after a spring shower." *SPS7d*

A melting

B sublimation

C evaporation

D fumigation

8 Which of the following is the best example of maintaining homeostasis? *SB1a*

A a horse sweating after a long ride

B a frog croaking to attract a mate

C a lizard changing colors to match its background

D worker ants protecting the queen

9 A refrigerator magnet is a permanent magnet, often made of strontium ferrite ($SrFe_{12}O_{19}$). If you place a refrigerator magnet on an electric toaster and it does not stick, you can draw several conclusions. Which one would NOT be correct? *SPS10c*

A The magnet has been de-magnetized.

B The surface of the toaster does not contain enough metal for a magnet to attract it.

C The magnet has recently been dropped or heated.

D The electrical field of the toaster is cancelling out the magnetic field of the magnet.

10 If a human somatic cell contains 46 chromosomes, how many chromosomes does a human reproductive cell contain? *SB2c*

A 46

B 23

C 92

D 12

11 The organism pictured below is usually associated with what type of species interaction? *SB4a*

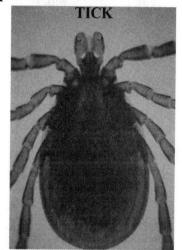

TICK

A mutualistic species

B commensalistic

C parasitic

D predator/prey

Go On

12 Fig. 1 shows a graduated cylinder that contains 25 ml of water. The mass of the cylinder and water is 68.0 g. Fig. 2 shows the same cylinder after a small stone was lowered into the cylinder. The water level rose to the 30.0 ml mark, and the mass of the cylinder, water and stone was 78.0 g. Select the density of the small stone.

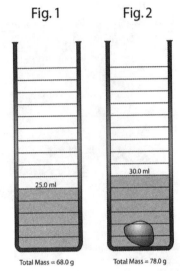

Fig. 1   Fig. 2

30.0 ml

25.0 ml

Total Mass = 68.0 g   Total Mass = 78.0 g

A   2.00 g/ml

B   10.0 g

C   0.50 ml/g

D   5.00 ml

13 Leon uses a screwdriver to open a can of paint. What simple machine is Leon using?

A   lever

B   wedge

C   resistance force

D   fulcrum

14 The macromolecule shown in the diagram below could be responsible for facilitating which cellular process?

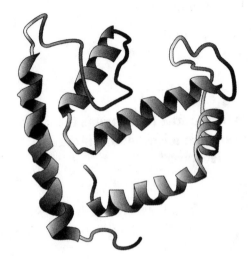

A   transcription

B   active transport

C   movement

D   osmosis

Go On

15 A molecule of methane consists of one carbon atom bound to four hydrogen atoms. How do these four covalent bonds create a chemically stable compound? SPS1b

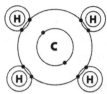

A The four C-H bonds give the carbon atom a full valence shell of eight electrons and each hydrogen atom a full valence shell of 2 electrons.

B The four C-H bonds give the carbon atom a full valence shell of ten electrons and each hydrogen atom a full valence shell of 2 electrons.

C The four C-H bonds are highly polar, which allows the methane molecule to engage in hydrogen bonding.

D The four C-H bonds are non-polar, which allows the methane molecule to engage in hydrogen bonding.

16 Examine the cladogram below and determine the most closely related organisms. SB3c, SB5b

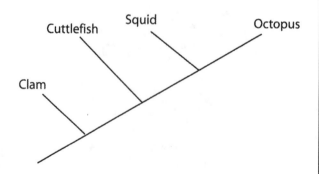

A clam and octopus

B cuttlefish and octopus

C squid and octopus

D clam and squid

17 Which of the following substances is the least chemically reactive? SPS4a

A H^+

B OH^-

C O^{2-}

D H_2O

18 Which of the following represents RNA in the figure below? SB2a

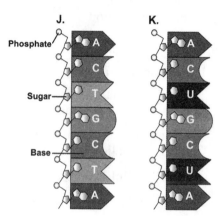

A J only

B both J and K

C K only

D neither J nor K

19 This diagram shows which process? SB2b

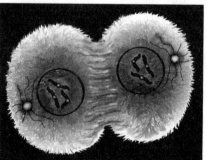

A anaphase

B metaphase

C cytokinesis

D interphase

Go On

20 A solution of salt in water is prepared. Under which conditions will additional salt dissolve quickest? *SPS6a*

   A   high temperature and high salt concentration

   B   high temperature and low salt concentration

   C   low temperature and low salt concentration

   D   low temperature and high salt concentration

21 The primary function of carbohydrates within a cell is to *SB1c*

   A   provide the main structural components of the cell membrane.

   B   regulate movement of materials into and out of cells.

   C   provide cellular energy.

   D   store cellular information.

22 The elements in the halogen family *SPS4b*

   A   need to give up one electron to become stable.

   B   need to gain one electron to become stable.

   C   are inert.

   D   are reactive metals.

23 Identify the main difference between plants and animals. *SB3b*

   A   Plants are made of cells while animals are not.

   B   Plants are producers while animals are consumers.

   C   Plants are green while animals are multicolored.

   D   Plants have roots while animals do not.

24 Trilobites are a class of extinct arthropods that flourished during the Cambrian period of the Paleozoic era. The Carboniferous period left behind huge fields of coal beds in Europe. During the Devonian period, the first fish evolved legs and started to walk on land as amphibians. The beginning of the Silurian period was marked by a mass extinction that destroyed nearly 60% of marine species. Given the following diagram, place these periods in order from oldest to most recent. *SB5c*

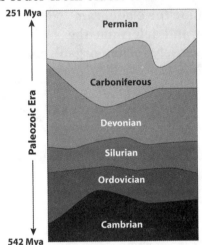

   A   Carboniferous, Devonian, Silurian, Cambrian

   B   Cambrian, Silurian, Devonian, Carboniferous

   C   Cambrian, Devonian, Silurian, Carboniferous

   D   Carboniferous, Silurian, Devonian, Cambrian

Go On

25 A sound wave will travel MOST quickly in which of the following media? ^SPS9e^

A	sand	**C**	water
B	granite	**D**	air

26 A small sailboat encounters a storm in the Atlantic Ocean. The boat sinks leaving its two crew members stranded in a life boat. After several days adrift, the two men begin to get dehydrated. Can the men survive until rescue by drinking ocean water? Why or why not? ^SB1d^

A Yes, the ocean water contains some water and will allow the men to survive.

B No, the high salt concentration of the ocean water will cause water to move out of the men's body and into the water in their gut.

C Yes, the high salt concentration of ocean water will cause salt to diffuse into the men's body and make them retain more water.

D No, ocean water contains toxins released by humans that become poisons when ingested.

Use the graph below to answer question 27.

Work vs Distance

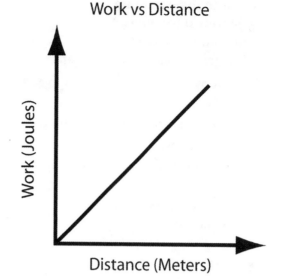

27 The slope of the graph would have units of ^SPS8a^

A newtons.

B watts.

C joules.

D seconds.

28 Select the product of radioactive decay that has the greatest ability to penetrate matter. ^SPS3a^

A alpha particles

B beta particles

C gamma rays

D neutrons

Go On

29 Genetic engineering is increasingly used to improve agricultural products. Which of the following is NOT a possible result of the genetic alteration of crops?   SB2f

    A Crops can be made resistant to certain diseases.

    B Crops can be made that will never die.

    C Crops can be made resistant to herbicides.

    D Increased crop yields can be achieved.

30 The diagram of a wave indicates two important properties of a wave: its wavelength and amplitude. Wavelength is inversely related to frequency: a longer wavelength indicates a lower frequency. Amplitude is proportional to the intensity of the energy that the wave can impart to matter: a greater amplitude indicates a greater intensity. Consider the following situation: Wave A has a wavelength 5λ and an amplitude 2γ, while Wave B has a wavelength 3λ and an amplitude 4γ. Which statement best describes these two waves?   SPS9b

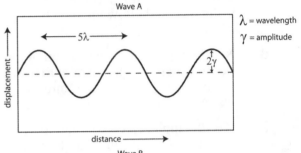

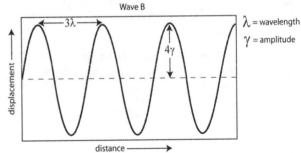

    A Wave A has a lower frequency and greater intensity than Wave B.

    B Wave A has a higher frequency and greater intensity than Wave B.

    C Wave A has a higher frequency and lower intensity than Wave B.

    D Wave A has a lower frequency and lower intensity than Wave B.

Go On

31 Samples of liquid nitrogen, gaseous nitrogen and a nitrogen plasma are being examined in physical science lab. Which sample (or samples) will turn out to be highly compressible? SPS5a, SPS5b

   A   gas only

   B   liquid only

   C   plasma and gas only

   D   plasma, liquid and gas only

32 Which of the following best describes a magnetic field? SPS10c

   A   The visible circles of force that surround magnets.

   B   The invisible lines of force between two poles of a magnet.

   C   A field of energy that is energized by metal objects.

   D   A field through which electricity cannot readily flow.

Arctic aquatic ecosystems can be very delicate. The US Fish and Game Service monitors the stocks of many economically important fish populations. One of these fish is the Alaskan Pollock. The population of these fish has decreased significantly due to overfishing. The result is a destabilization of the aquatic ecosystem of which the Alaskan Pollock is a member. The food web below shows the relationships between plants and animals in this ecosystem.

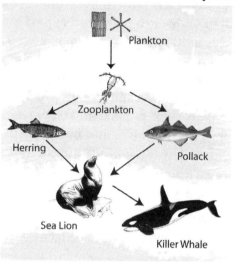

33 What is the nature of the relationship between the herring and the pollack? SB4b

   A   They are predator and prey.

   B   They are producers.

   C   They are primary consumers.

   D   They are competitors.

Go On

34 Select the situation that will result in the greatest gravitational force between two bodies.   SPS8c

  A   large combined mass and small distance apart

  B   large combined mass and great distance apart

  C   small combined mass and great distance apart

  D   small combined mass and small distance apart

35 The tundra is located near the north and south poles and experiences light rainfall. Summer temperatures average only 1°C. The subsoil of the tundra is permanently frozen. Grasses, mosses and lichens are present. Animals such as polar bears, caribou, hares, arctic wolves and birds live in the tundra. The amount of rainfall and temperature of this ecosystem are   SB4a

  A   biotic factors.

  B   abiotic factors.

  C   both biotic and abiotic factors.

  D   factors affecting symbiosis.

36 The diagram at right shows a ball at the top of a ramp. Select the statement that correctly describes the changes to the ball's kinetic energy (KE) and gravitation potential energy (PE) as it rolls down the ramp.   SPS7a

  A   KE and PE both decrease.

  B   KE and PE both increase.

  C   KE decreases and PE increases.

  D   KE increases and PE decreases.

37 One light bulb is removed from a string of 50 lights that are plugged in to a wall outlet. The other 49 bulbs remain lit. What does this tell you about how the bulbs are wired?   SPS10b

  A   The bulbs are wired in a series circuit.

  B   The bulbs are wired in a parallel circuit.

  C   There are too many leads on the circuit.

  D   More bulbs will burn out soon.

38 Which of the following correctly places the phases of water in order from the most dense to the least dense?   SPS5a

  A   solid, liquid, gas, plasma

  B   plasma, gas, liquid, solid

  C   liquid, solid, gas, plasma

  D   liquid, gas, plasma, solid

Go On

39 A state of matter that has no definite shape or volume is a(n) SPS5a

   A liquid.

   B solid.

   C mixture.

   D gas.

40 Magnesium (Mg) loses two electrons to form magnesium ions. Chlorine (Cl) gains one electron to form chloride ions. Select the correct formula for magnesium chloride. SPS2b

   A $MgCl$

   B Mg_2Cl

   C $MgCl_2$

   D Mg_2Cl_2

41 As illustrated in the diagram below, Carl investigated the change of mass during a chemical reaction. He massed a plastic bottle that contained 50 mL of water, a balloon and two seltzer tablets. The total mass of his experimental materials was 200g. Carl put the seltzer tablets inside the balloon and pulled the balloon over the neck of the bottle. He shook the balloon so the seltzer tablets fell into the water. Carl observed the tablets fizzing and the balloon expanding. Carl again massed his apparatus after the fizzing and the expansion of the balloon stopped. SPS2d

If the combined mass of the two seltzer tablets before they were dropped into the water was 5 g, select the mass of Carl's experimental materials at the end of his investigation.

   A 195 g

   B between 195 g and 200 g

   C 200 g

   D more than 200 g

42 The half-life of iodine-133 is 21 hours. How much iodine-133 would remain after 63 hours? SPS3c

   A one quarter

   B one-third

   C one-eighth

   D one-half

Go On

43 Which of the following is an element?   SPS1a

A   water

B   gold

C   sugar

D   aluminum oxide

44 Determine the number of neutrons that most copper atoms contain.   SPS1a

29
Cu
Copper
63.546
2,8,18,1

A   29   C   64

B   35   D   34

45 NaCl and H_2O are two compounds that bond differently. One bonds ionically; the other bonds covalently. Which of the following correctly represents the bonding of the ionic compound?   SPS1b

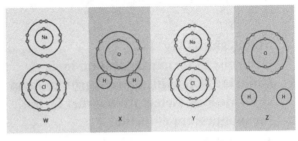

A   diagram W

B   diagram X

C   diagram Y

D   diagram Z

46 Which kingdom listed below contains organisms that do not have a cell wall?   SB3b

A   Plantae

B   Archaebacteria

C   Fungi

D   Animalia

Go On

47 The atomic number of beryllium is 4. Select the number of electrons a beryllium atom will gain or lose when it forms a beryllium ion.   SPS1a

A   gain 2

B   gain 4

C   lose 2

D   lose 4

48 What do sodium, magnesium, sulfur and chlorine all have in common?   SPS4a

A   They have the same number of valence electrons.

B   They are all Period 3 elements.

C   They all decay by alpha emission.

D   They are all Group 17 elements.

49 Identify the graph that correctly shows the effect on the current (I) flowing through a static 5-ohm resistor when the voltage (V) across the resistor is gradually increased.   SPS10b

A.

C.
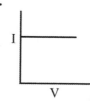

B.

D.

50 Fusion describes the process of   SPS3b

A   two small atoms joining together to produce one larger atom.

B   several small atoms joining together to produce one or more larger atoms.

C   several smaller atoms joining together to form a macromolecule.

D   two large atoms breaking apart to form smaller atoms.

51 No water is available in the area surrounding a plant cell. Which of the following is likely to happen if the plant cell is left this way for 24 hours?   SB2e

A   The plant cell will remain the same because of its impermeable cell wall.

B   The plant cell will expand with water and burst.

C   The plant cell will increase its rate of photosynthesis.

D   The plant cell will undergo plasmolysis.

52 Earthquakes produce seismic waves, which deform the ground surrounding the epicenter of the earthquake and radiate outwards. These waves get weaker the farther they get from the epicenter. Why is this?   SPS9a

A   The energy of the wave gets dispersed through its interaction with matter.

B   The energy of the wave disappears a certain distance from the epicenter.

C   The wave can only travel as far as its frequency will allow it to.

D   The wave only has a limited amount of time to exist, as defined by its period.

Go On

53 The African savanna has a wide range of highly specialized plants and animals which depend on each other to keep the environment in balance. In many parts of the savanna, the African people have begun to graze their livestock. What is the likely outcome of this activity? *SB4d*

A The savanna grasses will grow more quickly as they are eaten, so the area of the savanna will increase.

B The top consumers will leave the area, as there are no more animals to eat.

C The grasses will be diminished and will cease to hold water into the soil, so the savanna could convert to a desert biome.

D The loss of vegetation will cause groundwater to overflow, so the savannah biome will convert to a flooded grassland.

54 The Georgia State sport fish is the largemouth bass (*Micorpterus salmoides*). The adult largemouth bass is a top predator in its ecosystem. What trophic level does this fish belong in? *SB4b*

A producer

B primary consumer

C secondary consumer

D tertiary consumer

55 Given the following DNA strand, what is the correct arrangement of the complementary strand? *SB2a, SB2b*

– TTC AGT ACA –

A – AAG TCA TGG –

B – AAG TCA TGT –

C – AAG UCA UGU –

D – AAG UCA UGU –

56 When a neutral metal sphere is charged by contact with a positively charged glass rod, the sphere *SPS10a*

A loses electrons.

B loses protons.

C gains electrons.

D gains protons.

57 During his voyage aboard the HMS Beagle, Charles Darwin visited many places. Which place was of particular interest in developing his theory of evolution? *SB5a*

A The Galapagos Islands

B Brazil

C Cambridge

D Australia

58 Which of the following is true of a compound? *SPS2c*

A A compound must consist of covalently bound atoms.

B A compound must consist of ionically bound atoms.

C A compound must contain atoms of more than one element.

D A compound cannot remain bound when dissolved in a solvent.

Go On

59 Angiosperms are the most successful plants on Earth and have dominated the Earth's plant life for the past 65 million years. They can live almost anywhere on land and do not need to be near standing water to reproduce. Which of the following adaptations of angiosperms has allowed them to become fully adapted to life on land? *SB4e*

   A   seeds contained within protective fruits

   B   male and female parts contained in separate flowers

   C   less specialized xylem and phloem that require less energy from the plant to maintain function

   D   very small leaves that reduce water loss in the plant

60 Which of the following is not a strong acid? *SPS6d*

   A   hydrochloric acid

   B   sulfuric acid

   C   acetic acid

   D   nitric acid

61 Carbonated soda has carbon dioxide gas dissolved in the liquid to give it "fizz." Which of the following would be the best method of removing the carbon dioxide from the soda? *SPS6c*

   A   filtering the soda through a sieve

   B   increasing the pressure on the soda

   C   raising the temperature of the soda

   D   exposing the soda to an electromagnet

62 The leaves of a houseplant will turn toward a sunny window. This is an example of what behavior? *SB4e*

   A   photosynthesis

   B   gravity

   C   homeostasis

   D   phototropism

63 The Doppler effect results in the listener hearing *SPS9f*

   A   increased loudness.

   B   destructive interference.

   C   increased pitch.

   D   better sound quality.

Go On

Refer to the portion of the Periodic Table below to answer the question that follows.

11 Na Sodium 22.9898 2,8,1	12 Mg Magnesium 24.305 2,8,2	13 Al Aluminum 26.98154 2,8,3	14 Si Silicon 28.0855 2,8,4	15 P Phosphorus 30.97376 2,8,5	16 S Sulfur 32.06 2,8,6	17 Cl Chlorine 35.453 2,8,7	18 Ar Argon 39.948 2,8,8

64 Which element in this group would be the least likely to be chemically reactive?   SPS4b

   A sodium   **C** chlorine

   B silicon   **D** argon

Use this information to answer question 65.

Examine the food chains below.

plankton → herring → salmon

aquatic plants → tilapia

plankton → mollusks → small fish → tuna

65 Salmon, tilapia and tuna are three types of fish often raised by aquaculture for human consumption. Using your knowledge of human environmental impact, food chains and nutrient cycles, determine the most ecologically friendly fish to eat.   SB4d

   A salmon

   B tilapia

   C tuna

   D All three are equally ecologically friendly.

Go On

66 Energy is not destroyed, but rather converted from one form to another. Describe the conversion of energy in the following process: A power reactor utilizes the process of uranium fission to produce electricity. *SPS3d, SPS7a*

A nuclear to electrical

B nuclear to thermal to electrical

C nuclear to mechanical to thermal to electrical

D nuclear to thermal to mechanical to electrical

67 African Grey parrots (*Psittacus erithacus*) are well known for their ability to mimic human speech. Hand raised birds often have larger vocabularies and a better understanding of language than their wild caught counterparts. If a bird is caught in the wild as an adult bird, it can develop the ability to speak, but it does so at a slower rate. What does this suggest about how parrots develop the ability to speak? *SB4f*

A It is an innate behavior.

B It is a learned behavior.

C It is a diurnal behavior.

D It is a nocturnal behavior.

68 A landscaper crossed a tall silver maple tree with another tall silver maple tree. She noticed that 78% of the maples were tall and 22% were short. These results indicate that the allele for shortness is *SB2c*

A dominant.

B recessive.

C co-dominant.

D incompletely dominant.

69 The following figure describes the molecular motion of a sample of matter. Which of the following can you conclude is NOT the identity of the sample? *SPS7b, d*

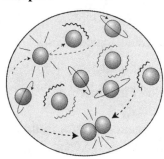

A hydrogen gas

B iron ore

C superheated steam

D liquid nitrogen

70 A skier traveling at 30.0 m/s falls and comes to rest 10.0 seconds later. What is her average acceleration? *SPS8a*

A 300 m/s^2 C -3.00 m/s^2

B 3.00 m/s^2 D -300 m/s^2

71 Scientists discovered a new species of cricket in the North Georgia Mountains. The new cricket is shown in Figure A. To determine the classification of the cricket, they compared it to three other species of cricket found above ground in the nearby area. All four cricket species are shown below. Based on the physical structure, which cricket is MOST related to the new species of cricket? *SB5b, d*

A. Cricket A is not visibly related to crickets B, C or D.

B. cricket B

C. cricket C

D. cricket D

Go On

72 A light beam strikes a mirror at a 30° angle to the plane of the mirror. What is the name of the angle formed when the light first hits the surface? SPS9d

A   angle of refraction

B   transverse angle

C   angle of reflection

D   angle of incidence

73 The chain reaction in a fission-powered nuclear reactor is mediated by control rods. The control rods prevent the chain reaction from proceeding too quickly and producing too much heat. Which statement best describes how control rods mediate the chain reaction? SPS3b, d

A   The control rods absorb neutrons produced by the joining of small atoms.

B   The control rods absorb neutrons produced by the splitting of large atoms.

C   The control rods absorb electrons produced by the joining of small atoms.

D   The control rods absorb electrons produced by the splitting of large atoms.

Use the following information to help you answer question 74.

Barth Syndrome is a name for a genetic disorder that affects individuals on the cellular level. Individuals affected with this disorder have mitochondria that fail to function properly. As a result, children with Barth Syndrome have delayed growth and are below average in weight and height. All muscles within the body have a reduced ability to produce energy. A weak heart, along with weakness in other skeletal muscles, is one symptom of this disease. Another symptom of the disease is increased susceptibility to infection.

74 The mitochondria do not function properly in people with Barth Syndrome because the mutated gene alters or inhibits the production of what biomolecule? SB1c, SB2b

A   nitrogenous base

B   protein

C   ribosome

D   lipid

75 Cellular respiration is to the mitochondria as photosynthesis is to the SB1a, 3a

A   chloroplast

B   Golgi apparatus

C   cytoplasm

D   vacuole

Go On

76 One class of biological molecules consists of proteins that function to speed up biochemical reactions. What are these called?   SB1b

A   carbohydrates

B   co-factors

C   enzymes

D   co-enzymes

77 What number should precede O_2 in the chemical equation below in order for the equation to be balanced?   SPS2e

$$H_2O_2\ (l)\ \rightarrow\ H_2O\ (l) + \underline{\quad}\ O_2\ (g)$$

A   1/2

B   2

C   3

D   4

78 DNA is largely made up of   SB1c, 2a

A   sugars and phosphates.

B   nitrogen and salt.

C   bacteria.

D   water and oxygen.

79 The process shown in the diagram below   SB2b

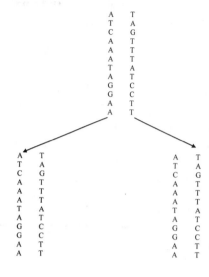

A   is transcription.

B   is the final process in the assembly of a protein.

C   is replication.

D   occurs on the surface of the ribosome.

80 The image here shows the landscape left after a glacier retreats. Which type of succession enables plants to once again grow on the rocky landscape?   SB4c

A   primary succession

B   secondary succession

C   aquatic succession

D   glaciation

EVALUATION CHART

GEORGIA HIGH SCHOOL GRADUATION DIAGNOSTIC TEST

Directions: On the following chart, circle the question numbers that you answered incorrectly and evaluate the results. Then turn to the appropriate topics (listed by chapters), read the explanations and complete the exercises. (Note that questions that address more than one standard may be covered in more than one chapter. These are typed in **bold**.) Finally, complete the Practice Tests to prepare for the Georgia High School Graduation Test.

Chapters	Question Numbers
Chapter 1: Cells and Cellular Transport	6, 8, **21**, 26, 75
Chapter 2: Chemistry of Biological Molecules	14, **21**, **74**, **76**, **78**
Chapter 3: Nucleic Acids and Cell Division	2, 3, 10, 14, 18, 19, 51, 55, **74**, **76**, **78**, 79
Chapter 4: Genetics Heredity and Biotechnology	1, 29, 68
Chapter 5: Taxonomy and Evolution	16, 23, 24, 46, 57, 59, 62, 67, 71
Chapter 6: Interactions in the Environment	11, 33, 35, 53, 54, 65, 80
Chapter 7: Nuclear Processes	28, 42, 50, **66**, 73
Chapter 8: Structure and Properties of Elements	15, 17, 22, 40, 41, 43, 44, 45, 47, 48, 58, 64, 77
Chapter 9: Matter and Energy	5, 7, 12, 20, 31, 38, 39, 60, 61, **69**
Chapter 10: Energy Transfer and Transformation	36, **66**, **69**
Chapter 11: Force, Mass, and Motion	4, 13, 27, 34, 70
Chapter 12: Electricity and Magnetism	9, 32, 37, 49, 56
Chapter 13: Waves	25, 30, 52, 63, 72

Chapter 1
Cells and Cellular Transport

GPS Standards	
SB1 a and d	Students will analyze the nature of the relationship between structures and functions in living cells.
SB3 d	Students will derive the relationship between single-celled and multi-celled organisms and the increasing complexity of systems.

CHARACTERISTICS OF LIFE

All living things, also called **organisms**, share the following characteristics:

1. Cells
2. Sensitivity (response to stimuli)
3. Growth
4. Homeostasis (stable internal environment)
5. Reproduction
6. Metabolism (transformation and use of energy)
7. Adaptation

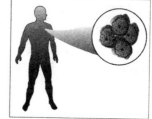

Figure 1.1 Cellular Makeup of Man

Characteristics Of Organisms

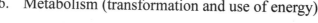

Cells:	Cells make up all living things. Cells can sometimes organize into complex structures. Multicellular organisms have many cells and unicellular organisms have only one cell.
Sensitivity:	Organisms respond to stimuli in the environment. A **stimulus** is a change in the environment. **Responses** are reactions to stimuli in the environment. Examples of responses to stimuli include a plant that grows toward a light source, or an animal that flees from a predator.
Growth:	Organisms change over their lifetime. This growth may be characterized by an increase in size, the development of new physical structures or the refinement of reasoning or behavior.
Homeostasis:	Organisms must maintain an internal environment that is suitable for life. Living things need the correct amount of fluids, salts, hormones and food sources in order to survive. **Homeostasis** is the ability of an organism to maintain a steady internal state, regardless of external influence.

Reproduction: All living things must be able to reproduce. Organisms can reproduce sexually or asexually. **Sexual reproduction** occurs when two organisms create offspring, and **asexual reproduction** occurs when one organism is capable of creating offspring by itself.

Metabolism: Organisms must get energy from the environment. The processes of extracting energy from the environment, using that energy and disposing of waste by-products are all chemical reactions. **Metabolism** is the sum of all chemical reactions within a cell or organism.

Adaptation: Over time, organisms can become specially suited to a particular environment. Sea turtles have long, flipper-like legs and cannot easily walk on land; they have become **adapted** to living in the ocean. **Adaptations** occur slowly, over the course of many generations.

Living things also carry out life processes. These are the specific events that allow cells to grow, respond to stimuli, maintain homeostasis, reproduce, metabolize and adapt. Non-living things cannot carry out these processes. A list of life processes is given in Table 1.1.

Table 1.1 Life Processes

Life Process	Description
Nutrition	the use of nutrients by an organism
Digestion	the process that breaks large food molecules into forms that can be used by the cell
Absorption	the ability of a cell to take in nutrients, water, gases and other substances from its surroundings
Transport	the movement of nutrients, water, gases and other substances into and out of the cell
Biosynthesis	the cellular process of building new chemical compounds for the purpose of growth, repair and reproduction
Secretion	the release of substances from a cell
Respiration	the release of energy from chemical breakdown of compounds within the cell
Excretion	the ability of the cell to rid itself of waste products
Response	the ability of a cell to react to stimuli from its environment
Reproduction	the process of fission in which one cell divides to form two identical new cells
Photosynthesis	the cellular process in which a plant makes food from water and carbon dioxide, using energy from the sun

Section Review 1: Characteristics of Life

A. Define the following terms.

stimulus	life	sexual reproduction	metabolism
response	homeostasis	asexual reproduction	

B. Choose the best answer.

1. Which of the following is NOT a characteristic of life?

    A. reproduction   B. homeostasis   C. sensitivity   D. transport

2. Which of the following is an example of how organisms maintain homeostasis?
    A. a damaged skin cell dividing into two newer skin cells
    B. a human shivering in cold weather
    C. a crow learning to retrieve a food reward in a laboratory experiment
    D. finches in the Galapagos developing different types of beaks

3. A runner eats a large pasta dinner the night before a big race. In this example, which characteristic of life is the runner using to help in her win the race?
    A. digestion   B. homeostasis   C. sensitivity   D. metabolism

4. How are life processes different from characteristics of life?
    A. Life processes are the specific actions that help organisms maintain characteristics of life.
    B. Characteristics of life are the specific actions that help organisms maintain life processes.
    C. Only organisms that show characteristics of life carryout life processes.
    D. Life process and characteristics are the exact same.

C. Answer the following questions.

1. List the seven characteristics all living things must show.

2. Based on what you know, how would you explain the fact that fire is not considered alive even though it grows and uses oxygen?

3. Look closely at all the life processes you listed. Which ones have to do with obtaining and processing food? Which do not?

CELLS

The **cell** is the structural and functional unit of all organisms. Some cells can operate independently to carry out all of life's processes. Some cells function using many small structures called organelles, while other cells do not have organelles. **Organelles**, or "little organs," are small, specialized cellular subunits separated from the rest of the cell by a membrane. Organelles help a cell to move molecules, create and store energy, store information and perform many other functions.

CELLULAR ORGANIZATION

PROKARYOTIC VS. EUKARYOTIC CELLS

There are two basic types of cells: prokaryotic and eukaryotic. A **prokaryotic** (*pro-* before; *karyotic-* nucleus) cell does not have a true nucleus. Although the genetic material is usually contained in a central location, a membrane does not surround it. Furthermore, prokaryotic cells have no membrane-bound organelles. Bacteria are prokaryotic. See Figure 1.2 for a schematic drawing of a prokaryotic cell.

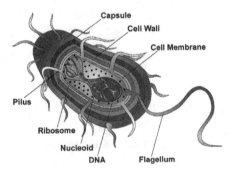

Figure 1.2 Prokaryotic Cell

Figure 1.3 Eukaryotic Cell

A **eukaryotic** (*eu-* true; *karyotic-* nucleus) cell has a nucleus surrounded by a nuclear membrane. It also has several membrane-bound organelles. Eukaryotic cells tend to be larger than prokaryotic cells. Plant and animal cells are both eukaryotic and, although similar in structure, contain unique cell parts. For instance, plant cells have a cell wall and chloroplasts, while animal cells have centrioles and some even have cilia and flagella. See Figures 1.3 and 1.4 for schematic drawings of eukaryotic cells, including plant and animal cells. Table 1.3 contains functions of eukaryotic cell parts.

CELLULAR PARTS

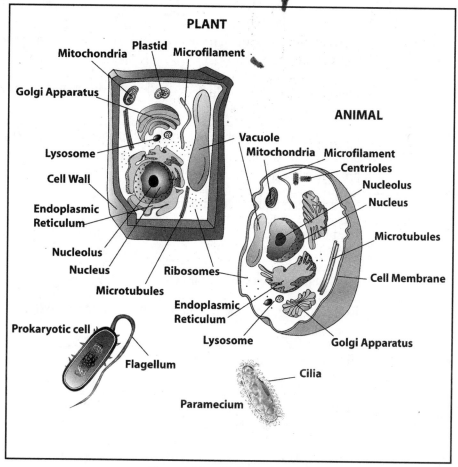

Figure 1.4 Specific Parts of the Cell

VIRUSES ARE NOT LIVING THINGS

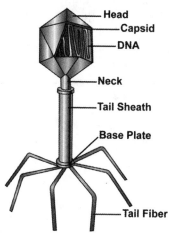

Figure 1.5 Virus Schematic

A **virus** is a small particle that contains proteins and hereditary material (DNA or RNA) but is not alive. The virus is surrounded by a protein coat, or capsid. A virus particle cannot eat, metabolize food and can only reproduce inside a cell. Outside the cell, a virus particle does nothing and remains inactive. Viruses are cell-specific, meaning they can only infect a cell if the capsid of the virus can fit into a receptor site in the host cell membrane. You can think of it like a lock and key: the virus has one of several thousand possible keys that may fit the lock on the surface of the cellular membrane.

Once the virus inserts its hereditary material into the cell, the protein coat falls away and the hereditary material then uses the cell's machinery to make more viral particles. The cell then dies and disintegrates releasing more virus particles into the organism's body.

Table 1.3 Parts of the Eukaryotic Cell

Name	Description
Cell Wall (plant cells only)	Rigid membrane around plant cell; made of cellulose and provides shape and support
Modified Cell Wall (bacteria and fungi only)	These organisms have cell walls made from different materials than plant cell walls; see Chapter 5
Plastids (plant cells only)	Group of structures (chloroplasts, leukoplasts, chromoplasts) used in photosynthesis and product storage; have a double membrane and provide color and cellular energy
Vacuoles	Spherical storage sac for food and water
Cell Membrane	Membrane surrounding the cell that allows some molecules to pass through
Golgi Bodies	Flattened membrane sacs for synthesis, packaging and distribution
Mitochondria	Rod-shaped double membranous structures where cellular respiration takes place
Microfilaments & Microtubules	Fibers and tubes of protein that help move internal cell parts
Endoplasmic Reticulum (ER)	Folded membranes having areas with and without ribosomes used for transport of RNA and proteins
Nucleolus	Dense body in the nucleus; site of ribosome production
Nucleus	Control center of the cell; location of hereditary information; surrounded by nuclear envelope
Nuclear envelope	Double membrane that surrounds the nucleus; fused at certain points to create nuclear pores; outer membrane is continuous with the ER.
Ribosomes	Structures that manufacture proteins; found on endoplasmic reticulum and floating in the cytoplasm
Centrioles (animal cell only)	Short tubes necessary for cell reproduction in some cells
Lysosomes	Spherical sac containing enzymes for digestive functions
Cilia (animal and bacteria cell only)	Short, hair-like extensions on the surface of some cells used for movement and food gathering
Flagella (animal and bacteria cell only)	Long, whip-like extension on the surface of some cells used for movement
Cytoplasm	Jelly-like substance in the cell around nucleus and organelles

Section Review 2: Cells

A. Define the following terms.

cell
organelles
cell theory
prokaryotic
eukaryotic
cell wall
plastids

golgi bodies
mitochondria
microfilaments & microtubules
endoplasmic reticulum (ER)
nucleolus

cilia
flagella
cytoplasm
unicellular
multicellular
tissue
organ

ribosomes
centrioles
lysosomes
vacuoles
cell membrane
organ system
nucleus

B. Choose the best answer.

1. The mitochondrion of a cell
   A. has only one membrane.
   B. has no membrane.
   C. is circular.
   D. is where cellular respiration occurs.

2. Ribosomes
   A. are the site of protein synthesis.
   B. are made by other ribosomes.
   C. have their own DNA.
   D. none of the above

3. A(n) _____ is an organelle that synthesizes, packages and distributes many different substances within the cell.
   A. vacuole   B. Golgi body   C. chloroplast   D. centriole

4. Structures that support and give shape to plant cells are
   A. microbodies.   B. Golgi bodies.   C. nucleus.   D. cell walls.

5. What are the two main types of cells?
   A. nuclear and non-nuclear
   B. plant and animal
   C. spherical and rod-shaped
   D. prokaryotic and eukaryotic

6. The storage of hereditary information in a eukaryotic cell is in the
   A. cytoplasm.   B. nucleus.   C. centrioles.   D. lysosomes.

C. Answer the following questions.

1. List five more examples of tissues, organs and organ systems not mentioned in the text.

2. Compare and contrast prokaryotic and eukaryotic cells.

3. Develop on analogy where you compare the school to the cell. Use all the cell parts and compare them to locations within your school.

SOLUTIONS

A **solution** is a liquid mixture of **solute** dissolved in **solvent**. Think of salt water, a solution in which salt (the solute) is dissolved in water (the solvent).

The interior of a cell is also a solution. The cytoplasm is a watery, jelly-like substance (the solvent) that contains a variety of substances, like salt and minerals (the solutes). Maintaining the concentration of solutes in the cytoplasm is critical to cell function — too much or too little of any component causes damage to the cell. This ideal balance of solutes within the cell is a state the cell strives to maintain through a variety of mechanisms. The process is referred to as maintaining **homeostasis.**

THE CELL MEMBRANE AND CELLULAR TRANSPORT

Hormones are chemical messengers that regulate some body functions in multicellular organisms. One function of hormones is to help maintain homeostasis. Other functions of hormones include the control of movement of oxygen into cells and the removal of carbon dioxide from cells, the maintenance of the internal temperature of an organism and the regulation of fluids. Individual cells move fluids and nutrients in and out through the semi-permeable cell membrane. They can move these materials by either passive or active transport mechanisms to maintain homeostasis.

CELL MEMBRANE

The main purpose of the cell membrane is to regulate the movement of materials into and out of the cell. The cell membrane is **semi-permeable**, or selectively permeable, meaning that only certain substances can go through.

The cell membrane is composed of a phospholipid bilayer, as shown in Figure 1.6. Each phospholipid layer consists of **phosphate groups** (phosphorous bonded with oxygen) attached to two fatty acid (lipid) tails. The layers arrange themselves so that the phosphate heads are on the outer edges of the membrane, and the fatty acid tails compose the interior of the membrane. Globular proteins used for various functions, such as transporting substances through the membrane, are embedded in the cell membrane. The **phospholipids** are free to move around, allowing the membrane to stretch and change shape. The situation is easy to visualize if you think of the phospholipids like balloons. One layer is a bunch of balloons on the ceiling and the other layer is a bunch of balloons on the floor. The balloons are free to move around in their bunch. Substances can pass between the individual balloons in much the same way as some substances pass through the cellular membrane. Substances that are physically too large to pass between the balloons must use specialized transport molecules that span the entire membrane.

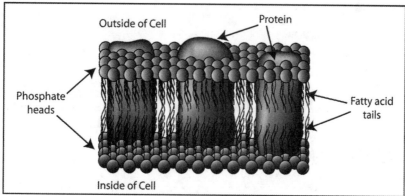

Figure 1.6 Phospholipid Bilayer

PASSIVE TRANSPORT

Passive transport is spontaneous and does not require energy. In **passive transport**, molecules move spontaneously through the cell membrane from areas of higher concentration to areas of lower concentration. This movement (from high to low) is said to be "with the **concentration gradient**." The three types of passive transport are diffusion, facilitated diffusion and osmosis.

Diffusion is the process by which substances move directly through the cell membrane as shown in Figure 1.6. **Facilitated diffusion** involves the help of a transport protein called a carrier protein to move a substance from one side of the cell membrane to the other. Facilitated diffusion allows the passage of molecules that are too large to fit between the phospholipids.

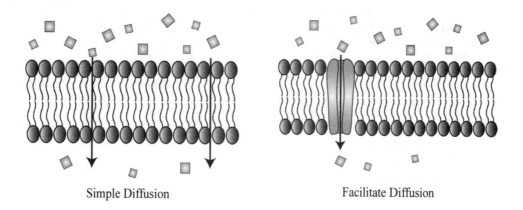

Simple Diffusion   Facilitate Diffusion

Figure 1.7 Diffusion

Osmosis is the movement of water from an area of high water concentration to an area of low water concentration through a semi-permeable membrane. Figure 1.8 shows osmosis through a membrane. Think of osmosis as the diffusion of water.

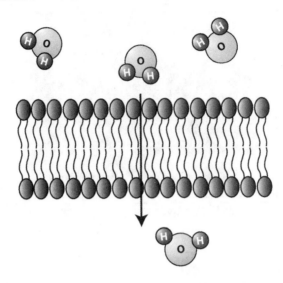

Figure 1.8 Osmosis

Osmosis can occur in either direction, depending on the concentration of dissolved material inside and outside the cell. Defining the solution concentrations *relative to one another* will predict the direction in which osmosis will occur. A **hypotonic** solution has the lower concentration of solute; this may be thought of as a higher concentration of water. A **hypertonic** solution has a higher concentration of dissolved solute, which may be thought of as a lower concentration of water. If the solute concentrates are the same inside and outside the cell membrane, the solutions are said to be **isotonic** to each other. Diffusion of water (osmosis) across a cell membrane always occurs from hypotonic to hypertonic. Three situations are possible:

a) The solution surrounding the cell membrane has a lower concentration of dissolved substances than the solution inside the cell membrane. Here, the solution outside the membrane is hypotonic with respect to the solution inside the cell membrane. The cell will experience a net gain of water and swell, as in Figure 1.4.

b) The solution surrounding the cell membrane has a higher concentration of dissolved solute than the solution inside the cell membrane. In this case, the solution outside the membrane is hypertonic with respect to the solution inside the cell membrane. The cell will lose water to its surroundings, causing it to shrink. This is shown in Table 1.4.

c) In the third case, the concentration of dissolved solutes is the same inside the cell as it is outside the cell. These solutions are said to be isotonic with respect to each other. There will be no net movement of water across the cell membrane. This is a state of equilibrium, which the cell often reaches only after a prior exchange of water across the membrane.

These situations are illustrated in Table 1.4 below.

Table 1.4 Relative Solution Concentration

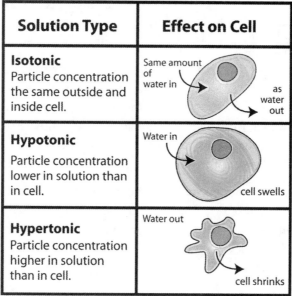

Solution Type	Effect on Cell
Isotonic Particle concentration the same outside and inside cell.	Same amount of water in → as water out
Hypotonic Particle concentration lower in solution than in cell.	Water in → cell swells
Hypertonic Particle concentration higher in solution than in cell.	Water out → cell shrinks

Placing plant cells in a hypertonic solution causes the plant cell membranes to shrink away from the cell wall. This process is called **plasmolysis**. Plasmolysis can result in plant cell death due to water loss. A wilted plant is showing signs of plasmolysis. Placing a plant in a hypotonic solution has an opposite effect: The cell will swell until the cell wall allows no more expansion. The plant now becomes very stiff and turgid.

Kidney dialysis is an example of a medical procedure that involves diffusion. Another example is food preserved by salting, sugar curing or pickling. All of these examples are methods of drawing water out of the cells through osmosis.

ACTIVE TRANSPORT

In some cases, the cell may need to move material across the cell membrane, against the concentration gradient. To do so, the cell must expend energy. The movement of substances from an area of low concentration to an area of high concentration is called **active transport**. The movement is characterized by its direction as exocytosis and endocytosis.

Exocytosis is a form of active transport that removes materials from the cell. A sac stores the material to be removed from the cell, and then moves near the cell membrane. The cell membrane opens and the substance is expelled from the cell. Waste materials, proteins and fats are examples of materials removed from the cell in this way.

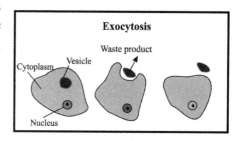

Figure 1.9 Exocytosis

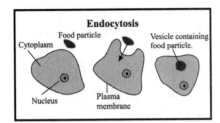

Figure 1.10 Endocytosis

Endocytosis, another form of active transport, brings materials into the cell without passing through the cell membrane. The membrane folds itself around the substance, creates a **vesicle**, and brings the substance into the cell. Some unicellular organisms, such as an amoeba, obtain food this way.

Active transport is a mechanism that allows certain organisms to survive in their environments. For instance, sea gulls can drink salt water because their cells remove excess salt from their bodies through active transport. However, freshwater fish are not able to remove excess salt from their cells and, therefore, would become dehydrated in a salt-water environment. Another example of active transport involves blood cells which use carrier proteins to transport molecules into the cell.

Carrier proteins are also used in active transport. Carrier proteins involved in active transport are special proteins embedded in the cell membrane, that have one binding site specific to the type of molecule it transports and another binding site for ATP. When both ATP and the molecule are bound to the protein, it changes shape and allows the molecule into the cell. The transported molecule and the ADP molecule are then released from the protein.

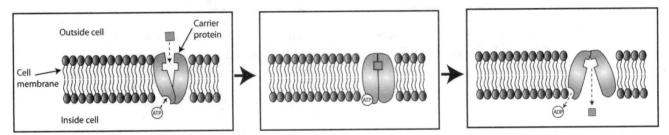

Figure 1.11 Active Transport

Activity

1. A cell which has no net gain or loss of water is in a(n) _____ solution.

2. The process of expending energy to move molecules across a membrane is _____ transport.

3. A plant cell that has swelled to its limits is referred to as _____; a shrunken plant cell has undergone _____.

Activity

Examine the situations below and determine the effect on the cell.

1. Internal cellular solution concentration of 11.4 mg/L placed in a solution with 9.9 mg/L.

2. Internal cellular solution concentration of 1.1 mg/L placed in a solution with 4.4 mg/L.

3. Internal cellular solution concentration of 0.01 mg/L placed in a solution with 0.1 mg/L.

4. Internal cellular solution concentration of 6.81 mg/L placed in a solution with 6.69 mg/L.

5. Internal cellular solution concentration of 8.03 mg/L placed in a solution with 2.21 mg/L.

Section Review 3: The Cell Membrane and Cellular Transport

A. Define the following terms.

hormones	diffusion	hypertonic	exocytosis
semi-permeable	facilitated diffusion	isotonic	endocytosis
passive transport	osmosis	plasmolysis	vesicle
solute	hypotonic	active transport	solvent
solution	homeostasis		

B. Choose the best answer.

1. The movement of substances into and out of a cell without the use of energy is called
   A. active transport.
   B. passive transport.
   C. exocytosis.
   D. endocytosis.

2. The movement of water across a semi-permeable membrane from an area of high water concentration to an area of low water concentration is called
   A. active transport.
   B. diffusion.
   C. osmosis.
   D. hypotonic.

3. A type of membrane which allows only certain molecules to pass through is called
   A. permeable.
   B. semi-permeable.
   C. active.
   D. porous.

4. A cell placed in a solution shrinks by the process of osmosis. What kind of solution is outside the cell?
   A. hypotonic   B. hypertonic   C. active   D. isotonic

5. If the solution surrounding a cell has a lower concentration of solutes than inside the cell, water will move into the cell through osmosis, causing it to expand. What kind of solution is surrounding the cell?
   A. active   B. passive   C. hypertonic   D. hypotonic

C. Answer the following questions.

1. How does active transport differ from diffusion?

2. Dried beans are soaked overnight in preparation for cooking. Explain the process affecting the beans. What will happen to the dried beans?

3. Describe the difference between exocytosis and endocytosis.

4. A celery stalk is placed in a solution. It begins to wilt. What is a likely component of that solution?

CHAPTER 1 REVIEW

Choose the best answer.

1. In order to be classified as living, an organism must have:

   A. a heart and lungs.

   B. the ability to nourish itself, grow and reproduce.

   C. the ability to photosynthesize and to eliminate waste products.

   D. a true nucleus and nuclear membrane.

2. _____ are the main products produced in a cell.

   A. Lipids   B. Amino acids   C. Proteins   D. Carbohydrates

3. A _____ is a type of cell that has a true nucleus.

   A. prokaryote   B. eukaryote   C. bacterium   D. virus

4. If a cell has a flagellum on its surface, it is

   A. an animal cell.   C. a prokaryotic cell.

   B. a plant cell.   D. a diseased cell.

5. If a plant cell is placed in distilled water, it will

   A. remain the same size.

   B. shrink.

   C. swell and eventually explode.

   D. swell, but stop when the cell wall prevents further expansion.

6. When you perspire on a hot, humid day, drinking water will restore _____ in your body.

   A. substances   B. oxygen   C. homeostasis   D. proteins

7. The process by which food is taken into the cell is called

   A. nourishment.   B. resuscitation.   C. absorption.   D. nutrition.

8. The ability of the cell to rid itself of waste products is called

   A. excretion.   B. elimination.   C. voiding.   D. absorption.

9. Two structures found in plant cells that are not found in animal cells are the

   A. mitochondria and ribosomes.   C. cell membrane and centrioles.

   B. cell wall and plastids.   D. nucleolus and endoplasmic reticulum.

10. Prokaryotic cells have no

    A.   nucleus.

    B.   energy exchange.

    C.   cell membrane.

    D.   metabolism.

11. When more water goes in through a cell membrane than out of it, the solution around the membrane is

    A.   isotonic.   B.   hypertonic.   C.   permeable.   D.   hypotonic.

12. Which organelle is the site of protein synthesis?

    A.   plastid   B.   ribosome   C.   nucleolus   D.   mitochondrion

13. Amoebas obtain food by wrapping the cell membrane around the food particle, creating a vesicle. The food is then brought into the cell. This process is called

    A.   exocytosis.

    B.   photosynthesis.

    C.   osmosis.

    D.   endocytosis.

Chapter 2
Chemistry of Biological Molecules

GEORGIA HSGT SCIENCE STANDARDS COVERED IN THIS CHAPTER INCLUDE:

GPS Standards	
SB1 b – c	Students will analyze the nature of the relationship between structures and functions in living cells.
SB3 a	Students will derive the relationship between single-celled and multi-celled organisms and the increasing complexity of systems.

All living things have in common several distinctive characteristics. As we have seen, the first among these is the existence of cells. Cells carry out the basic functions of life by organizing chemical features into a biological system. How is this done? Let us look at the basic chemistry and molecular components of a cell.

CHEMISTRY OF THE CELL

KEY ELEMENTS

An **element** is a type of matter composed of only one kind of atom which cannot be broken down to a simpler structure. There are six elements commonly found in living cells: **sulfur, phosphorous, oxygen, nitrogen, carbon** and **hydrogen** (easily remembered as **SPONCH**). These elements make up 99% of all living tissue and combine to form the molecules that are the basis of cellular function. Carbon is especially important because one carbon atom

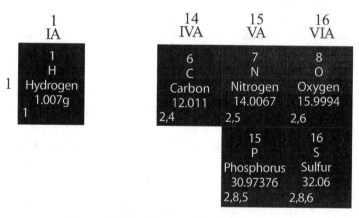

Figure 2.1 Key Elements in Living Cells

can make covalent bonds with four other atoms, resulting in the formation of very stable and complex structures. Carbon is in all living things, as well as in the remains of living things. Molecules containing carbon are called **organic molecules**, while those without carbon are called **inorganic molecules**. Water is the most important inorganic molecule for living things and serves as the medium in which cellular reactions take place.

Those cellular reactions occur in great part between biological molecules, often called **biomolecules**. The four primary classes of cellular biomolecules are carbohydrates, lipids, proteins and nucleic acids. Each of these is a **polymer** — that is, a long chain of small repeating units called **monomers**.

CARBOHYDRATES

Carbohydrates are often called sugars, and are an energy source. Structurally, they are chains of carbon units with hydroxyl groups (-OH) attached. The simplest carbohydrates are **monosaccharides**. The ends of these sugars bond and unbond continuously, so that the straight-chain and cyclic (ring-like) forms are in equilibrium. Figure 2.2 shows a Fischer diagram projection of glucose, a very common biomolecule. A Fischer projection depicts the straight chain form of a monosaccharide. Figure 2.3 shows a Hayworth representation of **ribose**, another common carbohydrate. A Hayworth representation indicates the structure of a cyclic monosaccharide.

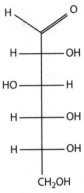

Figure 2.2
Fischer Diagram
of Glucose

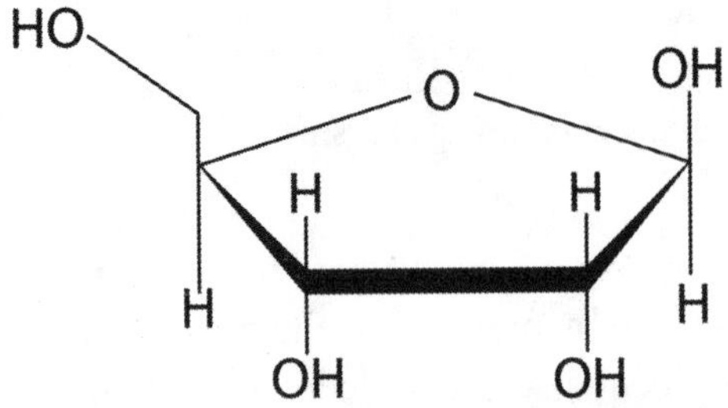

Figure 2.3 Hayworth Projection of Ribose

These monosaccharides may join together to form **disaccharides** (2), **oligosaccharides** (3 – 10) or **polysaccharides** (10+), depending on how many monosaccharides make up the polymeric carbohydrate. Disacchraides consist of two monosaccharide units. Common table sugar, or sucrose, is a disaccharide formed from the bound monosaccharides, fructose and glucose. Oligosaccarides are made up of 3 –10 monosaccharide units. Oligosaccarides are sugars that are either being assembled or broken down, so there aren't any well-known common names for them. Polysaccharides consist of ten or more monosaccharide units. Complex carbohydrates such as starch and cellulose are classified as polysaccharides.

Lab Activity 1: Testing for Carbohydrates in Food

Biologists use Benedict's solution to test for sugar. Use grapes, egg white and butter. Place bits of the different foods in test tubes. Add 10 drops of Benedict's solution to each test tube. Heat the contents of the tube gently for three minutes. Observe any color change.

- Brown means the food contains little or no sugar.
- Greenish-yellow means the food contains some sugar.
- Copper-orange means the food contains a lot of sugar.

Lab Activity 2: Testing for Starch

Iodine is useful in testing for the presence of starch. Use the same kind of food bits as Lab Activity 1. Place these bits of food on a paper towel. Put a drop of iodine on each bit of food. Observe any change in color.

- Reddish-brown means the food contains little or no starch.

- Yellow means the food contains some starch.

- Blue-black means the food contains a lot of starch.

LIPIDS

Lipids are fats; they are made up of chains of methyl (-CH) units. The chains may be long or short. They may be straight or fused into rings (cyclic). They have several functions but are most well known as fat molecules that store energy. They are also the structural components of the cell membrane. Several important lipids have names that you may recognize: waxes, steroids, fatty acids and **triglycerides**. The excess of triglycerides like the one pictured in Figure 2.4 is strongly linked to heart disease and stroke.

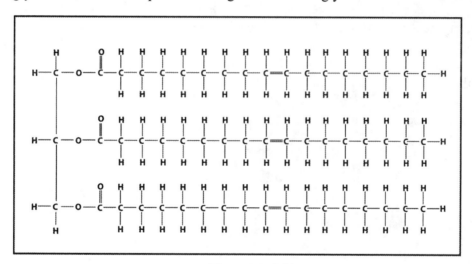

Figure 2.4 Lipid

After looking at Figure 2.4, can you guess why it is called a triglyceride? That's right: it has three carbon chains. Knowing that triglycerides are linked to heart disease, you may not be surprised to learn that butter contains triglycerides.

Lab Activity 3: Testing for Fats in Food

Use a piece of brown paper bag to test for fat. Use the same kind of food bits as Lab Activity 1. Rub the brown paper with each bit of food. Wait for 10 minutes. Hold the paper up to the light.

- If no fat is present, the paper will appear opaque.
- If some fat is present, the paper will appear semi-translucent.
- If a lot of fat is present, the paper will appear translucent.

PROTEINS

Proteins consist of long, linear chains of **polypeptides**. The polypeptide is itself a chain of **amino acid** monomers. There are 20 standard amino acids which combine to form every single protein needed by the human body; protein synthesis will be discussed in Chapter 3. Figure 2.5 shows a polypeptide; Figure 2.6 shows several polypeptides linked together to form a protein.

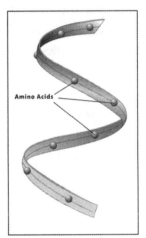

Figure 2.5 Polypeptide

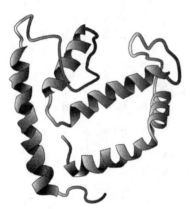

Figure 2.6 Protein

There are many different types of proteins which all have different biological functions. They include: structural proteins, regulatory proteins, contractile proteins, transport proteins, storage proteins, protective proteins, membrane proteins, toxins and enzymes. Despite the wide variation in function, shape and size, all proteins are made from the same 20 amino acids. Since mammals cannot make all 20 amino acids themselves, they must eat protein in order to maintain a healthy diet. Protein may be eaten in animal (meat) or vegetable (beans) form, but most organisms must have protein to survive.

NUCLEIC ACIDS

Nucleic acids are found in the nucleus of a cell. The nucleic acid polymer is made up of **nucleotide monomers**. The nucleotide monomer consists of a sugar, a phosphate group and a nitrogenous base. Nucleic acids are the backbone of the following genetic material:

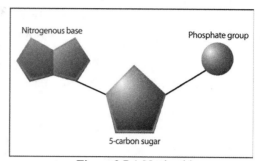

Figure 2.7 A Nucleotide

A. **DNA** (deoxyribonucleic acid) directs the activities of the cell and contains the sugar deoxyribose.

B. **RNA** (ribonucleic acid) is involved in protein synthesis and contains the sugar ribose.

Now that the biomolecules present in the cell have been introduced, can you guess which one makes up the bulk of a cell? Look at Figure 2.8. The bulk of a cell is not made up of a biomolecule — or even all the biomolecules put together! The bulk of the cell is made up of water.

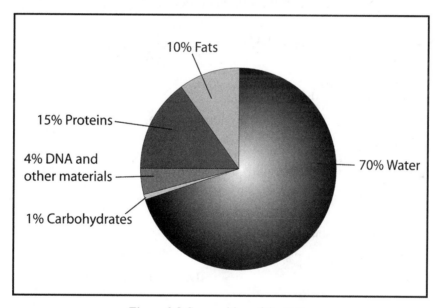

Figure 2.8 Composition of the Cell

Section Review 1: The Chemistry of the Cell

A. Define the following terms.

organic molecule	monomer	DNA	lipid	polymer
inorganic molecule	biomolecule	RNA	protein	polypeptide
nucleotide	nucleic acid	carbohydrate	amino acid	

B. Choose the best answer.

1. Carbon chains are principle features of both carbohydrates and lipids. What is the primary difference between these two types of biomolecules?

    A.   Lipids always have longer carbon chains that carbohydrates.

    B.   Carbohydrates carry hydroxyl groups on their carbon backbone.

    C.   Carbohydrates cannot form rings as lipids can.

    D.   Lipids provide energy, but carbohydrates do not.

2. What molecules make up the bulk of a cell?

    A.   carbohydrates   B.   lipids   C.   proteins   D.   water

3. Carbon is important to living things because

    A.   it metabolizes easily, creating a quick energy source.

    B.   it is abundant on the earth's surface.

    C.   it can form four covalent bonds with other atoms.

    D.   it has twelve protons and neutrons.

4. Nucleotides are to nucleic acids as amino acids are to

    A.   DNA.   C.   proteins.

    B.   polypeptides.   D.   carbohydrates.

C. Answer the following questions.

1. All living things have a common tie with the earth on which we live. Explain why this is true.

2. What are the six elements commonly found in living things?

3. Why is carbon important to living things?

D. Fill in the blanks.

1. One element found in all living and dead organisms is _____.

2. Chains of amino acids are called _____.

3. _____ is an example of a nucleic acid.

CELLULAR ENERGY

The life processes of a cell are the end result of a series of chemical reactions. Each chemical reaction requires energy. In many cases, chemical reactions also require substances to speed reaction time. Energy comes in the form of a molecule called **ATP**, and the substances used to push reactions along are called **enzymes**.

THE ROLE OF BONDING IN ENERGY PRODUCTION

When chemical bonds are formed, energy is stored, and when chemical bonds are broken, energy is released. The stronger the bond, the more energy that will be released when the bond is broken.

A **covalent bond** is the binding of two atoms where the atoms share electrons found in their outer electron shell. An **ionic bond** is the joining of two atoms based on their opposite electrical charges, which generate an electrostatic attraction. Covalent bonds generally occur between non-metallic elements, whereas metals tend to form ionic bonds.

A purely covalent bond is **nonpolar,** meaning that both atoms share electrons equally. Nonpolar bonding occurs between two atoms of the same element, like the carbon-carbon (C-C) bonds in an organic molecule, or the H-H bond in hydrogen gas (H_2). When atoms of different elements bond covalently, they bring to the bond their different electron configurations. This has the effect of one atom pulling electrons toward it more strongly than the other. These bonds are called **polar** covalent bonds. Water is a good example of polar covalent bonding: two hydrogen atoms are bound to one

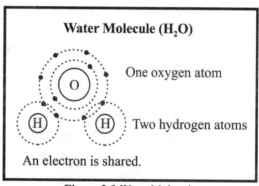

Figure 2.9 Water Molecule

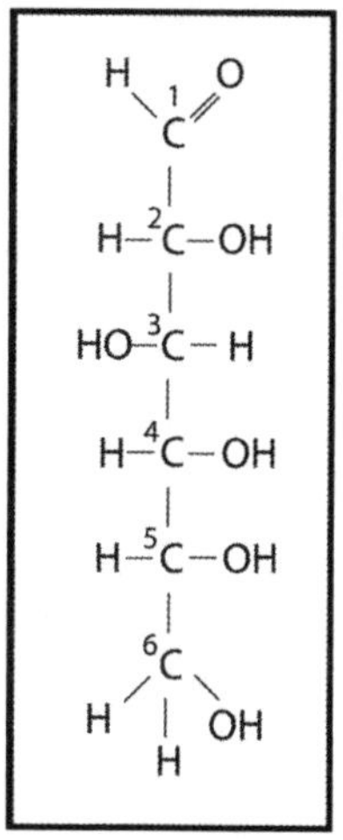

oxygen atom to form the water molecule. The H-O bonds are polar because oxygen pulls electrons toward it and away from hydrogen. Polar covalent bonds are often said to have "ionic character."

Figure 2.10
Bonding in Glucose

A glucose sugar molecule, which has the chemical formula of $C_6H_{12}O_6$, forms a molecule with 6 atoms of carbon, 12 atoms of hydrogen and 6 atoms of oxygen as shown in the modified Fischer projection of Figure 2.10. The atoms of the molecule are held together by covalent bonds, and electrons are shared within the molecule.

Bond strength is a measure of the amount of energy required to break a bond. It depends on several factors, including the number of electrons shared (a single, double or triple bond), the identity of the atoms involved in the bond and the polarity of the bond. In general, the greater the polarity of a bond, the easier it is to break, and the lower the bond strength. Bond strength is important because it can be a source of energy. When bonds break, energy is either released or consumed (depending on the bond strength). Bond strength is measured in joules; the joule is the SI unit of work or energy. As an example, the average bond energy for the O-H bonds in water is about 459 kJ/mol.

Free energy, or energy available to do work, is stored in chemical bonds of molecules. When a muscle contracts, it converts the free energy from glucose into energy that can be used to shorten muscle cells. The movement of the muscle is work. Free energy is released by glucose when its chemical bonds are broken. The energy conversion is not completely efficient and much of the free energy is lost as heat. However, the energy conversions in living cells are significantly more efficient than most types of energy conversion. One reason is that the cell has a variety of ways to store energy and break down processes into small energy saving steps. For instance, mitochondria are useful in the conversion of glucose because they break the chemical reaction into smaller steps, allowing organisms to harness the greatest amount of energy possible. The whole process of breaking down glucose is known as **cellular respiration** and is better than 40% efficient at transferring the chemical energy of glucose into the more useful form of ATP. By contrast, only 25% of the energy released from a gasoline engine is converted to work.

ATP

ATP (adenosine triphosphate) is a molecule that serves as the chemical energy supply for all cells. Adenine, the sugar ribose, and three phosphates compose ATP. The covalent bonds between the phosphate groups contain a great deal of energy. The release of that energy occurs when the last phosphate in ATP breaks off, forming **ADP (adenosine diphosphate)** and **P$_i$** (an inorganic phosphate molecule). The bonding of ATP is shown in Figure 2.11.

After the ATP molecule breaks down, ADP picks up free phosphate to form a new ATP molecule. Each ATP molecule is recycled in this way 2000 – 3000 times a day in the human body. The energy released during each cycle drives cellular processes. Examples of cellular processes that require energy include heat production, muscle contractions, photosynthesis, cellular respiration, locomotion and DNA replication.

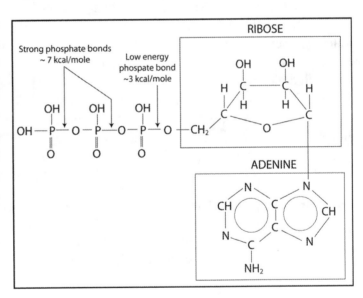

Figure 2.11 Bond Strength in ATP Molecule

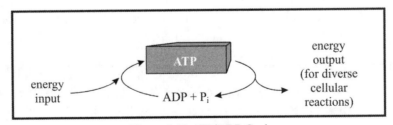

Figure 2.12 ATP/ADP Cycle

CATALYSTS AND ENZYMES

A **catalyst** is a substance that speeds up a chemical reaction without being chemically changed by the reaction. Catalysts decrease the amount of activation energy required for the reaction to occur. **Activation energy** is the amount of energy required in order for reactant molecules to begin a chemical reaction. When a molecule reaches its energy of activation, its chemical bonds are very weak and likely to break. Activation energy provides a barrier so that molecules will not spontaneously react with one another. One example of an inorganic catalyst is nickel, which is used in the

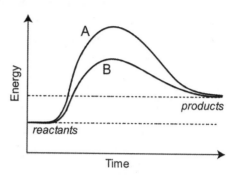

Figure 2.13 Effect of Catalysts on Activation Energy

hydrogenation of vegetable oil to make margarine. The nickel is recovered; it is not used up, and it is not part of the final product.

Our bodies use catalysts called enzymes to break down food and convert it to energy. Every cellular activity is a result of many biochemical reactions that take place at a cellular level. Substances that speed these reactions are called enzymes. **Enzymes** are specific proteins that combine with other substances called **substrates**. There is one enzyme for one substrate, and they fit together like pieces of a puzzle. Metabolism cannot occur unless the energy of activation has been reached. These biological reactions would eventually take place on their own; but in the presence of enzymes, the reactions take place about a million times faster. Enzymes help to lower the energy of activation, making some chemical processes occur with greater frequency.

Some reactions use **cofactors** to help enzymes by transporting electrons, ions or atoms between substances. A **cofactor** is either a **metal ion** (a metal atom that has lost or gained electrons) or a coenzyme. A **coenzyme** is a non-protein molecule that activates the enzyme. Important cofactors in photosynthesis and cellular respiration are **NADP+** (nicotinamide adenine dinucleotide phosphate) and **NAD+** (nicotinamide adenine dinucleotide). These cofactors pick up free hydrogen ions and electrons and transport them so the next stage of the reaction can take place. We will not be addressing the specific movement of molecules and bonds in this text, but it is a good idea to have an idea of what these cofactors look like. Figure 2.14 shows the structure of the coenzyme NAD+.

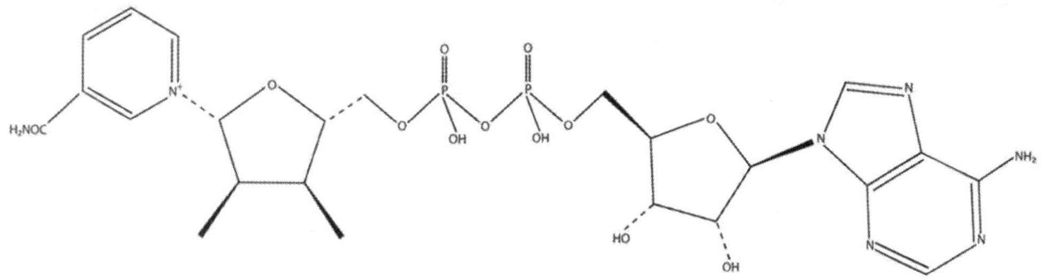

Figure 2.14 NAD+ (nicotinamide adenine dinucleotide)

Metabolic processes can occur without enzymes, though at biological temperatures, metabolism would happen so slowly most organisms would be unable to survive. Some enzyme failures result in disease or death of the organism.

Factors that influence the rate at which enzymes act include such things as temperature, pH and amount of substrate present. Most enzymes have an optimum temperature and pH. Their optimum temperature or pH is the range at which the enzyme functions best. Enzymes vary from one organism to another. Some bacteria have enzymes that have an optimum temperature of 70°C or higher; this temperature would destroy most human enzymes.

With a few exceptions, most enzymes have an optimum pH of between 6 and 8. Table 2.1 contains several enzymes and their optimal pH.

Table 2.1 pH for Optimum Activity

Enzyme	pH Optimum
Lipase – hydrolyzes glycerides (pancreas)	8.0
Lipse – hydrolyzes glycerides (stomach)	4.0 – 5.0
Pepsin – decomposition of proteins	1.5 – 1.6
Urease – hydrolysis of urea	7.0
Invertase – hydrolysis of sucrose	4.5
Maltase – hydrolysis of maltose to glucose	6.1 – 6.8
Amylase (pancreas) – hydrolysis of starch	6.7 – 7.0
Catalase – decomposition of hydrogen peroxide into water and oxygen	7.0

Recall that a pH of 7 is considered **neutral**. Water has a pH of about 7. Substances with a pH less than 7 are **acids** and substances with a pH greater than 7 are **bases**. One example of an enzyme is pepsin, an acidic enzyme found in the human stomach. Pepsin has an optimum pH of 1–2.

FOOD ENERGY

Organisms must use food to live. Organisms that obtain their food from other living things are called **consumers**. Consumers ingest food, digest the meal and then excrete waste. The food ingested by a consumer must be broken down into smaller molecules that the consumer can absorb and use. The proteins found in the food are broken down into amino acids and absorbed by the consumer. The consumer can then rearrange the amino acids into any desired form. For example, humans eat cow meat. The proteins contained in the cow meat are broken down and rearranged into human proteins. Through digestion, organisms can obtain energy, grow and carry out life's functions.

Section Review 2: Cellular Energy

A. Define the following terms.

ATP	catalyst	enzyme	coenzyme
ADP	activation energy	cofactor	free energy
covalent bond	acid	p_i	base
substrate	nonpolar	polar	neutral
ionic bond			

B. Choose the best answer.

1. What does ATP stand for?

    A.   adenosine triphosphate   C.   a triphosphate

    B.   adenine triphosphate   D.   none of the above

2. What are enzymes?

    A.   catalysts used by living things

    B.   catalysts used in all reactions

    C.   chemicals used to increase activation energy

    D.   fats used by living things to help speed up chemical reactions

3. Which statement below is true about enzymes?

    A.   Enzymes function at any temperature and pH.

    B.   Enzymes function at an optimum temperature and pH.

    C.   Enzymes increase the activation energy of a chemical reaction.

    D.   Enzymes aid in the formation of ATP.

4. Organic molecules most often form using

    A.   ionic bonds.   C.   polar ionic bonds.

    B.   covalent bonds.   D.   hydrogen bonds.

C. Answer the following questions.

1. In your own words, describe the relationship between ATP and ADP.

2. What is the purpose of ATP?

3. Briefly describe the function of enzymes.

OBTAINING CELLULAR ENERGY

PHOTOSYNTHESIS

Photosynthesis is the process of converting carbon dioxide, water and light energy into oxygen and high energy sugar molecules. The chemical equation representing this process is shown in Equation 2.1. Plants, algae and some bacteria can use the sugar molecules produced during photosynthesis to make **complex carbohydrates** such as starch or cellulose for food. The process of photosynthesis consists of two basic stages: **light-dependent reactions** and **light-independent reactions**. The light-independent reactions are also called the **Calvin cycle**.

$$6CO_2 + 6H_2O + \text{light} \rightarrow C_6H_{12}O_6 (\text{glucose}) + 6O_2$$

Equation 2.1

Photosynthesis takes place inside an organelle called a **chloroplast**. A chloroplast is all of a group of organelles called plastids. **Plastids** engage in photosynthesis and store the resulting food. The chloroplast is a specific organelle with a double membrane that contains stacks of sac-like membranes called **thylakoids**. The thylakoid membrane contains within itself a green pigment called **chlorophyll**. **Pigments** are substances that absorb light. Light-dependent reactions take place inside the thylakoid membrane. Light-independent reactions take place in the **stroma**, which is the region just outside the thylakoid membrane. In the **light-dependent phase**, sunlight hits the leaf of the plant where it is absorbed by the pigments in the leaf. There are several pigments in plant leaves, but the main one used in photosynthesis is chlorophyll, the green pigment. Chlorophyll is stored in the chloroplasts of the plant cell.

When light hits the chlorophyll, electrons absorb the energy, become excited, and leave the chlorophyll molecule. Carrier molecules transport the electrons, which follow an electron transport chain. Electron acceptor molecules pick up the electrons in a series and pass them from one molecule to another. As this occurs, energy is released, and ATP is formed. The final electron acceptor is NADP+.

Splitting a molecule of water replaces the electrons released from the chlorophyll. These electrons, now available, combine with the NADP+ to form **NADPH**. The next stage of photosynthesis uses the NADPH, while oxygen leaves as an end product of the reaction.

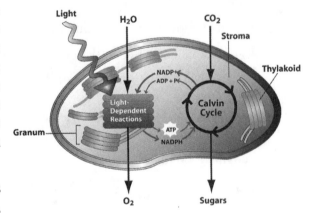

Figure 2.15 The Process of Photosynthesis

The end products of the light-dependent reactions are ATP, oxygen and NADPH. The ATP and NADPH will be used in the light-independent reactions, and the oxygen will be released into the atmosphere.

The next phase, the **light-independent** or **carbon fixation reactions**, uses the ATP formed during the light-dependent reaction as an energy source. In this phase, carbon – from carbon dioxide – and NADPH are used to form **glucose**. To accomplish this, a five-carbon sugar (a monosaccharide called a pentose) uses a carbon atom from carbon dioxide to create a six-carbon sugar (a **hexose**). Glucose is the end result, after several conversions have taken place. The glucose can then be used as food to enter cellular respiration, or it can be converted to other carbohydrate products, such as sucrose or starch.

CELLULAR RESPIRATION

Cellular respiration is the process of breaking down food molecules to release energy. Plants, algae, animals and some bacteria use cellular respiration to break down food molecules. There are two basic types of cellular respiration: aerobic and anaerobic. **Aerobic respiration** occurs in the presence of oxygen, and is represented by the chemical equation in Equation 2.2. The energy released through cellular respiration is used to create ATP. Cellular respiration occurs in three phases: **glycolysis**, **Krebs cycle** and **electron transport**. The process starts with a molecule of glucose. The reactions of cellular respiration occur with the use of enzymes. Respiration is the primary means by which cells obtain usable energy.

$$C_6H_{12}O_6 + 6O_2 \rightarrow 6CO_2 + 6H_2O + energy$$

Equation 2.2

Glycolysis is the first phase in cellular respiration. This step occurs in the cytoplasm of the cell, and it can occur whether or not oxygen is present. In this phase, the glucose molecule (a 6-carbon sugar) is broken in half through a series of reactions. The energy released by breaking down the glucose is used to produce ATP. Additionally, some high-energy electrons are removed from the sugar during glycolysis. These electrons pass on to an electron carrier called **NAD⁺**, converting it to **NADH**. These electrons will later be used to create more energy.

In aerobic respiration, the 3-carbon sugars produced from glycolysis enter the **mitochondria** along with the oxygen. As the sugars enter the mitochondria, they convert to citric acid in phase two of cellular respiration. The **citric acid cycle**, or **Krebs cycle**, is the cyclical process that breaks down the citric acid through a series of reactions. The citric acid cycle produces more ATP, as well as some **GTP** (a high-energy molecule similar to ATP). More high-energy electrons are released, forming NADH from NAD⁺.

The last phase of cellular respiration is the **electron transport chain**, which occurs on the inner mitochondrial membrane. In this phase, the NADH releases the hydrogen ions and high-energy electrons it picked up during glycolysis and the citric acid cycle. The energy from these electrons is used to convert large quantities of ADP into ATP. The electrons transfer through a series of carrier proteins. At the end of the electron transport chain the free electrons and H^+ ions bond with oxygen. The oxygen and H^+ ions form water, which is released from the cell as a waste product. Each electron transfer releases energy.

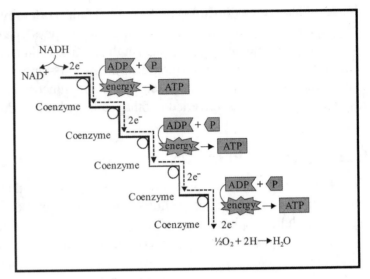

Figure 2.16 Electron Transport Chain

ANAEROBIC RESPIRATION

Anaerobic respiration or **fermentation**, is the process by which sugars break down in the absence of oxygen. Our muscle cells, fungi and some bacteria are capable of carrying out anaerobic respiration. These cells convert the products of glycolysis into either alcohol or **lactic acid**. Glycolysis releases energy, while the production of alcohol or lactic acid provides NAD^+, the electron carrier needed for glycolysis.

Yeast and some bacteria can carry out alcoholic fermentation. Yeast produces **ethanol** (C_2H_5OH) through a process called **alcoholic fermentation**. The chemical equation representing this process is shown in Equation 2.3. Carbon dioxide gas is released during alcohol formation. This carbon dioxide gas is responsible for the holes in bread. Yeast is commonly put in bread to make it rise. The fermentation of the yeast produces carbon dioxide which becomes trapped in the dough forming small bubbles and causing the bread to rise. Carbon dioxide produced by yeast in beer gives the beer its bubbles. Other uses of alcoholic fermentation are the making of breads, beer, wine and liquor.

$$C_6H_{12}O_6 \rightarrow 2C_2H_5OH + 2CO_2 + energy$$

Equation 2.3

Animal cells cannot perform alcoholic fermentation. Instead, they produce lactic acid from the products of glycolysis, through the process of **lactic acid fermentation**. Human muscle cells produce lactic acid during strenuous exercise. During strenuous exercise, a person cannot take in enough oxygen through breathing to supply all the muscles with the necessary oxygen. As a result, lactic acid fermentation occurs to supply the muscles with the needed energy. The day after intense physical activity, muscles are sore due to the presence of lactic acid. Some bacteria use lactic acid fermentation to obtain food energy.

COMPARING PHOTOSYNTHESIS AND CELLULAR RESPIRATION

All organisms must be able to obtain and convert energy to carry out life functions, such as growth and reproduction. **Photosynthesis** is one way that organisms can trap energy from the environment and convert it into a biologically useful energy source. **Cellular respiration** is a way that organisms can break down energy sources to carry out life's processes. Photosynthesis takes place in plants, algae and some bacteria. Cellular respiration takes place in all eukaryotic (have a true nucleus) cells and some prokaryotic (no true nucleus) cells.

Table 2.2 Comparison of Photosynthesis and Cellular Respiration

	Photosynthesis	**Cellular Respiration**
Function	energy storage	energy release
Location	chloroplasts	mitochondria
Reactants	CO_2 and H_2O	$C_6H_{12}O_6$ and O_2
Products	$C_6H_{12}O_6$ and O_2	CO_2 and H_2O
Chemical Equation	$6CO_2 + 6H_2O + light$ $C_6H_{12}O_6 + 6O_2$	$6O_2 + C_6H_{12}O_6$ $6CO_2 + 6H_2O + energy$

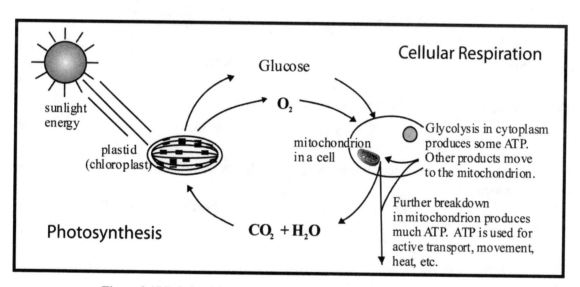

Figure 2.17 Relationship Between Photosynthesis and Cellular Respiration

Section Review 3:   Obtaining Cellular Energy

A. Define the following terms.

photosynthesis	light-dependent phase	glycolysis
Calvin cycle	light-independent phase	Krebs cycle
chloroplast	carbon fixation	electron transport chain
thylakoid	cellular respiration	alcoholic fermentation
chlorophyll	aerobic respiration	lactic acid fermentation
pigment	anaerobic respiration	
plastid		

B. Choose the best answer.

1. What form of energy is used by cells?

    A.   enzymes   B.   cofactors   C.   ATP   D.   DNA

2. The process of releasing energy from the chemical breakdown of compounds in a cell is
    A.   hesitation.   B.   expiration.   C.   elimination.   D.   respiration.

3. In photosynthesis, plants use carbon dioxide, water and light to produce
    A.   carbon monoxide.   C.   glucose and oxygen.

    B.   energy.   D.   chlorophyll.

4. What is released when ATP is broken down into ADP and one phosphate?
    A.   oxygen   B.   water   C.   energy   D.   hydrogen

5. The Krebs Cycle and the electron transport chain phases of cellular respiration take place in which organelle?
    A.   nucleus   B.   cytoplasm   C.   ribosome   D.   mitochon-drion

6. Photosynthesis takes place inside
    A.   mitochondria.   C.   animal cells.

    B.   chloroplasts.   D.   none of the above.

C. Answer the following questions.

1. Compare and contrast aerobic and anaerobic respiration.

2. Compare and contrast alcoholic and lactic acid fermentation.

3. What is the chemical equation for photosynthesis and cellular respiration?

CHAPTER 2 REVIEW

A. Choose the best answer.

1. Complex carbohydrates break down into

    A.   enzymes.

    B.   amino acids.

    C.   simple sugars.

    D.   ATP.

2. Which of the following biomolecules are fat molecules that store energy?

    A.   proteins

    C.   carbohydrates

    B.   nucleic acids

    D.   lipids

3. Which of the following elements can be found in all living and previously living organisms?

    A.   helium   B.   sulfur   C.   carbon   D.   nitrogen

4. Which biomolecule is a polymer assembled from some combination of the 20 amino acids?

    A.   lipids   B.   DNA   C.   protein   D.   nucleotide

5. Which proteins in the cell speed up chemical reactions?

    A.   lipids

    C.   enzymes

    B.   DNA

    D.   glucose

6. Cellular respiration takes place inside

    A.   an animal cell only.

    C.   both plant and animal cells.

    B.   a plant cell only.

    D.   neither plant or animal cells.

7. The chemical energy supply for all living cells is contained in a molecule that, when broken down, releases the energy so that it may be used for activities such as muscle contractions, photosynthesis and locomotion. This molecule that is a storehouse of energy is

    A.   ATP.

    C.   RNA.

    B.   DNA.

    D.   ADP.

8. To obtain and use cellular energy, plant cells use

    A.   photosynthesis only.

    B.   photosynthesis and cellular respiration.

    C.   cellular respiration only.

    D.   chemosynthesis.

9. Cellular energy is stored in the form of
   - A. chemical bonds.
   - B. enzymes.
   - C. membrane potential.
   - D. protein shapes.

10. Pepsin, a digestive enzyme in the human stomach, has an optimum pH that can be described as
    - A. basic.
    - B. neutral.
    - C. acidic.
    - D. very acidic.

11. _____ are the main product of the cell.
    - A. Lipids
    - B. Amino acids
    - C. Proteins
    - D. Carbohydrates

12. A coenzyme is a non-protein molecule that activates the enzyme. What is the difference in the molecular structure of the protein and the co-enzyme?
    - A. A cofactor contains amino acids, but a protein does not.
    - B. A protein contains amino acids, but a cofactor does not.
    - C. A cofactor contains high-energy ionic bonds, but a protein does not.
    - D. A protein contain high-energy ionic bonds, but a cofactor does not.

13. Which of the following foods represents the largest source of protein?
    - A. potato chips
    - B. oranges
    - C. chicken
    - D. cauliflower

14. What are the largest carbohydrates called?
    - A. monosaccharides
    - B. disaccharides
    - C. oligosaccharides
    - D. polysaccharides

Chapter 3
Nucleic Acids and Cell Division

Ga HSGT Science Standards covered in this chapter include:

GPS Standards	
SB2 a – e	Students will analyze how biological traits are passed on to successive generations.

THE ROLE OF DNA

The genetic basis of life is a molecule called **DNA** or **deoxyribonucleic acid**. DNA is carried in the nucleus of all cells and performs two primary functions. First, it carries the code for all the genes of an organism, which in turn create the proteins that perform all the work of living. Second, the code of the DNA itself is the template for future generations. First we will look at the role of DNA in protein synthesis and then its role in heredity.

DNA, RNA AND PROTEIN SYNTHESIS

DNA

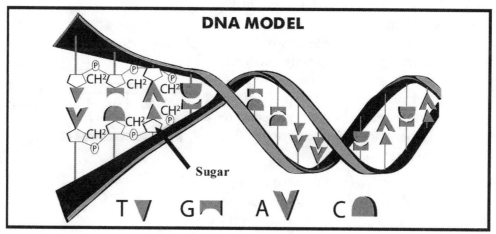

Figure 3.1 Model of DNA

DNA is a complex molecule with a double helix shape, like a twisted ladder. Each side of the helix is composed of a strand of **nucleotides** that are the building blocks of nucleic acids. Each nucleotide contains a phosphate group, the sugar **deoxyribose** and a **nitrogenous base**. There are four bases in DNA, and they form pairs. The bases are **adenine** (A), **thymine** (T), **guanine** (G) and **cytosine** (C). A and T always pair, and G and C always pair. The A-T and G-C pairings are called **complementary pairs**. Each pair forms one of the rungs of the ladder as shown in Figure 3.1.

The DNA molecule carries the code for all the genes of the organism. **Genes** are pieces of the DNA molecule that code for specific proteins. The process of making genes into proteins is called **protein synthesis**.

DNA is located in the nucleus of the cell. The assembly of proteins occurs outside of the nucleus, on the ribosome. So the manufacture of proteins involves three basic steps:

1. The DNA code of the gene segment must be copied, or transcribed, in the nucleus of the cell.

2. The code must then be carried from the nucleus into the cytoplasm and finally to a ribosome.

3. The protein is then assembled or translated from the code into an appropriate protein and then released from the ribosome.

These steps are carried out by RNA, or ribonucleic acid.

RNA

RNA (ribonucleic acid) is a molecule used to change the DNA code from the DNA molecule into protein. It is similar to DNA, except it is single stranded. Its sugar is **ribose**. RNA, like DNA, has four nitrogenous bases. It shares adenine, guanine and cytosine but replaces thymine with **uracil** (U). There are several types of RNA. Messenger, ribosomal and transfer RNA <u>all</u> are involved in protein synthesis.

Protein Synthesis[1]

There are many proteins within every cell. Proteins make up **enzymes** that help to carry out reactions within the cell. Proteins also compose **hormones**, which are chemical messengers that regulate some body functions. Proteins provide structure and act as energy sources. They transport other molecules and are part of our bodies' defenses against disease. In short, proteins are essential for survival because almost everything that happens in the cell involves proteins.

A major function of DNA is to code for the production of proteins by the cell. While DNA remains in the nucleus of a cell, proteins are made in the cytoplasm. RNA serves

TRANSCRIPTION

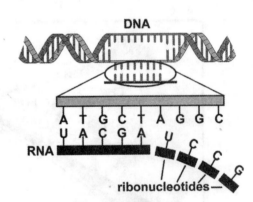

Figure 3.2 Transcription

as the messenger, carrying the genetic code from the nucleus to the cytoplasm. The genetic code begins with the DNA message. It is then changed into an RNA message, and it is then used to build proteins.

Transcription

The first step of protein synthesis is the manufacture of a specific kind of RNA called **messenger RNA (mRNA)**. This copying process is called **transcription**. Transcription begins when a region of the DNA double helix unwinds and separates, as shown in Figure 3.2. The separated segment is a gene, and it serves as a template for the forming mRNA strand.

---

1. To see a free downloadable animation of protein synthesis, go to www.americanbookcompany.com/science

The mRNA strand is assembled from individual RNA nucleotides that are present in the nucleus. An enzyme called **RNA polymerase** picks up these unattached nucleotide bases and matches them to their complementary bases on the DNA template strand. This continues until the entire gene segment has been paired, and a complete mRNA strand has been formed. This mRNA strand has a sequence that is complementary to the original gene segment. At that point, the mRNA separates and leaves the nucleus, moving out into the cytoplasm to settle on the **ribosome**, an organelle composed of another kind of RNA, called **ribosomal RNA (rRNA)**. Here on the surface of the ribosome, the process of translation begins.

TRANSLATION

Translation is the step in protein synthesis where mRNA is decoded (translated) and a corresponding polypeptide is formed. A polypeptide is made up of **amino acids**. There are exactly 20 amino acids. Let's look at the "language" of mRNA.

One way to think of a strand of mRNA is as a chain of nucleotides, as in:

AUGACAGAUUAG

While this is correct, a more accurate way of thinking of the chain is that it is divided into segments consisting of three nucleotides each, as in:

AUG ACA GAU UAG

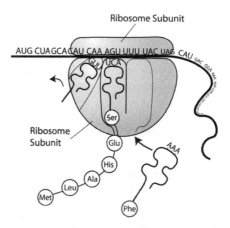

Figure 3.3 Translation

The mRNA strand is not *actually* divided, but writing its code in this way emphasizes an important concept: the **codon**. The three-nucleotide codon has the specific function of corresponding to a particular amino acid. Here is how it works: The molecule of mRNA is bound to the surface of the ribosome at the first three-nucleotide segment, called the **start codon**. The cytoplasm in which they float contains, among other things, amino acids and a third kind of RNA — **transfer RNA (tRNA)**. Transfer RNA is a molecule of RNA that contains a three-part nucleotide segment called an **anticodon**, which is the exact complement of one mRNA codon. The anticodon corresponds exactly to one of the 20 kinds of amino acids. Once the tRNA binds the amino acid, it travels to the ribosome surface. There the three tRNA nucleotide bases (the anticodon) pair with their

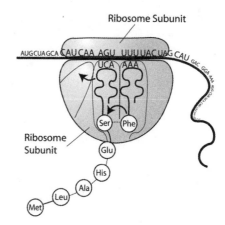

Figure 3.4 Translation

three complementary mRNA bases (the codon). The amino acid that is bound to the tRNA is then added to the growing polypeptide chain at the surface of the ribosome, as shown in Figures 3.3 and 3.4.

The ribosome facilitates this process by moving along the mRNA chain until it reaches a **stop codon**. A stop codon codes for a special protein called a **release factor**. The release factor binds to the ribosome similar to the way codon and anticodons pair during translation. The chemical structure of the release factor causes the ribosome to release the polypeptide chain. The ribosome then releases the newly-formed polypeptide chain, which moves out into the cell as a fully functioning protein.

Activity 1

Examine again the following mRNA chain.

AUG ACA GAU UAG

1. How many codons does it contain?

2. AUG stands for which nucleotide bases?

3. If you had not been told, how could you tell whether this was a segment of RNA or DNA?

4. AUG is a common start codon, and codes for the amino acid methionine. In the above mRNA chain, which codon segment is the stop codon?

5. If this mRNA strand was complete, how many amino acids would the resulting protein contain?

Section Review 1: DNA, RNA and Protein Synthesis

A. Define the following terms.

DNA	nucleotide	ribose	amino acid
gene	deoxyribose	transcription	translation
RNA	base	messenger RNA (mRNA)	transfer RNA (tRNA)
anticodon	ribosome	ribosomal RNA (rRNA)	enzyme
protein synthesis	adenine	codon	hormone
polymerase	cytosine	complementary pairs	thymine
guanine	uracil	stop codon	start codon

B. Choose the best answer.

1. Protein synthesis begins with the manufacture of a molecule of
   A. mRNA.   B. rRNA.   C. tRNA.   D. nucleotide.

2. What are ribosomes made of?
   A. mRNA.   B. rRNA.   C. tRNA.   D. protein.

3. Proteins are made up of polypeptide chains. Polypeptide chains are composed of
   A. mRNA.   B. rRNA.   C. tRNA.   D. amino acids.

4. Transfer RNA (tRNA) carries
   A. the mRNA to the ribosome.
   B. the nucleotide bases to the mRNA.
   C. an amino acid to the ribosome surface.
   D. an amino acid to the cytoplasm.

5. Which of the following is the first step in protein synthesis?
   A. tRNA bonds to an amino acid in the cytoplasm.
   B. DNA unravels to expose an mRNA segment.
   C. DNA unravels to expose a gene segment.
   D. mRNA bonds to tRNA.

C. Answer the following questions.

1. Describe the process of translation.
2. Which sugars are found in DNA and RNA?
3. What are proteins made of?
4. List the DNA bases that pair and the RNA bases that pair.
5. What role does DNA play in protein synthesis?

DNA REPLICATION

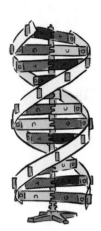

In the previous section, we examined the role that DNA plays in protein synthesis. In this section, we will examine the pivotal role that DNA plays in **cell division**.

Cells must be able to divide in order for the organism to grow, reproduce and repair itself. Multicellular organisms are made up of two kinds of cells: reproductive cells and somatic (or body) cells. Both kinds of cells contain DNA, which is stored in the nucleus in the form of chromatin. **Chromatin** consists of long strands of DNA, jumbled up with proteins, that together form a kind of disorganized mass of genetic material in the nucleus. When the cell is ready to divide, the chromatin coils and condenses to form chromosomes. **Reproductive cells** (sex cells) have a single set, or **haploid** number (n), of chromosomes. **Somatic cells** (body cells) have two sets, or a **diploid** number (2n), of chromosomes.

Figure 3.5 DNA   When the cell divides, the chromosomes must be distributed between the newly produced cells. This means that the DNA must be able to copy itself, which it does through the process of **replication**.

During replication, the double strands of the DNA helix break apart, unzipping like a zipper, to become two individual strands. In a process very similar to that of mRNA formation, new DNA strands are assembled from the free-floating nucleotides in the cell's nucleus. An enzyme called **DNA polymerase** collects the nucleotide bases and matches them to their complementary pair along the single-strand DNA. When the entire process is complete, two new DNA double helices, identical to the original helix, have been formed. The replication process is just one part of the cell cycle.

THE CELL CYCLE

The **cell cycle** is the sequence of stages through which a cell passes between one cell division and the next. The length of time it takes a cell to complete the cell cycle varies from one cell to another. Some cells complete the entire cycle in a few minutes, and other cells spend their entire life frozen in a particular phase.

Most of the cell cycle is spent in **interphase** as shown in Figure 3.6. Interphase consists of three major parts: G_1, S and G_2. During the G_1 phase of interphase, the cell grows in size. In the S phase, replication of the DNA containing the genetic material

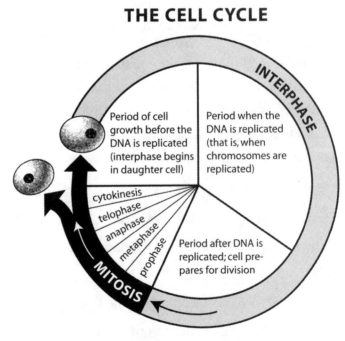

THE CELL CYCLE

Period of cell growth before the DNA is replicated (interphase begins in daughter cell)

Period when the DNA is replicated (that is, when chromosomes are replicated)

INTERPHASE

cytokinesis
telophase
anaphase
metaphase
prophase

Period after DNA is replicated; cell prepares for division

MITOSIS

Figure 3.6 The Cell Cycle

occurs, which gives the cell a double amount of DNA. In the G_2 phase, the cell prepares for mitosis by replicating organelles and increasing the amount of cytoplasm.

MITOSIS

All of the cells in the body, with the exception of reproductive cells, are called **somatic cells**. Some examples are heart cells, liver cells and skin cells. Somatic cells undergo a process called mitosis. **Mitosis** is a type of cell division that generates two daughter cells with the identical components of the mother cell.

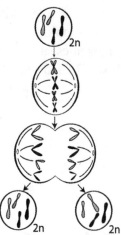

The daughter cells that result from mitotic cell division are identical to each other as well as to the parent cell. The daughter cells have the same (diploid) number of chromosomes as the parent cell. Mitosis is the mechanism for **asexual reproduction**, which only requires one parent. Mitosis also allows multicellular organisms to grow and replace cells. The stages of mitosis are:

Figure 3.7 Mitosis

Prophase:	The nucleus of the cell organizes the chromatin material into thread-like structures called chromosomes. The centriole, in animal cells only, divides and moves to each end of the cell. Spindles form between the centrioles.
Metaphase:	The chromosomes attached at the center, or centromeres, line up at the center of the cell.
Anaphase:	Chromosomes separate at their centromeres, and the spindles pull them toward either end of the cell. A nuclear membrane begins to form around the chromosomes as they disorganize.
Telophase:	Chromatin again forms from the chromosomes, and a cell membrane begins to grow across the center between the two new nuclei.

CYTOKINESIS

Cytokinesis, the division of the cell cytoplasm, usually follows mitosis. Cytokinesis generally begins during the telophase of mitosis. It finalizes the production of two new daughter cells, each with approximately half of the cytoplasm and organelles as well as one of the two nuclei formed during mitosis. The processes of mitosis and cytokinesis are together called **cell division**.

MEIOSIS

Meiosis is a type of cell division necessary for **sexual reproduction**. It is limited to the reproductive cells in the testes, namely the sperm cells, and the reproductive cells in the ovaries, namely the eggs. Meiosis produces four reproductive cells, or **gametes**. These four cells contain half the number (haploid) of chromosomes of the mother cell, and the chromosomes are not identical. There are two phases of cell division, **meiosis I** and **meiosis II**. Before meiosis begins, each pair of chromosomes replicates while the cell is in its resting phase (interphase).

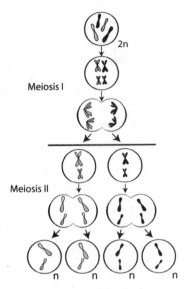

Figure 3.8 Meiosis

Figure 3.9 Crossing Over of Chromosomes

During meiosis I, each set of replicated chromosomes lines up with its homologous pair. **Homologous chromosomes** are matched pairs of chromosomes. Homologous chromosomes are similar in size and shape and carry the same kinds of genes. However, they are not identical because each set usually comes from a different parent. The homologous pairs of chromosomes can break and exchange segments during the **crossing over** process, a source of genetic variation. The homologous pairs of chromosomes separate. The cell then splits into two daughter cells, each containing one pair of the homologous chromosomes. **Interkinesis** is the resting period before meiosis II begins.

During meiosis II, the two daughter cells divide again without replication of the chromosomes. The result is four gametes, each having half the number of chromosomes of the mother cell.

In humans, the body cells have 23 different pairs or a diploid (2n) number of 46 chromosomes total. Each egg and each sperm have 23 single or haploid (n) number of chromosomes.

Section Review 2: Reproduction of Cells

A. Define the following terms.

reproductive cells	cell cycle	metaphase	sexual reproduction
haploid	interphase	anaphase	gamete
somatic cells	asexual reproduction	telophase	crossing over
diploid		cytokinesis	interkinesis
homologous chromosomes	prophase	cell division	polar bodies
chromatin	mitosis	meiosis	
	replication		

B. Choose the best answer.

1. The type of nuclear division that produces gametes is
   A. meiosis.   B. cytokinesis.   C. interphase.   D. mitosis.

2. When DNA is in long strands prior to coiling, it is in the form of
   A. chromosomes.   B. centromeres.   C. chromatin.   D. chromatids.

3. A type of nuclear division that takes place in somatic cells is
   A. meiosis.   B. cytokinesis.   C. interphase.   D. mitosis.

4. During interphase, the cell
   A.   splits its homologous pairs.
   B.   grows and replicates DNA.
   C.   divides the number of chromosomes in half.
   D.   becomes separated by a cellular membrane.

5. The length of time it takes for a cell to complete the cell cycle is
   A. around two hours.   C. the same for each kind of cell.
   B. different for each cell.   D. around two minutes.

C. Answer the following questions.

1. The normal number of chromosomes in a yellow pine tree is 24. With pictures taken from a high-powered microscope, you determine that the pollen from the yellow pine only has 12 chromosomes. How can this be explained?

2. Which type of cell division results in a diploid number of chromosomes in the new cells? Which type of cell division results in a haploid number of chromosomes in the new cells?

3. Anaphase in both mitosis and meiosis is the phase in which chromosomes get separated and pulled to opposite ends of the poles. Explain how anaphase in mitosis is different from anaphase I in meiosis. Draw a diagram of these two phases to help explain the difference.

ASEXUAL VS. SEXUAL REPRODUCTION

Asexual reproduction by mitosis is a careful copying mechanism. Some unicellular organisms like amoeba reproduce asexually. Many plants also reproduce asexually. There are several mechanisms by which this occurs. However, the offspring produced are always genetically identical to the parent.

In contrast, sexual reproduction by meiosis brings with it the enormous potential for genetic variability. The number of possible chromosome combinations in the gametes is 2^n, where n is the haploid chromosome number and 2 is the number of chromosomes in a homologous pair. Look at Figure 3.10, which shows the possible distribution of chromosomes into homologous pairs at meiosis in organisms with small numbers of chromosomes, in this case 2 and 3.

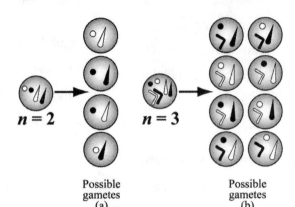

Figure 3.10 Chromosomal Combinations in Gametes

When n=2, four distinct distributions are possible. When n=3, eight distinct distributions are possible. If humans have a haploid number of n=23, then 2^{23} or 8,388,608 distinct distributions are possible.

Remember, this is only the genetic variation that occurs *before* fertilization.

Activity 2			
Great potential for genetic variability results from the number of potential combinations of chromosomes resulting from meiosis. Use the information given, along with a calculator, to determine the statistical number for the following organisms. Discuss your findings in class.			
Organism	**Diploid Number of Chromosomes (body cells)**	**Haploid Number of Chromosomes (gametes)**	**Number of Possible Chromosomes Combinations**
wheat	14		
earthworm	36		
domestic sheep	54		
algae	148		

FERTILIZATION AND CELL DIFFERENTIATION

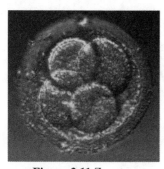

Figure 3.11 Zygote

The haploid gametes produced during meiosis are spermatozoa in males and ova in females. During **fertilization**, these gametes fuse to form a new diploid parent cell called the **zygote**. The zygote is one cell with a set of 2n chromosomes. Each parent contributes one homolog to each homologous pair of chromosomes. It then begins the process of mitosis to grow in size, becoming an **embryo**.

The group of cells produced in the very early stages of the embryo's growth are similar to the original zygote. They are called embryonic **stem cells**. Eventually, when the embryo reaches 20–150 cells in size, this group begins to produce cells that are different from themselves. This process is called **cell differentiation**. The cells become specialized and later become tissues. As each cell differentiates, it produces proteins characteristic to its specific function.

Stem cells have the capability to become any type of cell. This is possible because genes within the cell can be "turned on" or "turned off" at specific times. Every cell of the organism has the same genetic information that was present in the initial zygote. Thus, cell differentiation occurs by the selective activation or inactivation of only some of these genes. For example, some cells could become liver cells while other cells become skin cells, but both of these cell types contain genes for every other cell type within the organism.

In Chapter 4, we will discuss genes and the role they play in heredity.

Section Review 3: Asexual vs. Sexual Reproduction/Fertilization & Cell Differentiation

A. Define the following terms.

fertilization	embryo	stem cells
zygote	stem cells	cell differentiation

B. Choose the best answer.

1. In fertilization, gametes fuse to form a(n)
   - A. embryo.
   - B. somatic cell.
   - C. zygote.
   - D. reproductive cell.

2. Stem cells are
   - A. cells that can produce any type of offspring cell.
   - B. cells that contain stem structures used in reproduction.
   - C. haploid cells that can produce any type of offspring cell.
   - D. found only in plant cells.

3. A dove has a diploid number of 16 chromosomes. How many possible distributions of chromosomes can occur in the homologous pairs of a dove's gametes?
   - A. 16
   - B. 32
   - C. 256
   - D. 65,536

4. A zygote becomes an embryo through the process of
   - A. mitosis.
   - B. meiosis.
   - C. cell differentiation.
   - D. fertilization.

5. What process of reproduction brings with it the greatest potential for genetic variability?
   - A. mitosis
   - B. meiosis
   - C. cell differentiation
   - D. interkinesis

MUTATIONS

Mutations are mistakes or misconnections in the duplication of the chromatin material. Mutations usually occur in the nucleus of the cell during the replication process of cell division. Some mutations are harmful to an organism, and some are beneficial. Mutations play a significant role in creating the diversity of life on Earth today. Geneticists classify mutations into two groups: **gene mutations** and **chromosomal mutations**.

Gene mutations are mistakes that affect individual genes on a chromosome. For instance, one base on the DNA strand substitutes for another base. A substitution of bases will change the codon and, therefore, the amino acid. Consequently, the protein being synthesized may be different from what the DNA originally coded for, thus affecting one or more functions within the organism. Gene mutations also occur by the insertion or deletion of nucleotides from a gene.

Suppose a mutation caused a codon found in the gene to be GAA instead of GAU. This type of mutation is called a **substitution**, because one base is substituted for another. This single change could cause a different amino acid to be added to a growing polypeptide. Depending upon its location in the protein, this error may result in a defective protein within the organism, or it may have no major effect. A defective protein may cause serious illness or death of an organism.

Sometimes nucleotides can be left out of DNA strands altogether or an extra nucleotide can be added where there was no nucleotide before. These types of mutations are called **frameshift mutations** because they shift the "reading frame" of the mRNA strands that are transcribed. For example, if a normal mRNA has the following sequence:

UUAAUCGGCUAC

It is read like this:

UUA-AUC-GGC-UAC

And codes for the following amino acids:

Leucine-Isoleucine-Glycine-Tyrosine

Now suppose that a mutation causes the fourth base in this sequence to be deleted. The new mRNA sequence will be:

UUAUCGGCUAC

It is still read in groups of three:

UUA-UCG-GCU-AC

And the new amino acid sequence is:

Leucine-Serine-Glycine...

The deletion resulted in a shift of the codons, so every codon following the mutation will be affected. For this reason, frameshift mutations often have very serious consequences for the protein, as well as for the organism as a whole.

Chromosomal mutations are mistakes that affect the whole chromosome. Recall that during meiosis homologous chromosomes pair and may exchange segments through a process called **crossing over**. If errors occur during crossing over, chromosomal mutations result. There are four major categories of chromosomal mutations.

- **Duplication mutations** occur when a chromosome segment attaches to a homologous chromosome that has not lost the complementary segment. One chromosome will then carry two copies of one gene, or a set of genes.

- **Deletion mutations** occur when a chromosome segment breaks off and does not reattach itself. When cell division is complete, the new cell will lack the genes carried by the segment that broke off.

- **Inversion mutations** occur when a segment of chromosome breaks off and then reattaches itself to the original chromosome, but backwards.

- **Translocation mutations** occur when a chromosome segment attaches itself to a nonhomologous chromosome.

These mutations are illustrated in the example below, which carries six genes, genes A-F.

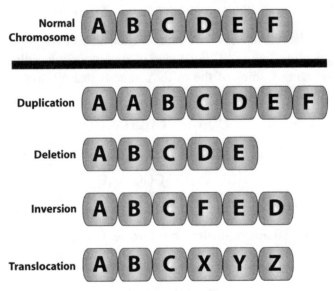

Figure 3.12 Types of Mutations

Mutations in the somatic cells affect only the tissues of the organism. Mutations occurring in the reproductive cells may be transmitted to the gametes formed in meiosis and thus pass on to future descendants. Some mutations are harmful to an organism, and some are beneficial. Many mutations do not have a noticeable effect on the functioning of the organism.

Activity 3

Your teacher will provide you with a plastic sandwich bag that contains 3 or 4 homologous pairs of "chromosomes" made with yarn. The "chromosomes" come in two colors, blue and pink. The color represents the chromosome's original donor (father or mother). On your "chromosomes" you might notice some knots. These knots represent different alleles for traits. You will notice that one knot from each pair is colored, this is the dominant allele.

Use the bag provided by your teacher to examine how traits are passed from parents to offspring by sexual and asexual reproduction. Begin by drawing a large circle on ½ of a blank sheet of paper. Next match the homologous chromosome pairs together.

NOTE: You will not use all of your yarn pieces in this step. Remember you will only have 3 or 4 pairs.

Continue by placing your "chromosomes" inside the circle. This is your parent cell. Next you will move your cell through the process of mitosis. You will do this by moving your "chromosomes" into daughter cells near the bottom of the page. Be sure you have the correct number of daughter cells for mitosis. Examine how the alleles were passed from the parent to the offspring.

Next, repeat the process, only this time you will move your cell through the process of meiosis.

As an extension, you can pretend to have mutations occur to your chromosomes by cutting (deletion) or adding (inserting) yarn to your chromosomes. Inversion mutations are simulated by twisting a loop into the yarn segment.

Examine the drawing below to help you.

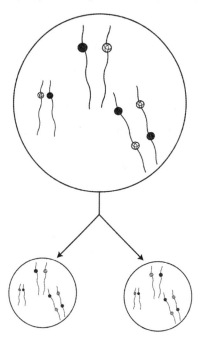

Section Review 4:   Mutations

A. Define the following terms.

mutation	chromosomal mutation	inversion mutation
gene mutation	deletion mutation	translocation mutation
		frameshift mutation

B. Choose the best answer.

1. A change in the chromosome structure caused by radiation, chemicals, pollutants or during replication is a/an

    A.   mutation.   B.   allele.   C.   gene.   D.   replicator.

2. A change in the nitrogen bases on the DNA strand is what kind of mutation?

    A.   chromosome mutation   C.   gene mutation

    B.   segregated mutation   D.   nondisjunction mutation

3. Which of the four types of mutations causes a change in the arrangement, rather than the number, of genes on a chromosome?

    A.   deletion   C.   translocation

    B.   deletion and translocation   D.   translocation and inversion

4. Which kind of mutation could cause a disease that might be passed along to one's offspring?

    A.   chromosomal mutation in the somatic cells

    B.   chromosomal mutation in the reproductive cells

    C.   gene mutation in the somatic cells

    D.   A and B only.

5. Which of the following is affected by a frameshift mutation?

    A.   nothing

    B.   only the codon where the mutation occurred

    C.   all the codons before the mutation

    D.   the codon where the mutation occurred, as well as all the codons after the mutation.

CHAPTER 3 REVIEW

A. Choose the best answer.

1. Chromosomes line up on spindles in the center of a cell during

   A. anaphase.

   B. telophase.

   C. metaphase.

   D. prophase.

2. In the DNA molecule, guanine pairs with another base called

   A. quinine.

   B. riboflavin.

   C. cytosine.

   D. thymine.

3. The long strands of DNA are made up of

   A. elastic rubber bases.

   B. sugar nucleotides and potassium.

   C. sugar and phosphates.

   D. oxygen and nucleotides.

4. The sections of DNA that resemble rungs on a ladder are called

   A. genetic codes.

   B. reprocessors.

   C. base pairs.

   D. lipid pairs.

5. Mitosis generates

   A. daughter cells identical to the mother cell.

   B. many reproductive cells.

   C. diseased cells.

   D. gametes.

6. Meiosis is a type of cell division that

   A. leads to genetic mutation.

   B. causes deformity.

   C. is necessary for sexual reproduction.

   D. causes alleles to deform.

7. DNA can make exact copies of itself. This process is called

   A. translation.

   B. duplication.

   C. replication.

   D. transcription.

8. A type of cellular reproduction when the nuclear division of somatic cells takes place is

   A. meiosis.   B. cytokinesis.   C. interphase.   D. mitosis.

9. When preparing for cell division, the chromatin condenses and becomes a

   A. gene.

   B. chromosome.

   C. protein.

   D. codon.

10. The molecule that transports the code of information from DNA to the ribosome is
    A. tRNA.   B. rRNA.   C. mRNA.   D. an amino acid.

11. The process in which paired twin chromosomes exchange pieces of DNA during meiosis is called
    A. crossing over.   C. self pollination.
    B. fertilization.   D. replication.

12. Somatic cells have two sets of chromosomes, one from the mother and one from the father. These matched pairs of chromosomes are called
    A. clones.   C. homologous chromosomes.
    B. gametes.   D. mutations.

13. During translation, adenine on mRNA will pair with which base on tRNA?
    A. uracil   B. guanine   C. thymine   D. cytosine

14. Amino acids that are not yet part of a polypeptide are found in which part of the cell?
    A. mitochondria   C. Golgi apparatus
    B. cytoplasm   D. nucleus

15. The number of chromosomes in gametes is referred to as
    A. chromatin.   C. heterozygous.
    B. haploid.   D. controlled.

16. Prior to cell differentiation, all the cells in an embryo are
    A. the same.   B. stem cells.   C. gametes.   D. A and B

17. A fruit fly has a haploid number of 4 chromosomes. How many possible distributions of chromosomes can occur in its homologous pairs?
    A. 4   B. 8   C. 16   D. 256

18. What is the function of a stop codon?
    A. to instruct tRNA to stop delivering amino acids to mRNA
    B. to instruct the ribosome to stop delivering amino acids to mRNA
    C. to bind to the ribosome and stop the translation process thereby releasing the protein
    D. to instruct the ribosome to stop the transcription process and release the protein

19. Which of the following occurs in a gene when a nucleotide is added or deleted by mistake?
    A. protein synthesis   C. frameshift mutation
    B. point mutation   D. transcription

Chapter 4
Genetics, Heredity and Biotechnology

GA HSGT SCIENCE STANDARDS COVERED IN THIS CHAPTER INCLUDE:

GPS Standards	
SB2 c and f	Students will analyze how biological traits are passed on to successive generations.

GENETIC EXPRESSION

Genes, which are specific portions of DNA, determine hereditary characteristics. Genes carry traits that can pass from one generation to the next. **Alleles** are different molecular forms of a gene. Each parent passes on one allele for each trait to the offspring. Each offspring has two alleles for each trait. The expression of physical characteristics depends on the genes that both parents contribute for that particular characteristic. **Genotype** is the term for the combination of alleles inherited from the parents.

Genes are either dominant or recessive. The **dominant gene** is the trait that will most likely express itself. If both alleles are dominant, or one is dominant and one is recessive, the trait expressed will be the dominant one. In order for expression of the **recessive gene** to occur, both alleles must be the recessive ones. For example, a mother might pass on a gene for having dimples, and the father might pass on a gene for not having dimples. Having dimples is dominant over not having dimples, so the offspring will have dimples even though it inherits one allele of each trait. For the offspring not to have dimples, both the mother and father must pass along the allele for not having dimples. The **phenotype** is the physical expression of the traits. The phenotype does not necessarily reveal the combination of alleles.

When studying the expression of the traits, geneticists use letters as symbols for the different traits. We use capital letters for dominant alleles and lowercase letters for recessive alleles. For dimples, the symbol could be D. For no dimples, the symbol could be d. The genotype of the offspring having one gene for dimples and one gene for no dimples is Dd. The phenotype for this example is having dimples.

If an individual inherits two of the same alleles, either dominant or recessive, for a particular characteristic, the individual is **homozygous**. If the offspring inherits one dominant allele and one recessive allele, such as in the example in the above paragraph, the individual is **heterozygous**.

Geneticists use the **Punnett square** to express the possible combinations for a certain trait an offspring may inherit from the parents. The Punnett square shows possible genotypes and phenotypes of one offspring. Figure 4.1 shows an example of a **monohybrid cross**, which involves one trait, done on a Punnett square.

The Punnett square

The Punnett square is a tool geneticists use to determine the possible genotype of one offspring. The possible alleles donated by one parent are written across the top and the possible alleles donated by the other parent are written along the left side. In the example, the cross between two heterozygous parents is examined.

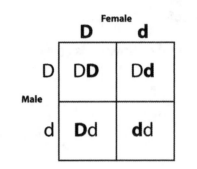

D = allele for dimples

d = allele for no dimples

Each time this male and female produce an offspring, there is a 3/4 or 75% chance the offspring will have dimples and a 1/4 or 25% chance the offspring will have no dimples

Figure 4.1 Punnett Square for Dimples/No Dimples

The phenotype depends not only on which genes are present but also on the environment. Environmental differences have an effect on the expression of traits in an organism. For example, a plant seed may have the genetic ability to have green tissues, to flower and to bear fruit, but it must be in the correct environmental conditions. If the required amount of light, water and nutrients are not present, those genes may not be expressed.

Temperature also affects the expression of genes. Primrose plants will bloom red flowers at room temperature and white at higher temperatures. Himalayan rabbits and Siamese cats have dark extremities like ears, nose and feet, at low temperatures. Warmer areas of the animals' bodies are lighter colored.

MENDEL'S CONTRIBUTION TO GENETICS

Around 1850, **Gregor Mendel** (1822 – 1884) began his work at an Austrian monastery. Many biologists call Mendel "the father of genetics" for his studies on plant inheritance. Mendel and his assistants grew, bred, counted and observed over 28,000 pea plants.

Pea plants are very useful when conducting genetic studies because the pea plant has a very simple genetic make up. It has only seven chromosomes, its traits can be easily observed, and it can **cross-pollinate** (have two different parents) or **self-pollinate** (have only one parent). Table 4.1 lists some of the pea plant traits, along with their attributes. To begin his experiments, Mendel used plants that were true breeders for one trait. **True breeders** have a known genetic history and will self-pollinate to produce offspring identical to itself.

Table 4.1 Possible Traits of Pea Plants

Seed Shape	Round* Wrinkled		Pod Color	Green* Yellow	
Seed Color	Yellow* Green		Flower Position	Axial* Terminal	
Seed Coat Color	Gray* White		Plant Height	Tall* Short	
Pod Shape	Smooth* Constricted				

*Dominant

PRINCIPLE OF DOMINANCE

Through his experiments, Mendel discovered a basic principle of genetics, the principle of dominance. Mendel's **principle of dominance** states that some forms of a gene or trait are dominant over other traits, which are called recessive. A dominant trait will mask or hide the presence of a recessive trait. When Mendel crossed a true breeding tall pea plant with a true breeding short pea plant, he saw that all the offspring plants were tall. The tallness trait *masks* the recessive shortness trait. The crossing of the true breeders is the **parental generation**, or the **P** generation. The offspring produced are the first filial generation or F_1 generation. The offspring of the F_1 generation are called the second filial or F_2 generation.

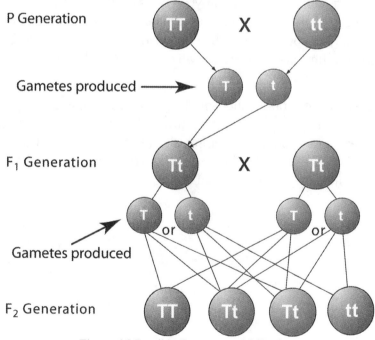

Figure 4.2 Possible Genotypes of Offspring

PRINCIPLE OF SEGREGATION

Crossing plants from the F_1 generation creates the F_2 generation. Mendel soon discovered that a predictable ratio of phenotypes appeared. For every one recessive plant, there were three dominant plants present. Mendel realized that this ratio could only occur if the alleles separate sometime during gamete formation.

As a result, Mendel developed his **principle of segregation**. This principle states that when forming sex cells, the paired alleles separate so that each egg or sperm only carries one form of the allele. The two forms of the allele come together again during fertilization.

PRINCIPLE OF INDEPENDENT ASSORTMENT

When Mendel began to study **dihybrid crosses**, which involve two traits, he noticed another interesting irregularity. Mendel crossed plants that were homozygous for two traits, seed color and seed texture. Round seed texture and green color are both dominant traits. Mendel assigned the dominant homozygous P generation the genotype of (RRGG). Wrinkled seed texture and yellow color are both recessive traits. The recessive homozygous P generation seeds were assigned the genotype (rrgg). When (RRGG) was crossed with (rrgg) the

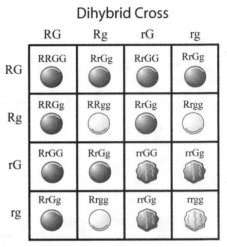

Dihybrid Cross

Figure 4.3 Dihybrid Cross of F1 Heterozygous Offspring

resulting F_1 generation was entirely heterozygous (RrGg). The F_1 generation was then allowed to self-pollinate, resulting in an F_1 dihybrid cross of (RrGg) with (RrGg). This resulted in an F_2 generation with a distinct distribution of traits, as depicted in Figure 4.3. Counting up the genotypes of the F_2 generation should give you the result that 9/16 of them will have the round, green phenotype, 3/16 will have the round, yellow phenotype, 3/16 will have the wrinkled, green phenotype and 1/16 will have the wrinkled, yellow phenotype.

The consistent observation of this trend led to the development of the **principle of independent assortment**. This principle states that each pair of alleles segregates independently during the formation of the egg or sperm. For example, the allele for green seed color may be accompanied by the allele for round texture in some gametes and by wrinkled texture in others. The alleles for seed color segregate independently of those for seed texture.

Section Review 1: Genetics

A. Define the following terms.

gene	phenotype	Gregory Mendel
allele	homozygous	true breeder
genotype	heterozygous	principle of dominance
dominant gene	Punnett square	principle of segregation
recessive gene	monohybrid cross	dihybrid
principle of independent assortment		gamete

B. Choose the best answer.

1. The combination of alleles inherited is called the
   A. heterozygote.
   B. phenotype.
   C. genotype.
   D. Punnett square.

2. The expression of traits is called the
   A. phenotype.
   B. genotype.
   C. mutation.
   D. allele.

3. If an individual inherits one dominant allele and one recessive allele, the genotype is
   A. homozygous.
   B. recessive.
   C. heterozygous.
   D. phenotype.

4. If an individual inherits two of the same allele, either both dominant or both recessive for a particular characteristic, the individual's genotype is
   A. heterozygous.
   B. phenotypic.
   C. homozygous.
   D. mutated.

5. Use a Punnett square to predict the cross of a homozygous green parent with a homozygous yellow parent if yellow is dominant over green. The phenotype of the offspring will be
   A. all yellow.
   B. all green.
   C. neither yellow nor green.
   D. some yellow and some green.

C. Answer the following questions.

1. The gene for cystic fibrosis is a recessive trait. This disorder causes the body cells to secrete large amounts of mucus that can damage the lungs, liver and pancreas. If one out of 20 people is a carrier of this disorder, why is only one out of 1,600 babies born with cystic fibrosis?

2. What is the relationship between phenotype and genotype?

3. Compare homozygous alleles to heterozygous alleles.

4. What specifically determines hereditary characteristics in an individual?

Modes of Inheritance

Sex-Linked Traits

Sex chromosomes are the chromosomes responsible for determining the sex of an organism. These chromosomes carry the genes responsible for sex determination as well as other traits. They are the 23rd pair of chromosomes and are sometimes called X or Y chromosomes. Males have the genotype XY and females have the genotype XX. In females, one X comes from their mother and one X comes from their father. In males, the X chromosome comes from their mother and the Y chromosome comes from their father.

Punnett Square for Color Blindness

	X^B	X^b
X^B	$X^B X^B$	$X^B X^b$
Y	$X^B Y$	$X^b Y$

B = Normal
b = Color Blind

Figure 4.4 Punnett Square for Color Blindness

If a recessive trait, like color blindness, is located on the X chromosome, it is not very likely that females will have the phenotype for this condition. It is more likely that males will have the condition since they only have one X chromosome. Males do not have another X chromosome or a duplicate copy of the gene. A female that has a recessive gene on one X chromosome is a **carrier** for that trait.

Examine the Punnett square in Figure 4.4, which shows the cross of a female who is heterozygous for color blindness with a normal male. This Punnett square shows how a mother contributes to the color blindness of her sons.

Incomplete Dominance

Incomplete dominance is the situation when one trait is not completely dominant over the other. Think of it as blending of the two traits. All of the offspring in the F_1 generation will show a phenotype that is a blending of both the parents. If the F_1 generation is self-pollinated, the ratio of phenotypes in the offspring (F_2 generation) will appear in a predictable pattern. One offspring will look like one parent, two offspring will look like both parents, and one offspring will look like the other parent.

A cross between a red and a white four o'clock flower demonstrates this point. One flower in the parental generation is red with genotype $R^1 R^1$. The other flower is white with genotype $R^2 R^2$. The offspring of this cross appear pink and have a genotype of $R^1 R^2$. See Figure 4.5 to the right for the genotypes and the phenotypes of the P, F_1 and F_2 generations.

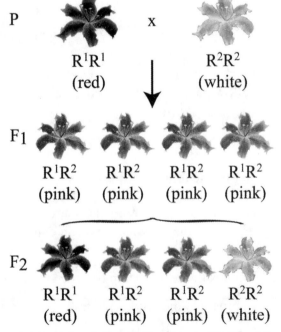

P

$R^1 R^1$ (red)   x $R^2 R^2$ (white)

F1

$R^1 R^2$ (pink) $R^1 R^2$ (pink) $R^1 R^2$ (pink) $R^1 R^2$ (pink)

F2

$R^1 R^1$ (red) $R^1 R^2$ (pink) $R^1 R^2$ (pink) $R^2 R^2$ (white)

Figure 4.5 Genotypes and Phenotypes of P, F_1 and F_2 Generations of 4 o'clock Flower

CO-DOMINANCE

When both traits appear in the F_1 generation and contribute to the phenotype of the offspring, the trait is **co-dominant**. One example occurs in horses in which the trait for red hair is co-dominant with the trait for white hair. A roan is a foal that has both traits. The horse appears to look pinkish-brown from far away. However, if you look closely at the coat of this animal, you will notice that both solid red and solid white hairs found on the coat give the animal its unique color.

Though they sound similar, there are two main differences between the situations of co-dominance and incomplete dominance. When one allele is incompletely dominant over another, the blended result occurs because *neither allele is fully expressed*. That is why the F_1 generation four o'clock flower is a *totally different color* (pink). In contrast, when two alleles are co-dominant, *both alleles are completely expressed*. The result is a combination of the two, rather than a blending. The roan horse's hair may look pink from afar, but it is actually a combination of distinct red hair and white hair.

MULTIPLE ALLELES AND POLYGENIC TRAITS

Certain traits like blood type, hair color and eye color are determined by two genes for every trait, one from each parent. Whenever there are different molecular forms of the same gene, each form is called an allele. Although each individual only has two alleles, there can be many different combinations of alleles in that same population. For instance, hamster hair color is controlled by one gene with alleles for black, brown, agouti (multi-colored), gray, albino and others. Each allele can result in a different coloration.

Polygenic traits are the result of the interaction of multiple genes. It is commonly known, for instance, that high blood pressure has a strong hereditary linkage. The phenotype for hypertension is not, however, controlled by a single gene that lends itself to elevating or lowering blood pressure. Rather, it is the result of the interaction between people's weight (partially controlled by one or more genes), their ability to process fats in general and cholesterol in particular (several metabolic genes), their ability to process and move various salts through the bloodstream (transport genes) and their lifestyle habits, such as smoking and drinking (which may or may not be the result of the expression of several genes that express themselves as addictive behavior). Of course, each of the genes involved may also have multiple alleles, which vastly expands the complexity of the interaction.

Section Review 2: Modes of Inheritance

A. Define the following terms.

sex chromosomes	carrier	incomplete dominance
co–dominance	multiple alleles	polygenic traits

B. Choose the best answer.

1. A male has the genotype XY. Which parent is responsible for giving the son the Y chromosome?

   A. mother

   B. father

   C. both the father and the mother

   D. neither the father nor the mother

2. What is the difference between co–dominance and incomplete dominance?

   A. Co–dominant traits are blended, and incompletely dominant traits appear together.

   B. Co–dominant traits are recessive, and incompletely dominant traits appear together.

   C. Co-dominant traits appear together, and incompletely dominant traits are blended.

   D. Co-dominant traits are recessive, and incompletely dominant traits are blended

3. A cross between a black guinea pig and a white guinea pig produces a grayish guinea pig. What information do you need to determine if the production of a greyish offspring is a result of co–dominance or multiple alleles?

   A. the phenotype of the guinea pig's litter mates

   B. the number of alleles per gene

   C. the genotype of both parents

   D. either A or B

4. Roan horse and cattle fur is a common example of

   A. incomplete dominance.

   B. co–dominance.

   C. multiple alleles.

   D. polygenic traits.

C. Answer the following questions.

1. The phenotype for blood type is an example of a multiple allele trait. The three alleles are A, B, and O. A and B are co-dominant to O. Determine the phenotypes of the offspring in each of the situations to the right.

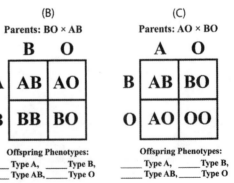

(A)
Parents: AO × AA

	A	O
A	AA	AO
A	AA	AO

Offspring Phenotypes:
____ Type A, ____ Type B,
____ Type AB, ____ Type O

(B)
Parents: BO × AB

	B	O
A	AB	AO
B	BB	BO

Offspring Phenotypes:
____ Type A, ____ Type B,
____ Type AB, ____ Type O

(C)
Parents: AO × BO

	A	O
B	AB	BO
O	AO	OO

Offspring Phenotypes:
____ Type A, ____ Type B,
____ Type AB, ____ Type O

2. Given the information that the offspring phenotypes for blood type are 2/4 AB and 2/4 AO, draw a corresponding Punnett square.

BIOTECHNOLOGY

Biotechnology is the commercial application of biological products and has been in existence for thousands of years. It includes the production of wine, beer, cheese and antibiotics, but today it more commonly refers to processes that manipulate DNA. DNA technologies, or biotechnology, manipulate DNA to benefit humans. DNA technologies have impacted the following three areas of modern life: forensics, medicine and agriculture.

FORENSICS

Forensics uses scientific techniques to collect evidence for the legal system. DNA is used in forensics to collect and analyze different samples found at crime scenes. Sometimes a sample of DNA is found at a crime scene. This unknown DNA sample is analyzed and compared with a database containing known DNA samples. This process is known as DNA fingerprinting.

DNA FINGERPRINTING

With the exception of identical twins, every person's DNA is different. **DNA fingerprinting** is the identification of a person using his DNA. Laboratory tests are performed by forensic scientists to determine if the suspect of a crime, for example, was present at the scene of the crime. It is also used to determine paternity or the father of a child. This process has a high degree of accuracy, greater than 99%. A DNA fingerprint is not the same as an actual fingerprint taken by inking your finger. Neither is it a blueprint of your entire DNA sequence. Rather, it is the analysis of a small number of sequences of DNA that are known to vary a great deal among individuals. These sequences are analyzed to get a probability of a match. That means that DNA fingerprinting can be used to compare sample DNA from, say, a crime scene to sample DNA taken from a suspect. It cannot be used to tell who you are, independent of a comparative sample.

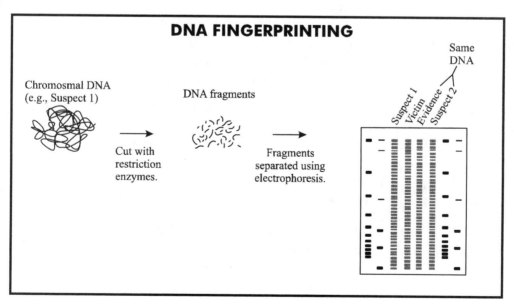

Figure 4.6 DNA Fingerprinting

DNA fingerprinting is performed by cutting DNA with enzymes and separating the fragments using electrophoresis. **Electrophoresis** uses electrical charges to separate pieces of molecules based on both size and charge. The nucleic acids of DNA have a consistent negative charge imparted by their phosphate backbone, and thus migrate toward the positive terminal of the electrophoresis apparatus! The speed at which they migrate depends on both the size and molecular structure of the fragments. The result is a column of bands, each representing a specific fragment of DNA. Since two identical samples of DNA will both fragment and migrate in the same fashion, matching bands indicate that the DNA of those samples is the same, and thus the person from which those samples came is one and the same person.

In years past, there have been errors in the results of DNA fingerprinting. Today, however, there is only a tiny possibility of error, a fraction of a percent, since such advances have been made in the precision and accuracy of electrophoretic techniques that DNA sequences differing by a single base pair can now be easily resolved.

BIOTECHNOLOGY IN MEDICINE

Figure 4.7 Biotech Analyst

The medical establishment is a strong proponent of **biotechnology**. Biotechnological research is encouraged in government, academic and private laboratories. This has generated a need for many analysts and researchers with a biochemistry background. Every year, greater advances are made in biotech medicines and therapies.

Recombinant DNA technology uses the natural process of transcription and translation to alter organisms. The DNA containing the desired gene is cut into segments by humans. The fragment that contains the desired gene is inserted into the genome of a microscopic biological agent like a bacteria or virus. The newly inserted DNA segment will now produce the desired protein. The biological agent now contains the recombinant (re-combined) DNA. Once inserted into a human, it reproduces, inserting the desired DNA segment into other cells. The **vaccine** for Hepatitis B is a recombinant product. Human insulin and growth hormone as well as a clot-dissolving medication have been created using recombinant DNA technology. **Interferon** is a recombinant product used to fight cancer and a broad array of other diseases.

Monoclonal antibodies are exact copies of an antibody that bind to a specific antigen, such as a cancer cell. Once the binding takes place, the immune system detects and responds to the target cancer cell. These antibodies have been created and are used as therapy for breast cancer and non-Hodgkin's lymphoma. Research is ongoing to produce antibodies to target cells responsible for causing other diseases. As with all medications, side effects are evaluated, and each drug must prove to be more beneficial than harmful before it is approved for use.

In addition to medications, **gene therapy** is used to help cure diseases. The idea is that if a defective protein is replaced with a good one, then the disease caused by the defective protein can be eliminated. Gene therapy has the greatest potential for success in treating diseases with only one defective gene.

Gene therapy is currently used in people who have SCID, severe combined immunodeficiency. People with this disease are also called "bubble babies" because they must be kept in sterile, bubble-like environments to prevent even minor infections which can kill them. To treat the disease, cells with the gene to make a certain protein are introduced into the body via the white blood cells. The new cells can then multiply and produce the protein necessary to have a functional immune system.

STEM CELL RESEARCH

Stem cells are cells found in the human body that have yet to become a specialized type of cell. They are a "pre cell." Stem cells have the amazing ability to become any type of cell or tissue. For example, a stem cell could develop into a nerve cell, skin cell or a liver cell. The potential for using stem cells to help cure many chronic human diseases is great. There are three main sources of stem cells available. Stem cells can be harvested from adult bone marrow, umbilical cord blood after delivery or from human embryos. The harvesting of stem cells from human embryos results in the death of that embryo. For this reason, many people oppose using embryonic stem cells in medicine. There are other avenues of harvesting stem cells, however:

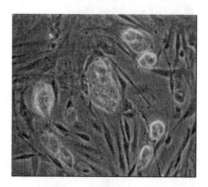

Figure 4.8 Stem Cells

sources such as bone marrow and umbilical cord blood are being researched as possible alternatives to the use of embryonic stem cells. More research is needed to determine the full range of therapeutic possibilities of stem cells.

CLONING

Cloning is the creation of genetically identical organisms. The cloning of Dolly the sheep from a somatic cell of an adult sheep created great debate about the possibility of cloning humans. The possible benefits of human cloning include allowing a childless couple to have a child, creating tissues for transplantation that would not be rejected by their host and using genetically altered cells to treat people with Alzheimer's or Parkinson's, both diseases caused by the death of specific cells within the brain. Another application is to create therapeutic proteins, like antibodies, through the modification of the cells and then cloning the cells to have several copies.

Figure 4.9 Dolly and Her Offspring Bonnie

Although creating a human clone is theoretically possible, it would be very difficult. Dolly was the 277th attempt in cloning a mammal and her death sparked a huge array of new research questions. Both scientific and moral questions must be debated, researched and solved if cloning technology is ever to become mainstream science. In the United States, federal research funds are not given to scientists who research human cloning, but the research is not banned.

GENETIC ENGINEERING OF AGRICULTURAL CROPS

Figure 4.10 Crops

Many scientists and researchers believe that recombinant technology holds great potential for improvements in agricultural products. There have already been many successes with the technology. These modified crops and animals allow farms to produce higher quality and more bountiful products, which in turn give the farmers a greater earning potential. For centuries, traditional methods of plant hybridization have been widely used to improve the genetic characteristics of various agricultural products. Recombinant technology takes this to an improved level by allowing scientists to transfer specific genetic material in a very precise and controlled manner and in a shorter period of time than traditional methods. For example, in plant crops the characteristics of pest resistance and improved product quality are highly desirable.

Recombinant technology has already resulted in improved strains of corn, soybeans and cotton. The desirable genes inserted into the plants' DNA enable crops to resist certain insects or tolerate herbicides used to kill weeds. These improvements also enable farmers to reduce the use of chemicals, which reduces costs for the farmers, as well as helping to reduce environmental damage and run-off pollution. Rot-resistant tomatoes have been made possible by agricultural biotechnology. This improved variety allows grocery stores to offer naturally vine-ripened tomatoes instead of tomatoes that were picked green and artificially ripened on their way to the store.

Some improved products show promise for a global impact on the problem of malnutrition. Researchers working in cooperation with the International Rice Research Institute have used genetic engineering to develop an improved variety of rice. This hybrid "golden rice" has been designed to overcome Vitamin A deficiency and to combat iron-deficiency anemia. A diet containing this improved rice could prevent blindness in millions of children in Third World countries. Another product in development is a variety of rice that will grow in the 33 million acres of land in China that have salty soil.

Figure 4.11 Rice Farm

There are many questions about the possible long term effects of these genetic technologies. One concern is that genetically modified foods may be detrimental to human health. Genetically engineered foods may cause unexpected allergic reactions in people, since proteins not naturally found in the product have been inserted. Without labeling, a person with allergies may find it difficult to avoid a known food allergen if part of the food causing the allergy is genetically added into another food product. In many European and Asian countries, modified foods must be labeled as such, but, in the United States, the FDA has not yet required consumer information labeling.

Genetically modified crops could pose some threat to the environment. Since herbicide-tolerant crop plants do not die when exposed to the weed-killing chemicals, some crops might be sprayed more heavily to ensure greater weed control. Some studies have indicated that the destruction of plant life naturally surrounding the crops reduces the habitats and food supplies of birds and beneficial insects.

Genetic pollution can occur through the cross-pollination of genetically modified and non-genetically modified plants by wind, birds and insects. Also, farmers who want to grow non-genetically modified crops may have a hard time avoiding genetic pollution if their farms are located near fields with genetically modified plants.

Section Review 3: Biotechnology

A. Define the following terms.

biotechnology   monoclonal antibody   cloning

recombinant DNA   gene therapy   DNA fingerprinting

genetic pollution   stem cell   electrophoresis

B. Choose the best answer.

1. What is the commercial application of biological products?
    A. illegal
    B. biotechnology
    C. unethical
    D. agricultural

2. What is a DNA fingerprint?
    A. a blue print of the entire DNA
    B. a print made by inking your finger.
    C. an analysis of a small segment of DNA
    D. transformed loop

3. Strawberries have been created to resist the harmful effects of frost. This is an application of what?
    A. genetic engineering
    B. gene therapy
    C. DNA fingerprinting
    D. cloning

4. A person with a defect in a gene that codes for a specific protein could be a candidate for which of the following?
    A. cloning
    B. DNA fingerprinting
    C. gene therapy
    D. protein injections

5. Which of the following is a potential carrier of DNA to create recombinant products?
    A. clone
    B. virus
    C. enzyme
    D. electrophoresis

C. Answer the following questions.

1. What are the positive and negative aspects of cloning humans?

2. How is genetically modified food beneficial to farmers? How can it be harmful?

3. Give an example of an advance in biotechnology that you have heard about in the news or read about in this chapter. Explain the benefits of the application of biotechnology as well as possible negative effects.

CHAPTER 4 REVIEW

A. Choose the best answer.

1. Down's syndrome is caused by

    A. hemophilia.

    B. thyroid disease.

    C. chromosome mutation.

    D. injury during pregnancy.

2. Use a Punnett square to predict the cross of a homozygous tall parent with a homozygous short parent if tall is dominant over short. The phenotypes of the offspring will be

    A. all tall.

    B. all short.

    C. neither short nor tall.

    D. some tall and some short.

3. What kind of alleles are present in the heterozygous genotype?

    A. two identical alleles

    B. two recessive alleles

    C. two non-identical alleles

    D. two dominant alleles

4. If a person receives the Blood Type A allele from one parent and the Blood Type B allele from the other parent, there is a chance that they will have the phenotype for Type AB blood. Type AB blood has characteristics of both Type A and Type B blood. This is an example of

    A. incomplete dominance.

    B. co-dominance.

    C. a polygenic trait.

    D. a sex-linked trait.

5. The F_2 generation of snapdragon plants reveals the distinct phenotypes that were present in the P generation but lost in the F_1 generation. What is the reason for this?

    A. The two plants crossed in the P generation had alleles that were incompletely dominant to each other.

    B. The two plants crossed in the P generation had alleles that were co-dominant to each other.

    C. The F_1 generation consisted of only heterozygous genotypes.

    D. The F_1 generation consisted of only homozygous genotypes.

Use the Punnett square to answer questions 6 and 7.

6. What is the probability that the offspring of this cross will be homozygous recessive?

    A. 0%   B. 25%   C. 50%   D. 100%

7. What is the probability that the offspring of this cross will be homozygous dominant?

    A. 0%   B. 25%   C. 50%   D. 100%

Use the following Punnett square and phenotype key to answer questions 8 and 9.

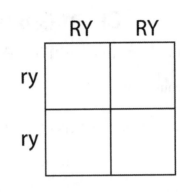

Key:
R : Allele for round seed shape
r : Allele for wrinkled seed shape
Y: Allele for yellow seed color
y: Allele for green seed color

8. What is the genotype ratio of the off-spring in this dihybrid cross?
   A. 100% RrYy
   B. 50% RRYY and 50% rryy
   C. 25% RRYY, 50% RrYy and 25% rryy
   D. 25% RRYY, 75% RrYy and 0% rryy

9. What will the phenotype of the offspring be?
   A. all round and green
   B. all round and yellow
   C. half round and yellow, half wrinkled and green
   D. three quarters round and yellow, one quarter wrinkled and green

10. The medical industry is helped by technology
    A. through the development of better treatments and drugs.
    B. through the more effective disposal of wastes.
    C. by better helping people deal with loss of a loved one.
    D. through better care for the ill members of society.

11. Stem cells
    A. only come from human embryos.
    B. can cure most diseases.
    C. are found on the ends of neurons.
    D. are undifferentiated cells capable of becoming any tissue.

12. A police officer is at a crime scene and is collecting samples of blood, hair and skin. What is the officer probably going to do with the samples?
    A. The officer is cleaning the crime scene based on protocol.
    B. The officer is keeping samples to be filed with the police report.
    C. The officer is going to have the samples analyzed for a DNA fingerprint.
    D. The officer will show them to the victim's family, the judge, and the prosecutor.

Chapter 5
Taxonomy and Evolution

GA HSGT SCIENCE STANDARDS COVERED IN THIS CHAPTER INCLUDE:

GPS Standards	
SB3 b – c	Students will derive the relationship between single-celled and multi-celled organisms and the increasing complexity of systems.
SB4 e – f	Students will assess the dependence of all organisms on one another and the flow of energy and matter within their ecosystems
SB5 a – e	Students will evaluate the role of natural selection in the development of the theory of evolution

BIOLOGICAL CLASSIFICATION

Biologists classify living things according to the traits they share. **Taxonomy** is the classification of an organism based on several features, such as structure, behavior, development, genetic makeup (DNA), nutritional needs and methods of obtaining food. Evolutionary theory is the basis for this classification system. Taxonomy divides organisms into several categories that start out broadly and become more specific. These categories are **kingdom**, **phylum**, **class**, **order**, **family**, **genus** and **species**.

Occasionally, subphylum, subclasses and suborders are used to further delineate characteristics among the primary classifications.

Table 5.1 lists the six **kingdoms** based on general characteristics. Each kingdom further divides into **phylum**, to name organisms in the kingdoms of Eubacteria. Phylum further break down into **classes**, and classes break down into **orders**. The categories become progressively more detailed and include fewer organisms as they are further broken down into **family**, **genus** and **species**. The species is the most specific category. Organisms of the same species can breed and produce fertile offspring.

To remember the order of the subdivisions, memorize the silly sentence, "King Phillip Came Over From Greece Sneezing." The first letter of each of the words in this sentence is also the first letter of each of the classification categories for organisms.

Figure 5.1 Classification System for Organisms

Table 5.1 The Six Kingdoms

Super Kingdom	Kingdom	Basic Characteristic	Example
Prokaryotes	Eubacteria	found everywhere	cyanobacteria
	Archaebacteria	live without oxygen, get their energy from inorganic matter or light, found in extreme habitats	halophiles
Eukaryotes	Protista	one-celled or multicellular, true nucleus	amoeba
	Fungi	multicellular, food from dead organisms, cannot move	mushroom
	Plantae	multicellular, cannot move, make their own food, cell walls	tree
	Animalia	multicellular, move about, depend on others for food	horse

Aristotle (384 – 322 BC) made the first recorded attempt at classification of plants and animals. He grouped all living things into two main categories: plants and animals. According to Aristotle, animals were further divided into two groups: blooded and bloodless. Blooded animals included viviparous quadrupeds (live-bearing four legged), birds, oviparous quadrupeds (egg laying four legged), fish and cetaceans (whales). Bloodless animals included land arthropods (insects), aquatic arthropods (crustaceans), shelled animals (mollusks), soft animals (octopus) and plant-animals (jelly fish).

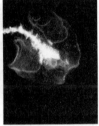

Figure 5.2 Two of Aristotles' Bloodless Animals

Aristotle's classification system had many flaws because the relatedness and reproductive strategies of organisms was not completely understood in his time. However, Aristotle's contribution to taxonomy was important because early on it promoted the scientific way of organizing information.

Figure 5.3 Carl Linnaeus

Carl Linnaeus (1707 – 1778), a Swedish botanist, devised the current system for classifying organisms. Linnaeus used **binomial nomenclature**, a system of naming organisms using a two-part name to label the species. The binomial name is written in Latin and is considered the scientific name. It consists of the generic name (genus) and the specific epithet (species). The entire scientific name is italicized or underlined, and the genus name is capitalized, as in *Homo sapiens* for humans. Table 5.2 is a complete classification of three members of the kingdom Animalia, which we will examine later in the chapter.

A classification system is necessary to distinguish among the great number of organisms and to avoid confusion created by the use of common names. Common names are used for many organisms, but not all organisms have common names, and some have multiple common names.

Table 5.2 Examples of Classifications

Example:	Human	Grasshopper	Dog
Kingdom	Animalia	Animalia	Animalia
Phylum	Chordata	Arthropoda	Chordata
Class	Mammalia	Insecta	Mammalia
Order	Primate	Orthoptera	Carnivora
Family	Homindae	Locuslidea	Canidae
Genus	*Homo*	*Schistocerca*	*Canis*
Species	*sapiens*	*americana*	*familiaris*

The hierarchical classification devised by Linnaeus has been, and still is, quite useful in organizing organisms. However, limitations do exist. For instance, even though classification is based on evolutionary theory, it does not reflect the idea that evolutionary processes are continual, and species are not fixed. Changes will occur over time and, therefore, classification will also have to change. Also, classification does not take into account the variation that exists among individuals within a species. All domestic dogs have the scientific name *Canis lupus familiaris*, but a great deal of variation exists among different breeds of dogs and even among individual dogs of the same breed.

Finally, the most definitive test to determine if organisms are of the same species is to confirm their ability to breed successfully, producing fertile offspring. However, controlled breeding of wild organisms for the purpose of observation and study can sometimes be impractical, if not impossible. Also, sometimes closely related species can interbreed, such as in the mating of a horse and donkey to produce a mule. Classification has been instrumental in bringing about an understanding of similarities and possible evolutionary relationships of organisms. However, it is not static and may need to change with the discovery of new organisms and as more evidence of evolutionary patterns surfaces.

Six Kingdoms

As you might expect from an examination of Table 5.2, organisms vary greatly in form between the six kingdoms. Think of all the different types of organisms found in the world. From a single celled bacterium to a multicellular human, organisms can have a great diversity of structures. However, all living things are composed of ordered systems of structures that work together to sustain life by carrying out life processes (Chapter 1). In this text, we will only discuss major highlights of structure and function found in each kingdom.

One major characteristic of each kingdom is how its members obtain food.

Archaebacteria

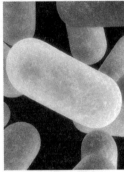

Figure 5.4 Microbes

The Kingdom **Archaebacteria** contains prokaryotic bacteria that thrive in many habitats including harsh environments previously thought uninhabitable. The prefix *archa-* means ancient. The organisms in this kingdom are believed to be similar to the first types of living things found on planet Earth. These bacteria can be single celled or cluster together to form filaments. Archaebacteria have a uniquely structured cell wall, cell membrane and ribosomal RNA. The cell walls of archaebacteria lack peptidoglycan, a protein-carbohydrate molecule found in all other bacterial cell walls. Archaebacteria are **anaerobic**, meaning they do not require oxygen, and live in many habitats.

Archaebacteria are classified according to the environment in which they live. **Methanogens** produce methane gas and live in places such as the soil and the intestines of herbivores. **Halophiles** live in extremely salty environments like the Dead Sea. **Thermoacidophiles** live in areas like the acidic sulfur springs of Yellowstone National Park and undersea vents. These bacteria live in areas where temperatures are near 80°Celsius (176°F) and the pH is as low as 2. Archaebacteria can reproduce using asexual reproduction through budding or binary fission, or through a type of sexual reproduction called **conjugation**, using a sex pilus.

Eubacteria

The Kingdom **Eubacteria** are the "true bacteria." The prefix *eu-* means true. These bacteria can be single celled or cluster together to form colonies. Because they are bacteria, Eubacteria are prokaryotic. Eubacteria have a cell wall, cell membrane and circular DNA called a **plasmid**. The cell wall of Eubacteria is made up different materials and is more complex than the cell walls of plants or fungi. Eubacteria are classified as heterotrophic, autotrophic or chemotrophic. **Heterotrophs,** found nearly everywhere, need organic molecules as an energy source and feed on living organisms, dead organisms or organic wastes. **Autotrophs** are photosynthetic and are found in

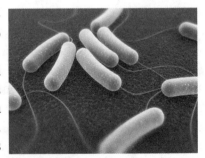

Figure 5.5 *E.coli* Bacteria

ponds, lakes, streams and most areas of land. Cyanobacteria, also called blue-green algae, are a type of autotrophic Eubacteria. **Chemotrophs** obtain energy from the breakdown of inorganic, or non-living, substances such as nitrogen and sulfur compounds. Eubacteria are found everywhere, and most are harmless. Eubacteria are used to make cheese, vinegar, soy sauce and yogurt. Some Eubacteria are decomposers and are important to the proper functioning of many ecosystems. Eubacteria can also reproduce using asexual reproduction through budding or binary fission or through conjugation using a sex pilus.

PROTISTA

Figure 5.6 Slime Mold

Kingdom **Protista** contains a diverse group of unicellular and multicellular organisms. All protist cells are eukaryotic with a membrane-bound nucleus. Protists can be *plant-like, animal-like or fungus-like*. **Plant-like protists** are known as algae and may be unicellular or multicellular. Although algae come in different colors, all algae have chlorophyll-containing chloroplasts and are **autotrophs**, meaning they can make their own food. **Animal-like protists** are one-celled organisms known as protozoa. They cannot make their own food, so they are called **heterotrophs**. Many protozoa are parasites living in water, on soil and on living and dead organisms. Protozoa can move using a **flagella** or **cilia**.

Fungus-like protists include several phyla that have features of both protists and fungi. They obtain energy from decomposing organic material. The Slime Mold phylum is a group of fungus-like protists found in damp soil and on rotting wood.

FUNGI

Fungi are heterotrophic organisms that secrete enzymes, allowing them to digest their food. They are also **saprophytes**, which are organisms that live in or on matter that they decompose as they use it for food. Fungi can be unicellular or multicellular organisms and are made of eukaryotic cells surrounded by a cell wall. Some fungi are edible, while other species are poisonous. Fungi live in aquatic or moist environments like soil, mud and decaying plants. They include black bread mold, yeast, mushrooms and truffles. The fungus *Penicillium* is responsible for the flavors of Roquefort and Camembert cheeses. The widely-used antibiotic penicillin is also derived from a species of this group.

Figure 5.7 Fungi

Fungi reproduce sexually and asexually with reproductive cells called **spores**. Spores are produced sexually by the fruiting body, usually the visible portion of a mushroom. The fruiting body forms gametes that reproduce sexually. Fungi reproduce asexually through mitosis or **budding**. Budding occurs when a piece of the organism becomes detached and continues to live and grow on its own as a complete structure. Fungi, along with bacteria, are the great recyclers. Together they keep the Earth from becoming buried under mountains of waste.

PLANTAE

Figure 5.8 Moss

The Kingdom **Plantae** consists of multicellular organisms that have eukaryotic cells. Almost all use photosynthesis to obtain food and are producers in most ecosystems. There are many different types of plants with a variety of structure types. Plants can be non-vascular, vascular seedless or vascular seed-bearing. **Non-vascular plants** lack tissues used to transport substances like water and sugars. Instead they absorb nutrients through their cells. As a result, non-vascular plants tend to remain small in size. Bryophytes are a type of non-vascular, seedless plant. Bryophytes live in a moist habitat. They include the mosses, liverworts and hornworts.

Vascular plants contain specialized structures for conducting substances and, as a result, can live in drier environments than the non-vascular plants. Vascular plants are divided into two main groups: seedless and seed bearing. The seedless vascular plants produce spores and include the ferns, whiskbrooms, lycophytes and horseferns. They must live in moist environments because their gametes require water for fertilization to take place. The seed bearing plants grow from seeds and include gymnosperms and angiosperms. **Gymnosperms** include most conifers

Figure 5.9 Vascular Plants

and *Ginkgo biloba*. Gymnosperms can live in dry, wet, hot or cold environments. **Angiosperms** include flowering plants and can. because they reproduce using seeds contained in protective fruit, live and reproduce in nearly all environments. Plant reproduction is a complicated cycle called alteration of generations that will not be addressed here. What is important for you to understand is that plants can reproduce using sexual reproduction with flowers or asexual reproduction with budding or vegetative propagation.

ANIMALIA

All members of Kingdom **Animalia** are multicellular organisms made of eukaryotic cells. Animal cells group together to form tissues which then group to form organs which further group into organ systems. Some animals have complex organ systems capable of carrying out highly complicated tasks. Animals are heterotrophic. They are diploid organisms and most reproduce sexually, although some reproduce asexually. Animals produce haploid gametes through meiosis. A diploid zygote is formed upon fertilization. The zygote undergoes mitosis and cell differentiation to grow into a multi-celled body. Some animals provide parental care but most do not. Animals are capable of movement at some stage in their lives and are either invertebrates, without a backbone, or vertebrates, with a backbone.

Figure 5.10 Starfish

Invertebrates are animals without a backbone; they are the most abundant group. They are all multicellular and most form tissues, organs and organ systems. Invertebrates can reproduce asexually and sexually. They are comprised of the following phyla: porifera (sponges), cnidarians (jellyfish, anemones and corals), platyhelminthes (flatworms), nematoda (roundworms), annelida (earthworms), mollusca (mollusks), echinodermata (starfish and sea urchins) and arthropods (crustaceans, insects and spiders).

Vertebrates are animals that share several distinct characteristics sometime during their life cycle and belong to the phylum Chordata. These characteristics are: a notochord, gill slits and an endoskeleton. A notochord is a firm, flexible rod that provides support and stability. It often changes into a vertebral column later in life. Gill slits (aka pharyngeal pouches) are openings used in respiration that lead to the outside of an animal's body. The gill slits take oxygen into the body and release carbon dioxide. An endoskeleton is an internal skeleton composed of bones, cartilage or both. It grows with the animal. Fish, amphibians, reptiles, birds and mammals are all vertebrates and are all members of phylum Chordata.

Figure 5.11 Tibetan Fox

It is important to remember that the complexity of organisms can sometimes be inferred by examining their taxonomic classification. Organisms found in the kingdoms Eubacteria or Protista are *generally* less complex when compared to organisms found in the kingdoms Plantae or Animalia.

Activity

In this activity, you will examine specific examples of organisms from different kingdoms. We will begin by selecting one specific example of an organism from each of the six kingdoms. If you are having trouble thinking of specific organisms from Archaebacteria, Eubacteria, Protista and Fungi, use the Internet or your text book to help you. We will discover how the structures found in these organisms help it to function as a living organism. Use a table to examine the methods and structures organisms use for reproduction, movement, growth, obtaining energy, waste removal and body systems.

Activity

Divide the class into six groups. Assign each group one of the six kingdoms. Have each group prepare a presentation about organisms found in their respective kingdoms. The presentations should include information about the following: the methods and structures used by the organism for reproduction, movement, growth, obtaining energy, waste removal and body systems. Students should include pictures of specific types of organisms found in their kingdom along with notable characteristics of their kingdom. Then have each group present their project to the class.

Section Review 1: Six Kingdoms

A. Define the following terms.

methanogens	genus	heterotrophs	Animalia
halophiles	species	autotrophs	invertebrates
thermoacidophiles	plasmid	chemotrophs	vertebrates
kingdom	Protista	saprophytes	taxonomy
phylum	Fungi	vascular plants	gymnosperms
class	Plantae	anaerobic	angiosperms
order	non-vascular plants	Archaebacteria	
family	binomial nomenclature	Eubacteria	

B. Choose the best answer.

1. Why are archaebacteria placed in a kingdom separate from eubacteria?

    A. They are structurally and functionally different from all other types of life on planet Earth.

    B. They are used in the food making process and must be separated from wild types of bacteria.

    C. Because their DNA forms a special ring called a plasmid.

    D. They are not placed in a kingdom separated from other types of bacteria.

2. Which kingdom below contains organisms that are made up of eukaryotic cells?

    A. Eubacteria   C. Fungi

    B. Archaebacteria   D. none of the above

3. Which group of animals can reproduce asexually?

    A. vertebrates   B. invertebrates   C. fish   D. amphibians

4. Which kingdom listed below contains eukaryotic cells surrounded by a cell wall?

    A. Fungi   B. Plantae   C. Animalia   D. both A and B

5. Which organism listed below is an invertebrate animal?

    A. kangaroo   B. gymnosperm   C. cyanobacteria   D. sponge

C. Do the following activities.

1. Make a VENN diagram comparing different structures found in the six kingdoms (see Appendix A for instructions on creating Venn Diagrams).

2. Describe, in your own words, the varying complexity of the six kingdoms.

USING A DICHOTOMOUS KEY

The identification of biological organisms can be performed using tools such as the **dichotomous key**. A dichotomous key is an organized set of questions, each with yes or no answers. The paired answers indicate mutually exclusive characteristics of biological organisms. You simply compare the characteristics of an unknown organism against an appropriate dichotomous key. The key begins with general characteristics and leads to questions which indicate progressively more specific characteristics. By following the key and making the correct choices, you should be able to identify your specimen to the indicated taxonomic level. An example using known organisms follows: pick an organism and follow the key to determine its taxonomic classification.

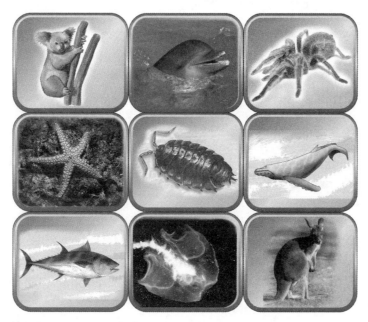

1. Does the organism have an exoskeleton?

    Yes... Go to question 2.
    No... Go to question 4.

2. Does the organism have 8 legs?
    Yes... It is of Class Arachnida, Order Araneae.
    No... Go to question 3.

3. Does the organism dwell exclusively on land?
    Yes... It is of Phylum Arthropoda, Subphylum Crustacean, Class Malacostraca, Order Isapoda, Suborder Dniscidea.
    No... Go to question 4.

4. Does the organism have an endoskeleton?
    Yes... Go to question 5.
    No... Go to question 6.

5. Does the organism dwell exclusively in the water?

   Yes...Go to question 6

   No... Go to question 7

6. Does the organism have stinging tentacles?

   Yes... It is of Phylm Cnidaria, Class Scyphozoa

   No... Go to question 7.

7. Does the organism have 5 legs?

   a. Yes... It is of Phylum Echinodermata, Class Asteroidea

   b. No... Go to question 8.

8. Does the organism carry live young in a pouch?

   a. Yes... Go to question 9.

   b. No... Go to question 10.

9. Does it climb trees?

   a. Yes... It is of Class Mammalia, Subclass Marsupialia, Order Diprodonia, Suborder Vombatiformes.

   b. No... It is of Class Mammalia, Subclass Marsupialia, Order Diprodonia, Suborder Phalangerida, Genua Macropus

10. Is the organism a mammal?

   a. Yes.... Go to 11.

   b. No... It is of Phylum Chordata, Class Actinoptergii, Order Perciformes, Family Scrombridae, Genus Thunnus

11. Does the adult organism have teeth?

   a. Yes... It is of Phylum Chordata, Class Mammalia, Order Cetacea, Suborder Odontoceti.

   b. No... It is of Phylum Chordata, Class Mammalia, Order Cetacea, Suborder Mysticeti.

Were you able to identify all the animals? If not, one glitch might be that some of these sub-categories go beyond the knowledge that has been outlined in our text. These are easily investigated by going online and searching simply for the animal name. You will be surprised at how much you learn.

Activity

Try this as a practice exercise: Use Wikipedia®, the free encyclopedia (online at http://en.wikipedia.org/) to search the term Vombatiformes. If you answered the questions in the dichotomous key correctly, you know that one member of this sub-order is the koala. There is only one other member of this sub-order; all the others are extinct. Find out what other animal belongs to the sub-order Vombatiformes.

BIODIVERSITY

Scientists estimate that there may be up to 14 million different species inhabiting the planet. Approximately 1.75 million species have been scientifically named and described, including 250,000 plant species and 792,000 animal species. The variation among organisms is called **biodiversity**.

According to the theory of **evolution**, new species evolve from preexisting species over long periods of time. This evolution of new species promotes diversity. However, evolution does not always affect the entire species. Organisms within the same species may evolve differently over time, or remain unchanged, depending on their needs and environment. **Adaptation** is a change in structure or function that allows an organism to be more successful. Adaptation is another way species can diversify. **Extinction** is the condition where there are no living representatives of an organism. Extinction impacts biodiversity by reducing the number of species.

CLASSIFICATION WITH EVOLUTION

In the last section, we discussed structures and functions that are characteristic of different kingdoms. How were these organisms classified, though? Scientists use similarities in reproductive strategies and nutritional strategies to classify organisms. Evolutionary relationships are also a major factor when classifying living things. Biologists assume that organisms with common traits come from a common ancestor. Physical structures, embryo development and genetic makeup are all studied for clues.

ANATOMICAL SIMILARITIES

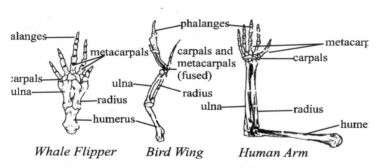

Figure 5.12 Examples of Homologous Structures

Anatomical similarities are evident in the study of homologous structures and vestigial organs. **Homologous structures** develop from a common ancestor and are similar in shape, but have different functions. The human arm, the wing of a bird and the flipper of a whale are all homologous structures. They contain the same bones. In fact, we see a similar pattern of limb arrangement in all land dwelling (or previously land dwelling) organisms. The limb pattern is one bone, two bones and then many bones. Biologists believe these structures come from a common ancestor. Their different functions correspond to their use in different environments. A whale uses a flipper for swimming, and a bird uses a wing for flying. A whale, a bird and a human all belong in the same phylum, Chordata.

Vestigial organs, structures that are no longer used or have greatly decreased in importance, are another anatomical similarity. A whale and some snakes have a pelvis and femur, structures necessary for walking, but whales and snakes no longer have any use for these structures. These structures may have become smaller since they are unused. Their presence also suggests a common ancestor.

EMBRYONIC DEVELOPMENT

Scientists agree that studying the embryonic development of an organism often leads to a greater understanding of the evolutionary history of that organism. The early development of an embryo is the most important time during its life cycle. Like laying a foundation for a house, the structures and tissues formed at the beginning of development lay the basis for many other tissues later in life. Vertebrates (organisms with a backbone or spine) pass through some stages that are similar to each other. The more closely related an organism is, the more similar its stages of development will be.

GENETIC MAKEUP

Biochemical similarities demonstrate relationships among various organisms. DNA sequences are studied and compared. The closer the sequences, the more closely related the organisms. Humans and chimpanzees show a great deal of overlap in their DNA sequences. Humans and reptiles show some similarities, but there is less overlap than between the human and chimpanzee sequences. When the DNA from humans and yeast are compared, there is very little overlap. This suggests that humans and chimpanzees are much more closely related than humans and yeast. Another example is the horseshoe crab. The horseshoe crab was once grouped with other crabs, but is now grouped with the spiders based on genetic data. Figure 5.13 shows a comparison of chromosome #7 from different organisms.

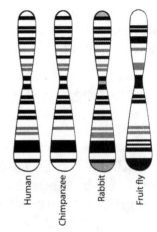

Figure 5.13 Comparison of Chromosome in Animal Kingdom

Section Review 2: Biological Classification

A. Define the following terms.

biodiversity	adaptation	evolution	homologous structure
	extinction		vestigial organ

B. Choose the best answer.

1. The dodo bird was a flightless bird that became extinct in the last century. Although its disappearance had no significant recorded impact on other members of the ecosystem, its disappearance did affect what aspect of the ecosystem?

    A. The ability for other species to adapt.

    B. The genetic diversity of other species.

    C. The biodiversity of the ecosystem as a whole.

    D. The process of evolution within the ecosystem.

Use the following scenario to answer questions 2 – 3:

> Lake Lanier is a man-made like in Georgia. The floor of the lake is filled with dead trees and construction debris remaining from the time of its construction. Over time, these items have become the natural habitat of the organisms living in the lake.

2. If a new species of fish were transferred from a natural lake to Lake Lanier, which of the following would be altered?

    A. the fish's ability to adapt

    B. the ecosystem of the fish

    C. the ecosystem of the lake

    D. the ability of other fish to adapt

3. Wisdom teeth are the common name for the third molar in humans. They generally appear much later than all other adult teeth, and usually not until the age of 18. The teeth have no noticeable purpose to the modern human and are often pulled to make room for the other teeth in the mouth. The continued presence of wisdom teeth is a good example of

    A. homologous structures in humans.

    B. vestigial structures in humans.

    C. genetic diversity in humans.

    D. adaptation to better dental care.

DEVELOPMENT OF EVOLUTIONARY THOUGHT

Figure 5.14 Ostrich

Figure 5.15 Emu

Scientists observe the natural world and come up with many questions. How can a rhea in South America, an ostrich in Africa and an emu in Australia look so much alike but be different birds? How can the finches on the Galapagos Islands all have different beaks? How can sharks and dolphins have similar-looking structures when one is a fish and one is a mammal? The theory of evolution attempts to answer such questions and more.

The theory of evolution states that organisms go through a process of change over time and develop new species from preexisting ones. **Phylogeny** is the evolutionary history of one organism or a group of related organisms. The following sections will describe the mechanisms and patterns of modern evolutionary theory.

DARWIN

Charles Darwin (1809 – 1882), who was born in England, attended Cambridge to train for the ministry after a short period of study at a medical school. While at Cambridge, he developed a passion for studying biology and geology. Through the efforts of his professors, he was able to get aboard a British science ship, the *Beagle*, bound on a five-year trip around the world.

Figure 5.16 Darwin

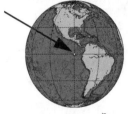

Figure 5.17 Galapagos on the Globe

During this trip, Darwin observed fossils on many different continents. Darwin observed and collected many different organisms from places all around the globe. He took notes about every place he visited. One place that was of particular interest to Darwin was the Galapagos Islands off the coast of South America.

Figure 5.18 Evolution of Finches on the Galapagos Islands

Darwin noticed that all the organisms on this island looked very similar to the organisms on the South American continent, especially the finches. On the South American continent, finches only eat seeds and have very few species. Every bird Darwin saw on the Galapagos Islands was a type of modified finch. The finches were about the same size and all very similar in color. The only differences in the finches Darwin saw were their beaks and what they ate. There were finches that ate insects, seeds, plant matter, egg yolks and blood. The finches on the

Galapagos Islands looked very similar to one type of finch on the South American continent, but none of the Galapagos Island types of finches were found on the South American mainland.

The types of finches seen were indeed very diverse. Darwin began to ask many questions; one of which began to plague him above all others: "How did one species change into a different species?" It is important to note that scientists in the 19th century did not know how a trait passes from one animal to its offspring; they did not know of the existence of DNA. They could breed horses for speed and dogs for hunting ability by choosing parents with those traits, but they did not know what biological process was at work. After the trip on the *Beagle,* Darwin studied his collection of organisms as well as many different books and readings. He also talked with several domestic animal breeders.

After 20 years of study, Darwin published his book, *The Origin of Species*, in 1859. In this book, Darwin describes his theory of how one species changes into another species. According to Darwin, in all living populations of organisms there is some natural variation between individual organisms.

Darwin had repeatedly observed that environmental pressures can change how an organism interacts with its environment. He developed a theory based on these observations and called it the theory of natural selection.

Recall that the entire diet of the Galapagos finches changed in response to their isolated environment. That was a modification of behavior (eating habits) in response to environmental pressure (limited food resources). The existence of certain physical traits may also be modified over time. As the finches began to eat more varied food items, the actual function of their beaks began to change. Finches that began to eat insects needed longer beaks for digging beetles out of their burrows. Finches that ate seeds or nuts required stronger jaw muscles to crack the shells.

Figure 5.19 Finch

Figure 5.20 Finch

How did the finches change their beaks in response to these needs? Modern science now views the process of natural selection in this way. The finches' beaks did not change overnight, but rather over many, many generations. Among the population of beetle-eating finches, those that were born with longer, sharper beaks naturally had access to more beetles than those finches with blunter beaks. The sharp-beaked finches thrived, and had many offspring, while the blunt-beaked finches gradually died out. The sharp beak was a trait that was, in effect, *selected* by nature to thrive. The same thing happened in each finch population, until finches from a given population began to look similar to each other and different than other finches.

This process of **natural selection** is distinct from the common breeding practices of **artificial selection**, which is how animal breeders obtain desired traits.

To be clear: the individual physical traits of a finch are not modified by the finch (his beak does not grow and change to suit his changing needs). Rather, the animals who already possess a trait that is favored by the current environmental pressures survive and pass that trait on to their offspring. This insures that, over time, the expression of the favored trait becomes more pronounced, and other traits disappear. This is why Darwin's theory of natural selection is also called the **survival of the fittest**.

Figure 5.21 Giraffes with Their Offspring

Section Review 3: Development of Evolutionary Thought

A. Define the following terms.

phylogeny   natural selection

survival of the fittest   artificial selection

B. Choose the best answer.

1. Ideas about evolution

    A. have already been thought.   C. may change based on new data.

    B. are perfect and need no refinement.   D. only involve animals.

2. What is genetic drift?

    A. The random change in genes within a population.

    B. The formation of a new species.

    C. The isolation of individual organisms of a population.

    D. The ability of an organism to survive in its environment.

       Oncillas, margays and ocelots are all small cats, common in South America. All three are spotted cats with long tails. The oncilla and margay are nearly the same size, 2–3 kg; the ocelot is a little larger, 10–15 kg. All three cats are equipped for an arboreal lifestyle, but the margay is the only one that dwells almost exclusively in the trees. The margay is one of only two cats that can climb headfirst down a tree, owing to its extremely flexible ankles. (The only other cat that can do this is the leopard.)

Use the following table to answer questions 3 – 4.

	Oncilla	Margay	Ocelot
Leopardus	*tigrinus*	*wiedii*	*pardalis*

3. What taxonomic category do all three cats share?

    A. Genus   B. Species   C. Order   D. Family

4. Choose the sentence that could correctly describe the evolution of the margay.

    A. Micro evolution is responsible for the differences between the margay and the oncilla.

    B. The margay is a tree-dwelling oncilla.

    C. The margay likely evolved to become a strictly arboreal species because of its small size and flexible ankles.

    D. The margay's small size and flexible ankles evolved in response to habitat changes that oncillas and ocelots were unable to respond to.

THE FOSSIL RECORD: MORE EVIDENCE OF EVOLUTION

The evolutionary relationships used to classify organisms provide evidence for evolution, such as the existence of homologous structures, vestigial organs and biochemical similarities. Fossils also provide evidence for the change in organisms over time. Darwin himself observed fossils found on many different continents while aboard the HMS Beagle. Fossil evidence was instrumental in the development of Darwin's ideas on evolution. A **fossil** is the recognizable remains or body impressions of an organism that lived in the past. The existence of animal life on land is relatively recent. Fossils indicate that insects first came onto land around 440 million years ago, and vertebrate animals moved onto land about 417 million years ago (mya).

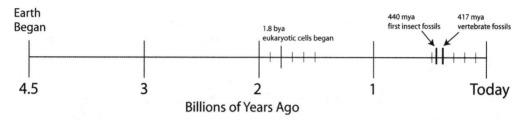

Figure 5.22 Timeline of Earth's Existence

In general, fossils come from organisms that are now extinct. One exception is the **living fossil**. This is an organism, like a horseshoe crab or a ginkgo tree, that has remained essentially unchanged from earlier geologic times. Fossils found of these organisms look very similar to the living organism today. These organisms have many successful characteristics that do not need extensive modification and so remain virtually unchanged for long periods of time. This is not to say they have ceased to evolve, think of it like more like changing very little. Crocodilians are one example; they have changed very little over their 84 million year history. They have had some variation in size over the years. After all, crocodiles that ate dinosaurs would have to be much larger than today's crocodiles!

Why is it important to know that organisms change over time? The answer is that if there is change, then there must be a cause of the change. Discovering both the cause of, and the mechanism through which, the change occurs is central to the survival of organisms and the ecosystems they populate. Of course, the study of fossils also gives us a fascinating historical perspective — snapshots from an Earth of long ago. Taken together, these snapshots are referred to as the **fossil record**.

Scientists use the body of evidence accumulated from the fossil record to make hypotheses about organism development and migration over the course of history of the planet.

MECHANISMS OF EVOLUTION

Mechanisms of evolution deal with how evolution occurs. Most scientists consider natural selection one of the most important mechanisms of evolution, but other mechanisms like mutations, gene flow and genetic drift are also significant.

NATURAL SELECTION

Naturalist Charles Darwin proposed the idea of natural selection in 1859. **Natural selection** states that organisms best suited to the environment are the ones most likely to survive and reproduce. A few important points Darwin made in his book, *The Origin of Species*, are:

- **Resources are limited in all environments**. The availability of food, water and shelter in an environment is limited. This leads to competition among organisms. **Competition** is the fight among living things to get what they need for survival. For example, moths must find food before other moths take all the food.

- **Most organisms have more offspring than the environment can support**. For example, a moth lays thousands of eggs or one tree produces millions of seeds.

Figure 5.23 Tree Seeds

- **There is natural variation within a population**. A **variation** is a difference in a trait between organisms within a population. Not all organisms are exactly alike. For example, not all moths are the exact same color. Another example of variation is that not all humans are the same height.

- **Natural selection is always taking place**. Organisms with traits that are the most desirable are selected to survive. Organisms in any environment have a specific fitness for that environment. **Fitness** is the ability of an organism to live, survive and reproduce in that environment. Not all of the individual animals within a population have the same fitness.

Figure 5.24 Natural Variation in Human Height

Figure 5.25 The Cheetah

Variations in physical characteristics make some organisms better suited, or more fit, to live in their environments. Much of this variation is inherited. For example, the fastest cheetah is better equipped to hunt than a slower cheetah. As a result, the faster cheetah will get more food. The most successful cheetah lives the longest and is, therefore, able to produce the most offspring. Scientists would say that the fastest cheetahs are the most fit for their environment. This is where the idea of survival of the fittest comes from.

Inherited traits that are more versatile than others improve the chances of the organisms' survival and reproduction. For example, having long legs and a skinny body helps a cheetah stay cool. These adaptations also help the cheetah to run fast. These traits are favorable for more than one reason, making them highly likely to pass on to offspring.

An improved chance of survival allows organisms to produce offspring that will make up more of the next generation, while passing along their favorable traits. Unfavorable traits will eventually be lost since there is less reproduction among the individuals with such traits.

The slowest cheetahs will get the least amount of food, and will, therefore, have a greater chance of dying. These slow cheetahs are said to be less fit, or unfit, for their environments. In many cases, the most successful traits are maintained and change very little over a long period of time. Sharks, turtles, crocodiles and ferns are examples of organisms that have successful traits that have remained virtually unchanged over millions of years. Remember the living fossil?

ENVIRONMENT AND VARIATIONS

Environmental conditions also contribute to variations in traits among individuals of the same species. The size of house sparrows in North America varies depending on location. House sparrows living in colder climates are larger than those living in the warmer climates. As a general rule, the larger the body size of an animal, the more body heat it can trap or conserve.

The size of extremities, such as ears or legs in some animals, also demonstrates environmental differences. Since extremities give off heat to help cool the animals' bodies, mammals living in hot climates tend to have larger ears and longer legs than their cousins in cooler climates. A desert jackrabbit has much larger ears than a rabbit found in a temperate (cooler winter) climate.

Figure 5.26 Desert and Temperate Rabbits

Natural variation within a population allows for some individuals to survive over other individuals in a changing environment. This natural variation can eventually lead to the formation of new species, which is also called **speciation**.

MUTATIONS

Mutations are random changes in DNA that act as another mechanism for evolution. These changes result in a variation in traits, which then pass from one generation to the next. Mutations can be beneficial, neutral or harmful to an organism. Mutations beneficial to the organism in a particular environment lead to furthering of the species. For example, a mutation can result in the production of an enzyme that breaks down a particular food product predominant in an area. Individuals with the expression of that gene have more food choices, giving them greater survival chances, and allowing them to be more successful. Another example could be a mutation in color pigments that leads to an individual that is a different color than the normal population.

GENE FLOW

Gene flow is the change in the occurrence of genes in a population. Population refers to the group of organisms of the same species in a given geographic area. Gene flow occurs when an individual leaves a population or a new individual joins a population. Gene flow tends to increase the similarity of individuals from different populations, since these individuals share their genes with each other through reproduction.

Gene flow happens easily in plants that have seeds carried by wind. The wind carries the seeds of a plant from one population to another population. When these new seeds grow into plants, the plants can cross-pollinate with the existing plants, and genes from different populations are shared.

GENETIC DRIFT

Genetic drift provides random changes in the occurrence of genes through chance events. It can occur if a large number of the population is killed because of disease, starvation, change in natural environment or a natural disaster. When this happens to a population, it is called **bottlenecking**. A large population is reduced to a few individuals, and the genes of subsequent generations become very similar.

Inbreeding between these few individuals leads to populations that have very few genetic differences. It is believed that African cheetahs went through two bottlenecks, one about 10,000 years ago and one about 100 years ago. All African cheetahs alive today are descendents of a few cheetahs, and possibly only three females. Because cheetahs are genetically similar, they have become very susceptible to diseases.

Figure 5.27
Bottleneck

Section Review 4:   Mechanisms and Patterns of Evolution and the Fossil Record

A. Define the following terms.

natural selection	gene flow	bottlenecking
competition	immigration	convergent evolution
variation	emigration	divergent evolution
fitness	fossil	co-evolution
	fossil record	

B. Choose the best answer.

1. What are the effects of genetic drift and gene flow?

    A. change in gene occurrences   C. change in DNA replication patterns

    B. change in vision acuity   D. change in organism size

2. Which event listed below does NOT lead to fossil formation?

    A. floods   B. forest fires   C. earthquakes   D. mudslides

3. When is it hypothesized that the first living organisms appeared on Earth?

    A. 3.8 billion years ago   C. 440 million years ago

    B. 1.8 billion years ago   D. 3.8 million years ago

4. Which of the following describes the effect of a bottleneck in a population?

    A. A large number of the population dies.

    B. The genetic diversity of the population decreases.

    C. The genetic diversity of the population increases.

    D. Competition increases.

C. Answer the following questions.

1. Explain the theory of natural selection.

2. How is variation beneficial to an organism? How is it harmful?

ADAPTATIONS AND BEHAVIOR

ADAPTATION

Adaptations are physical and behavioral changes that make organisms better suited to their environments. Plants and animals adapt in a variety of ways in an effort to protect themselves from predators and survive in their environment. There are many, many different plant and animal adaptations. In fact, we could probably fill the rest of this book with examples of plant and animal adaptations! (Don't worry, we won't.)

PLANT ADAPTATIONS

Figure 5.28 Animal Seed Dispersal

Plants cannot flee from predators, but they do have spines, thorns and leathery leaves to discourage herbivores from consuming them. Some plants manufacture chemicals that are poisonous or have a foul odor to keep animals away. Milkweed, tobacco and peyote cactus are three such plants. The Venus flytrap plant has adapted a unique way to gather food by catching insects within its modified leaves. Some plants have developed unique methods of spreading seeds. Some plants have seeds with spines that attach to animal fur. Some have seeds with "wings" or parachutes used to harness the wind and some seeds have watertight buoyant outer shells used to travel in the water.

Figure 5.29
Wind Seed Dispersal

Mechanical stress — such as wind, rain and animal — has an effect on the growth of plants. Indoor plants will grow taller than outdoor plants of the same species because they are protected from the weather. Adaptations to mechanical stress include shorter, thicker stems, which helps outdoor plants withstand the stress and increases their survival chances, even if the plants' overall growth is inhibited.

BEHAVIORAL PLANT ADAPTATIONS

Response to internal and external stimuli by an organism is called **behavior**. Plants respond to stimuli in a variety of ways to increase their chances for survival.

Tropisms are the growth of a plant in response to a stimulus. **Positive tropisms** are toward the stimulus and **negative tropisms** are away from the stimulus.

Phototropism is the response to light. Light is important to plants, since they use it to trap energy and make glucose. Plants are **photosynthetic**. Photosynthetic structures, like leaves and stems, are positively phototropic. These plant tissues will grow in a variety of directions to get the best possible light. Roots are negatively phototropic; they grow away from the light source.

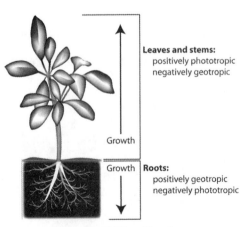

Leaves and stems:
positively phototropic
negatively geotropic

Growth

Growth **Roots:**
positively geotropic
negatively phototropic

Figure 5.30 Plant Tropisms

Geotropism is a plant's response to gravity. Roots are positively geotropic. They grow toward the Earth in response to gravity. Stems and leaves are negatively geotropic. Plants also respond to touch. This is called **thigmotropism.** Climbing plants, like kudzu, honeysuckle or beans, generally have weak stems and will wrap around another plant, wall, fence or other structure for support. The tentacles of climbing plants respond to the touch of something else and coil around the object, sometimes in a matter of hours.

OTHER PLANT BEHAVIORS

Figure 5.31 Venus Fly Trap

Nastic movements are the responses of plants to stimulus regardless of direction. Examples include flowers opening and closing in response to light, or mimosa leaves curling up when touched by an object or blown by wind. Carnivorous plants, like the Venus flytrap, will close in response to something touching the little hair-like structures inside their leaves, which helps them obtain food.

Plants also follow circadian rhythms. **Circadian rhythms** are behavior cycles that follow roughly 24 hour patterns of activity. Some plants fold their leaves and flowers during the night and open them during the day, to preserve water. For many plants, light stimulates growth hormones. Other plants have adapted to secreting perfumes and nectars at times when their pollinators are active, increasing chances of fertilization.

Plants can send communication signals to predators and other plants. They have the ability to secrete foul-tasting substances, so herbivores will avoid eating them. Even leaves damaged by an herbivore can secrete the chemical warning to other plants. The other plants then produce the chemical substance. The plants only secrete the protective substance when needed.

Flower blooming follows a photoperiodic trend. **Photoperiodism** is the response of plant processes to the amount of daylight. Photoperiodism explains why plants bloom in different seasons. The amount of daylight in fall and winter is less than the amount of daylight in spring and summer. The photoperiods of various plants are summarized in Table 5.3 below.

Table 5.3 Photoperiods

Short-Day Plants	Flowers bloom in fall and winter. Includes ragweed, goldenrod and chrysanthemums.
Long-Day Plants	Flowers bloom in spring and summer. Includes spinach, clover and iris.
Day-Neutral Plants	Flowers bloom over a range of photoperiods. Examples include roses, tomatoes and beans.

BEHAVIORS OF UNICELLULAR ORGANISMS

Bacteria, amoeba and paramecia also have behaviors. For instance, they respond to light and chemical signals. Photosynthetic bacteria, cyanobacteria and protists gravitate toward light in a process called phototaxis, to ensure survival. Monerans and protists can detect chemical signals given off by food sources, ensuring their survival. Some bacteria even have magnetic crystals inside their bodies that direct their movements. One-celled organisms are also capable of avoiding negative stimuli, such as temperature and chemical changes in their environments.

ANIMAL ADAPTATIONS

Most animals have also developed special adaptations. Animals show physical, chemical and behavioral adaptations to increase their chances for survival and reproduction.

PHYSICAL ANIMAL ADAPTATIONS

Physical adaptations help animals survive and flourish in their environment. Many species living in cold climates grow thick fur during the winter and shed it during the summer months. Animals that live in cold climates typically have short extremities (limbs, ears, tails). Shorter extremities reduce heat loss from the animals body. Animals that live in dry deserts like camels, giraffes and African deer can survive for long periods without water. Some desert frogs have special adaptations that allow them to absorb water directly from the air, some frogs can change color to a pale white to reflect heat during the hottest part of the day. Animals that live in hot climates typically have large, long extremities, which allow them to cool off.

Animals also adapt in response to predator/prey interactions. Porcupines and spiny anteaters grow sharp quills for protection against predators. Turtles retreat inside a bony shell for protection. Some animals produce venom or poison for hunting or protection. Armadillos have armor-like skin that protects the animal when it flees from predators into thorny patches. The American alligator has eyes and nostrils located on the top of its head allowing the body of the animal to remain hidden. Cottonmouth snakes and other pit vipers have special heat-sensing organs, located on the front of their head.

Figure 5.32 Alligator

Figure 5.33 Predator

Most land-dwelling predators have eyes located close together on the front of the head. This allows the predator to focus specifically on its prey. Most prey have eyes located far apart on either side of the head. This allows the prey to see more of the area around it, perhaps helping their escape.

Figure 5.34 Prey

ANIMAL BEHAVIOR

Ethology is the study of animal behavior. Scientists evaluate animal behavior to see how their responses relate to their goals — survival and reproduction. Behavior is broadly divided into innate behavior and learned behavior. Behavior is influenced by hormones and by the nervous system. Hormones direct certain behaviors, and the nervous system allows an animal to respond to stimuli.

INNATE BEHAVIOR

Innate behaviors are those that are under genetic control and are inherited like physical traits. Innate behaviors are animals' instincts and are performed perfectly without any learning. A baby is behaving on instinct when he or she sees a human face and smiles. Innate behavior causes a baby cuckoo bird to push an unhatched egg out of the nest so it does not have to share food and space. Instinct allows a female digger wasp to emerge from her pupa, make a nest, mate, hunt and lay eggs all within her short life span of only a few weeks. Some examples of innate behavior are territoriality, protective behaviors, courting behavior, hibernation and migration.

BEHAVIORAL ANIMAL ADAPTATIONS

Animals use behavioral adaptations for survival and reproduction. **Territoriality** is a behavioral adaptation that ensures adequate space and resources for reproduction. For example, male elephant seals battle for specific beach territories during the breeding season. When female seals arrive, they remain on the beach within the territory of a single male seal. Large, strong males typically have the largest territories, and the most females. In this way, they are assured to pass along their genes to a large portion of the next generation of elephant seals. Remember that not all elephant seal pups will survive to adulthood. Fathering many offspring is one way males ensure reproductive success.

Figure 5.35 Territorial Elephant Seals

Many animals have adapted behaviors that protect them from predators. Birds flock together, fish school together and insects form swarms to increase their chances for survival.

Some animals help others of their kind by giving a signal that a predator is near. For instance, the whitetail deer signals alarm to other nearby deer by raising its characteristic white tail while fleeing from danger.

Figure 5.36 Flock of Birds

Figure 5.37 Bird of Paradise

Courting behavior is a behavioral adaptation that helps to ensure beneficial genes are passed along to offspring. Mates that can build the best nests, sing exuberant mating calls or have the brightest colors are healthy and strong and will likely produce the strongest offspring. The courting behavior of insects, birds, amphibians, mammals or fish can be complex visual or auditory displays. Lightening bugs display bright lights to attract mates. Birds build nests, do dances, sing songs or grow specialized feathers to attract mates. Birds of the Genus Paridisaeidae are commonly called birds of paradise; males of this genus are renowned for their ornamental plumage. Frogs, alligators and whales call for a mate with elaborate songs.

Hormones organize and activate specific forms of innate behavior. Mating behavior in many animals and singing behavior in some birds are activated by hormones. For example, some animals — usually males — engage in elaborate rituals to lure a mate. Many male mammals fight with other males, and some birds will decorate nests, perform dances or puff up colorful feathers. The females generally select the males with the best traits, and those genes are passed along to offspring.

Animals, like plants, follow circadian rhythms, which are innate behavior cycles. Some animals are active during the day. They are **diurnal** animals, like squirrels and blue jays. Animals active at night are **nocturnal**, like bats and racoons.

Figure 5.38 Bear

Some animals hibernate, estivate or migrate to escape extremes in weather. These activities are innate behaviors. **Hibernation** is a period of dormancy during cold months. When animals enter a period of **dormancy**, which is a period of biological rest or inactivity, food supplies are limited, and the animal lives off its fat stores. Metabolism, breathing and body temperature all drop to conserve energy. Growth and development also cease during the dormant period. Bears hibernate in winter. **Estivation** is dormancy in hot climates. Lungfish estivate. Other animals **migrate**, or move to new locations in response to weather changes to stay close to food sources. These animals, like geese, usually follow the same routes every year.

LEARNED BEHAVIOR

Learned behavior is a result of an animal's experiences. It allows animals to adapt, so survival chances are enhanced. There are several types of learned behaviors, and it is generally believed that only animals with complex nervous systems are capable of learning. Learned behaviors are related to life span and parental care. Animals with short life spans and little or no parental care have fewer learned behaviors. Table 5.4, summarizes these learned behaviors.

Table 5.4 Learned Behavior

Type of Learning	Description	Example
Imprinting	A rapid form of learning that occurs at a young age during a critical period of development.	Some birds use imprinting.
Habituation	An animal learns not to respond to repeated stimulus.	Dogs stop barking at familiar people entering the house.
Reasoning or Insight	An animal uses past knowledge to solve unfamiliar problems.	An octopus opens a jar to get the food inside.
Spatial or Latent	The animal creates a mental map of its environment.	Blue jays know where they have hidden food, even if food is stored in up to one hundred locations.
Classical Conditioning	An animal learns to associate a stimulus with a response that would not normally occur.	Pavlov's dogs salivated at the sound of a bell.
Operant Conditioning	An animal learns to associate an activity with a consequence.	Toads flick their tongues at flying insects, their food source. If they are stung by a bee, they learn to associate the sting with insects that have stripes, and they avoid them in the future.

Activity

Read each statement and decide if it is a learned behavior or an innate behavior. Mark L for learned and I for innate.

1. _____ humans jump when hearing a sudden loud noise

2. _____ toads avoid eating bees

3. _____ dogs no longer bark at familiar person

4. _____ humpback whales move from warm oceans to polar oceans

5. _____ newborn infant smiling at human face

6. _____ conditioning

7. _____ imprinting

8. _____ squirrels know where to find their hidden food

9. _____ baby ducks follow mother duck after hatching from egg.

10. _____ cat salivating at sound of can opener

11. _____ wildebeests cover thousands of miles every year in October

12. _____ a child showing a fear response to stuffed teddy bears

13. _____ opossums being active only at night

14. _____ chimpanzees aggressively defend their territory from rival groups

15. _____ a crow using car traffic to crack open hard nut shells in Japan

Section Review 5:   Adaptations and Behavior

A. Define the following terms.

ethology	hibernation	adaptations	estivation	innate behavior
diurnal	courting behavior	nocturnal	learned behavior	trophism
migrate	nastic movements	geotropism	phototropism	behavior
territoriality	circadian rhythms	thigmotropism	photoperiodism	photosynthetic
			migrate	dormancy

B. Choose the best answer.

1. Which of the following is true about the connection between parental care and learning?

    A. more parental care, more learned behaviors

    B. more parental care, fewer learned behaviors

    C. less parental care, more learned behaviors

    D. less parental care, all behavior is learned

2. A cat might raise the hair on its back to

    A. appear gentle.   C. attract a mate.

    B. appear intimidating.   D. conserve heat.

3. Milkweed, tobacco and peyote have adapted which type of measures to protect themselves?

    A. behavioral   B. physical   C. chemical   D. territorial

4. Why is it beneficial for some insects to be able to blend in with their surroundings?

    A. It protects them from predators.

    B. It allows them to regulate body temperature.

    C. It helps them find a mate.

    D. It protects their territory.

C. Answer the following questions.

1. Name two adaptations plants have developed to disperse their seeds.

2. What are some reasons that animals emit sounds?

CHAPTER 5 REVIEW

1. Why do scientists find it useful to use a classification system to group organisms?

   A. easier to learn about them

   B. helps avoid duplication of names

   C. organizes all information

   D. all of the above

2. What is formed during the process of fertilization when gametes fuse?

   A. fetus B. embryo C. zygote D. larva

3. One group of animals provides parental care, and their bodies produce food for their young. Which group is it?

   A. reptiles B. mammals C. birds D. amphibians

4. What characteristics do all vertebrates share in common at some time in their lives?

   A. gill slits and exoskeleton

   B. spinal cord and endoskeleton

   C. notochord and exoskeleton

   D. gill slits and endoskeleton

5. The two major divisions of the Kingdom Plantae are

   A. gymnosperms and angiosperms.

   B. vascular and non-vascular.

   C. mosses and ferns.

   D. monocots and dicots.

6. An eyespot is a simple photoreceptor found in some organisms. This organelle senses light and directs the movement of the organism closer to the source. Chloroplasts can then produce the greatest amount of energy. What kingdom do you suppose contains organisms with an eyespot?

   A. Animalia

   B. Plantae

   C. Protista

   D. Archaebacteria

7. What tool would a scientist use to classify a newly discovered plant?

   A. Punnett square

   B. pedigree

   C. binomial nomenclature

   D. dichotomous key

8. What group of tissues do plants use to transport substances?

   A. circulatory system

   B. nervous system

   C. vascular tissues

   D. pharyngeal pouches

9. Which of the following is an example of a eukaryote?

   A. amoeba

   B. mushroom

   C. maple tree

   D. all of the above

10. Identify the evidence for evolution below.

    A. cave drawings, ancient stories and ceremonial rites.

    B. homologous structures, DNA and embryonic evidence.

    C. eukaryotes, symbiosis and competition.

    D. nephrons, antibodies and homeostasis.

11. Natural selection states that individuals

    A. with adaptive traits are more likely to survive.

    B. on the bottom level of the hierarchy have the greatest reproductive success.

    C. demonstrating altruistic behavior are the ones with the most mutations.

    D. remain unchanged over a period of time.

12. Biochemical similarities exist among organisms and indicate relationships. How are these biochemical characteristics studied?

    A. observations of plant and animal behavior

    B. fossil records

    C. observations of various cells under a microscope

    D. DNA sequences

13. Increased use of antibiotics has killed off bacterial populations that were most susceptible to antibiotic treatment. Consequently, many strains of bacteria are resistant to prescription drugs. What is the mechanism by which these resistant bacteria have been allowed to thrive?

    A. natural selection   C. speciation

    B. mutation   D. germination

14. Which statement below is true concerning mixing of gene pools?

    A. It promotes diversity.   C. It reduces the number of organisms.

    B. It increases the number of organisms.   D. It reduces diversity.

15. Identify the mechanisms of evolution below.

    A. natural selection, mutations, genetic drift and gene flow

    B. gradualistic model and punctuational model

    C. co-evolution, convergent evolution and divergent evolution

    D. innate and learned behavior

Chapter 6
Interactions in the Environment

Ga HSGT Science Standards covered in this chapter include:

GPS Standards	
SB4 a – d	Students will assess the dependence of all organisms on one another and the flow of energy and matter within their ecosystems.
SB5 e	Students will evaluate the role of natural selection in the development of the theory of evolution.

Earth's Major Ecological Systems

How Climate Relates to Biome

Plants comprise the ecological foundation for most ecosystems. Plants are the main pathway by which energy enters the ecosystems. Because plants are generally stationary organisms, they cannot respond to rapidly changing environmental conditions. If the amount of rainfall or sunlight received in an area changed suddenly and permanently, most plant species would become extinct. The general climate found in an area determines the plant species that will grow under those conditions. A hot, humid and rainy climate will be favorable to jungle-like plants. The plant types found in an area will determine the animal species that live there. There are **six major terrestrial ecological systems** and **three major aquatic ecological systems**.

TERRESTRIAL ECOSYSTEMS

Large land areas characterized by a dominant form of plant life and climate type that make up large ecosystems are called **biomes**. Organisms living in biomes have adapted to the climate of the geographic region. Distinct boundaries between biomes are not apparent; instead, one area gradually merges into the next. The approximate location of the **six major biomes** are shown in Figure 6.1 below.

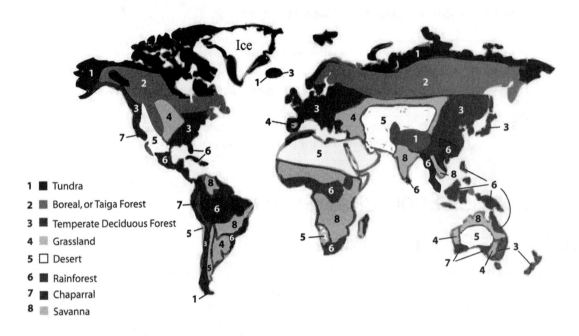

1 ■ Tundra
2 ■ Boreal, or Taiga Forest
3 ■ Temperate Deciduous Forest
4 ■ Grassland
5 □ Desert
6 ■ Rainforest
7 ■ Chaparral
8 ■ Savanna

Figure 6.1 Biomes of Earth

Figure 6.2 Tundra Biome

The **tundra** biome is located near the North and South Poles. Rainfall is light and summer temperatures average only 1° C (34°F). The land in the tundra has gently rolling plains with subsoil that is permanently frozen. There are many lakes, ponds, and bogs. Grasses are present, but only a very few small trees grow there. The small plants mostly consist of mosses, lichens and reindeer moss. Examples of animals found in tundra areas are *reindeer*, *caribou*, *polar bears*, *arctic wolves*, *foxes*, *hares*, *lemmings*, *birds* and *insects*.

The **coniferous forest** biomes are found above 60°N latitude. Rainfall is medium, and the average summer temperature is around 12°C (54°F). In the coniferous forest, the subsoil thaws for a few weeks in summer. The land is dotted with lakes, ponds and bogs. The trees are mostly coniferous, such as spruce and fir. There are only a few deciduous trees, which shed or lose their leaves at the end of the growing season. Examples of animals living in coniferous forest areas are *moose*, *black bears*, *wolves*, *lynx*, *wolverines*, *martens*, *porcupines* and *birds*.

The **deciduous forest** biomes are found in the middle latitudes between 20° and 60°N latitude. The deciduous forest has variations in rainfall, but in general, the rainfall is medium. The average summer temperature is around 24°C (75°F). The deciduous forest has trees that are broad-leaved with foliage that changes color in autumn. The animals consist mostly of *squirrels, deer, foxes* and *bears*. The state of Georgia falls into this biome.

Figure 6.3 Deciduous Forest Biome

Figure 6.4 The Grasslands

The **grasslands** are located in mid-continent areas of middle latitudes. They are found in regions that have warm and cold cycles as well as in the tropic regions on the **savannas** with wet and dry cycles. In general, the rainfall is low, and the average summer temperature is 20°C (68°F). There are large herbivores on the savannas such as *bison, pronghorn antelope* and *zebras*, as well as smaller ones such as *burrowing rodents* and *prairie dogs*.

The **tropical rain forest** biomes are found near the equator and near mountain ranges. They have abundant rainfall and are very humid. The average summer temperature is 25°C (77°F). The trees are very tall with dense canopies. The floor of the tropical rain forest does not get much sunlight, but it does keep a fairly constant temperature. There is a great diversity of species of both the plants and animals. Many different types of plants like *vines, hardwood trees* and *orchids* live in the rainforest. Animals like **orangutans**, *insects, sloths, birds* and *jaguars* live in the rainforest.

The **deserts** are found on either side of the equator between 0° and 20° latitudes. They get little rain and have extreme temperature fluctuations. The average summer temperature is 30°C (86°F). There is not much grass in the desert, but what is there is very drought resistant. Other plants, like *sage- brush, euphorbia, mesquite* and *cacti*, have also adapted to desert conditions. Animals common to the desert are the *kangaroo rat, snakes, lizards*, some *birds, spiders* and *insects*.

AQUATIC ECOSYSTEMS

Aquatic ecosystems depend on a number of different factors such as amount of light, oxygen and the **salinity** (salt) level of the water. The amount of salt in the water is the most important factor in determining the type of organisms in the ecosystem. Light and oxygen are important for photosynthesis. Temperature is less important in aquatic systems since water temperatures do not fluctuate a great deal. Aquatic ecosystems include **marine areas**, **freshwater areas** and **estuaries**, all of which are determined by the salinity of the area.

Figure 6.5 Desert

Freshwater ecosystems consist of streams, rivers, lakes, marshes and swamps. All have a low salinity level. Fresh water is important in recycling the Earth's water supply through the water cycle. Freshwater ecosystems are found in areas with differing temperatures and support a wide variety of animal and plant life.

Marine ecosystems are divided into the intertidal, pelagic and benthic zones. All have a high salinity level.

The intertidal zone is the area of shore that can be seen between low and high tides. It is the most biologically active area in a marine ecosystem, with a high level of light and nutrients. Because of the high tides and shifting sand, this area is also under the most stress. Animals like sand crabs often move to find protection. Rocky shores provide good places for kelp and invertebrates to attach themselves, but these organisms also have to deal with changing water levels, the physical stress of the waves and the sand.

HOWARD H. CLEAVE

Figure 6.6 Marine Ecosystem

The largest ocean area is the **pelagic** zone, which is further divided into two areas. The more shallow area is closer to shore and has a maximum depth of 200 meters (600 feet). There is good light for photosynthetic organisms in this relatively shallow area. Many types of fish like *tuna*, *herring*, *sardines*, *sharks*, and *rays* live in this area along with *whales* and *porpoises*. The deeper part of the pelagic zone comprises most of the oceans in the world. This area is deeper than 200 meters. It receives little light, has cold water temperatures, and high pressure. Many different organisms are adapted to the various characteristics of the ocean depths. Some fish have no eyes or have developed luminescent organs. *Lantern fish*, *eels* and *grenadier fish* live in this area.

The **benthic** zone is the ocean floor. Animals like *worms*, *clams*, *hagfish* and *crabs* can be found in deep benthic areas, in addition to bacteria. In deep benthic areas, hydrothermal vents can form the basis of a complex food web supporting a variety of animals. Coral reefs are commonly found in warm, shallow benthic areas. The reefs prevent erosion and provide habitats for many organisms like *sea stars*, *plankton*, *sponges* and a *variety of fish*.

Figure 6.7 An Estuary

An **estuary** is where fresh and salt-water meet in a coastal area. The salinity level in an estuary fluctuates, but is generally not as high as in the ocean ecosystems. The water is partly surrounded by land with access to open ocean and rivers. Estuaries contain salt marshes and swampy areas and are among the most biologically diverse locations on Earth. The diversity is attributed to the large amount of nutrients, the tides that circulate the nutrients, and remove waste and the abundance of different types of plants. The outer banks of North Carolina are the third largest estuary system in the world.

Section Review 1: Earth's Major Ecological Systems

A. Define the following terms.

biome	grasslands	freshwater ecosystem	pelagic zone
tundra	tropical rain forest	estuary	benthic zone
coniferous forest	desert	marine ecosystems	
deciduous forest	salinity	intertidal zone	

B. Choose the best answer.

1. Tundra biomes generally occur near which latitudes?
   A. equatorial
   B. mid-continent
   C. middle
   D. polar

2. The eastern United States is predominately a
   A. grassland biome.
   B. desert biome.
   C. coniferous biome.
   D. deciduous biome.

3. Which of the following is a correct statement about tropical rain forests?
   A. They have little to no rainfall.
   B. They have a diversity of species.
   C. They fluctuate greatly in yearly temperatures.
   D. They are found between the 0° and 20° latitudes.

4. Which biotic factor listed below determines <u>all</u> other biotic factors in a particular biome?
   A. plants   B. animals   C. rocks   D. temperature

5. Holden goes on a class trip to another country. They observe plants adapted to fire and drought like eucalyptus and euphorbis. Many different types of marsupials, reptiles, spiders and insects are also observed. The daytime temperature reaches over 90° F with little rainfall all week. Which biome is Holden's class visiting?
   A. tropical rain forest
   B. desert
   C. tundra
   D. intertidal

C. Answer the following questions.

1. What are the differences and similarities between marine and freshwater biomes?

2. Why is climate important to biotic factors in a biome?

ORGANIZATION OF ECOSYSTEMS

ECOSYSTEM

An **ecosystem** is the interdependence of plant and animal communities and the physical environment in which they live. The **biosphere** is the zone around the Earth that contains several self-sustaining systems composed of biotic and abiotic factors. **Biotic** factors include all living things, such as birds, insects, trees and flowers. **Abiotic** factors are those components of the ecosystem that are not living, but are integral in determining the number and types of organisms that are present. Examples of abiotic factors include soil, water, temperature and amount of light. In order for an ecosystem to succeed, its biotic factors must obtain and store energy. In addition, the biotic and abiotic factors of the ecosystem must recycle water, oxygen, carbon and nitrogen.

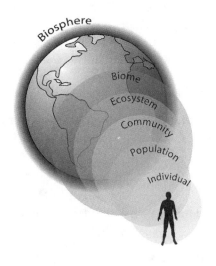

Figure 6.8 Organization of Life

COMMUNITY

A community is a collection of the different biotic factors in a particular ecosystem. Communities include many different species of plants and animals that live in close proximity to one another. For example, in a marine ecosystem a coral reef supports a large community of plants and animals. In this example the community of fishes, shrimps, mammals, algae, sharks, corals, urchins, sea stars and clams all live together and interact with one another. A community might have very different types of plants and animals living in one area. The members of a community interrelate with each other. Deer grazing in a clearing in the forest may be alert to the activity or movement of birds that warn them of approaching danger. In turn, the birds may depend on the deer grazing in a clearing to disturb insects hiding in the grass, thus causing them to become visible.

Figure 6.9 A Forest Community

Each member of a community has its own **habitat**. A habitat is the dwelling place where an organism seeks food and shelter. A woodpecker lives in a hole in a tree. It eats the insects that live in the bark of the tree. A robin builds its nest and raises its young in the same tree. A mouse lives in a burrow at the base of the tree. An owl sleeps on a branch of the same tree. The tree supports a whole community of organisms and becomes their habitat. The habitat provides food and shelter for the members of the community. In turn, each species of the tree community has its own **niche**. A niche is the role that an organism plays in its community, such as what it eats, what eats it, and where it nests.

POPULATION

A community of living things is composed of populations. **Populations** are made up of the individual species in a community. For example, in a forest community ecosystem, there are populations of various plant and animal species such as deer, squirrels, birds, insects and trees.

Figure 6.10 A Population of Deer

SPECIES

A **species** is a group of similar organisms that can breed with one another to produce fertile offspring. Organisms of the same species share similar characteristics common to all organisms within the population. For example, all domestic cats can breed to produce kittens. All domestic cats have whiskers, retractable claws, canine teeth, eat meat and can land on their feet; these characteristics are common to all cats.

Some natural variation exists within all members of a species. Not all cats have whiskers of the same length or bodies of the same size. However, all domestic cats can breed to produce offspring.

Two organisms are part of a different species when they cannot breed and produce fertile offspring. A horse and a donkey can breed, but they produce a mule, which is almost always infertile. Therefore, a horse and a donkey are different species.

Figure 6.11 Cat Species

Section Review 2: Organization of Ecosystems

A. Define the following terms.

ecosystem	abiotic	niche
biosphere	community	population
biotic	habitat	species

B. Choose the best answer.

1. The area in which certain types of plants or animals can be found living in close proximity to each other is called a

   A. habitat.　　　　B. community.　　　　C. niche.　　　　D. kingdom.

2. A British ecologist stated the importance of realizing an organism's role in the ecosystem as follows: "When an ecologist sees a badger, they should include in their thoughts some definitive idea of the animal's place in the community to which it belongs." What does this statement describe?

   A. an animal's habitat　　　　　　　　C. an animal's community

   B. an animal's niche　　　　　　　　　D. an animal's ecosystem

3. The giant noctule bat (Nyctalus lasiopterus bat) predates mainly upon insects during the summer months, and on migrating songbirds during the autumn and spring. The bat attacks the birds at night from several hundred meters in the air. During the day, the bat roosts in trees. What do these sentences describe?

   A. community　　　　B. habitat　　　　C. biome　　　　D. niche

4. Nitrogen, oxygen and carbon dioxide are among the most biologically important atmospheric gases. What are these called?

   A. abiotic factors　　　　　　　　　C. biospheric factors

   B. biotic factors　　　　　　　　　　D. habitat factors

5. A hinny is the offspring of a male horse and a female donkey. Like mules, hinnies are almost always sterile (unable to breed). This confirms that

   A. a mule and a donkey are different species.

   B. a mule and a hinny are different species.

   C. a horse and a donkey are different species.

   D. a horse and a hinny are different species.

C. Answer the following question.

1. Name four abiotic conditions that might determine the kind of ecosystem in an area.

RELATIONSHIPS AMONG ORGANISMS

Each organism in an ecosystem interrelates with the other members. These relationships fall into one of three categories: **symbiosis**, **competition** or **predation**.

SYMBIOSIS

A **symbiotic relationship** is a long-term association between two members of a community in which one or both parties benefit. There are three types of symbiotic relationships: commensalism, mutualism and parasitism.

- **Commensalism** is a symbiotic relationship in which one member benefits and the other is unaffected. Hermit crabs that live in snail shells are one example of this type of relationship. Some argue that one member in most commensalistic relationships is harmed in some way by the relationship. For example, orchids are a type of epiphytic plant that grows on top of the branches of rainforest trees. Having a *few* orchids in its branches does not harm the tree. However, the accumulation of many epiphytic plants could cause the tree to loose limbs, sunlight or nutrients. For this reason, true commensalistic relationships are rare in nature.

Figure 6.12
A Commensalistic Relationship

- **Mutualism** is a symbiotic relationship that is beneficial to both organisms. In South America, the tree *Acacia cornigera* and a species of ant (*Pseudomyrmex ferruginea*) are one example of mutualism. The acacia tree provides a home for the ants by growing hollow thorns. The tree also provides food for the ants in the form of protein-lipid and a carbohydrate-rich nectar from structures on the leaf stalk called nodules. The ants in turn, protect the tree from predators by biting or stinging them and other plant

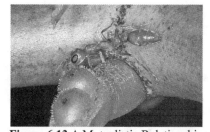

Figure 6.13 A Mutualistic Relationship

  competitors by killing all plant life that comes into contact with the branches. There are many examples of mutualism in nature, including cleaner fish in the ocean, remoras and sharks and clown fish and sea anemones.

- **Parasitism** is a symbiotic relationship that benefits one organism (the parasite), but harms the other (the host). For example, heartworms in dogs (and humans) are parasites (see Figure 6.14). The heartworm benefits by getting its nutrition from the bloodstream of its animal host. The host, however, is harmed because blood flow is restricted and nutrients are lost to the parasite. There are many examples of parasitism in nature, including fleas, tapeworms, live flukes and ticks.

Figure 6.14 A Parasitic Relationship

COMPETITION

When two or more organisms seek the same resource that is in limited supply, they **compete** with each other. A **resource** could be food, water, light, ground space or nesting space. Competition can be intraspecific or interspecific. **Intraspecific competition** occurs between members of the same species, whereas **interspecific competition** occurs between members of different species.

PREDATION

Ecosystems maintain an **ecological balance** within themselves. This balance can be helpful or harmful to the members that make up the community depending upon whether they are the predator or the prey. A **predator** is an organism that feeds on other living things. The organism it feeds on is the **prey**. For instance, wild dogs will hunt down and kill zebra, separating out weak and sick animals from the herd. As you will soon see, the predator/prey relationship is the way energy passes up the food chain of the ecosystem.

Figure 6.15 Predator-Prey Relationship Between a Wild Dog and Zebra

---

Activity

Use books, magazines or the Internet to observe the interactions of organisms. Mount each interaction image on poster board then classify the relationship as commensalistic, mutualistic, parasitic, competition or predator/prey.

Section Review 3:   Relationships among Organisms

A. Define the following terms.

symbiotic relationship	parasite	interspecific competition
commensalism	host	predation
mutualism	competition	predator
parasitism	intraspecific competition	prey

B. Choose the best answer.

1. The relationship between two members of a community in which one member harms another by its presence is

    A. parasitism.   C. mutualism.

    B. commensalism.   D. dependency.

2. A bee goes from flower to flower, gathering nectar. At each stop, the furry body and legs accumulate pollen from the flower, which the bee transfers as it moves. The flower needs pollen to reproduce and the bee needs nectar to eat. What kind of relationship is this?

    A. parasitism   B. mutualism   C. commensalism   D. predation

3. Tapeworms are long, flat parasites that can live in the intestines of animals, including humans. The tapeworm feeds off the food that the host animal consumes, and the host animal loses nutrition as a result. What kind of relationship is this?

    A. parasitism   B. mutualism   C. commensalism   D. predation

4. A mother cuckoo lays her egg in the nest of a warbler, then flies away. The warbler raises the baby cuckoo along with her own babies. The cuckoo baby grows quickly, becoming massive compared to the warbler babies. At some point, the baby cuckoo pushes the warbler babies out of the nest in order to make more room for itself. What does this scenario describe?

    A. parasitism   C. intraspecies competition

    B. predation   D. interspecies competition

5. Which of the following is <u>not</u> true regarding predation?

    A. Predation helps maintain an ecological balance.

    B. Predators keep the numbers of prey animals under control.

    C. Predators choose the sick and weak prey because they are easier to catch.

    D. Predators choose the sick and weak prey because they are trying to maintain ecological balance.

C. Do the following exercise.

1. Compare mutualism and parasitism. Provide examples of each.

POPULATION DYNAMICS

A **population** is a group of organisms of the same species living in the same geographic area. Important characteristics of populations include the growth rate, density and distribution of a population. The study of these characteristics is called **population dynamics**.

GROWTH

The **growth rate** of a population is the change in population size per unit time. Growth rates are typically reported as the increase in the number of organisms per unit time per number of organisms present. The size of a population depends on the number of organisms entering and exiting it. Organisms can enter the population through birth or immigration. Organisms can leave the population by death or emigration. **Immigration** occurs when organisms move into a population. **Emigration** occurs when organisms move out of a population. If a population has more births than deaths and immigration and emigration rates are equal, then the population will grow. Ecologists observe the growth rate of a population over a number of hours, years or decades. It can be zero, positive or negative. Growth rate graphs often plot the number of individuals against time.

A population will grow exponentially if the birth and death rates are constant, and the birth rate is greater than the death rate. **Exponential growth** occurs when the population growth starts out slowly and then increases rapidly as the number of reproducing individuals increase. Exponential growth is also sometimes called a **J-shaped curve**. In most cases, the population cannot continue to grow exponentially without reaching some environmental limit such as lack of nutrients, energy, living space and other resources. These environmental limits will cause the population size to stabilize, which we will discuss shortly.

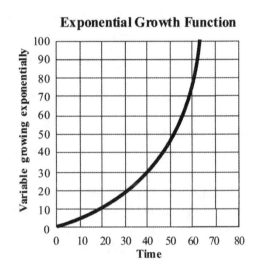

Figure 6.16   J-Shaped Curve

DENSITY AND DISTRIBUTION

The **density** of a population refers to the number of organisms per unit area. For example, there could be an average distribution of 100 maple trees per square kilometer in the eastern United States. However, population density does not reveal how organisms are distributed in space.

The **distribution** of a population refers to the pattern of where the organisms live. The areas in which populations are found can range in size from a few millimeters in the case of bacteria cells, to a few thousand kilometers in the case of African wildebeests. Organisms within the population can have random, clumped or even distribution within the ecosystem.

Several factors, including the location of resources and the social behavior of animals, affect the dispersion of a population. A **random distribution** is one in which there is no set pattern of individuals within the ecosystem. This pattern is rare in nature. A **clumped distribution** is one in which individuals are found in close-knit groups, usually located near a resource. Clumped distributions frequently form among highly social animals like baboons. This distribution pattern is common in nature. **Even distribution** occurs when a set pattern or even spacing is seen among individuals. This distribution sometimes occurs with highly territorial animals that require a well-defined living space apart from others of their species. Orangutans are an example. Even distributions are less common than clumped distributions. All distributions will tend to vary seasonally and at times of ecological change.

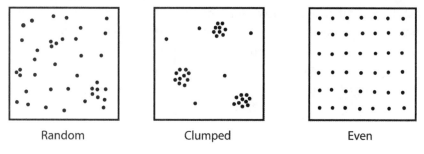

Random   Clumped   Even

Figure 6.17 Possible Population Distributions

CARRYING CAPACITY

As the population uses up available resources, the overall growth of the population will slow or stop. Population growth will slow or decrease when the birth rate decreases, or the death rate increases. Eventually, the number of births will equal the number of deaths. The **carrying capacity** is the number of individuals the environment can support in a given area. The population size will eventually fluctuate around the carrying capacity. When the population size exceeds the carrying capacity, the number of births will *decrease* and

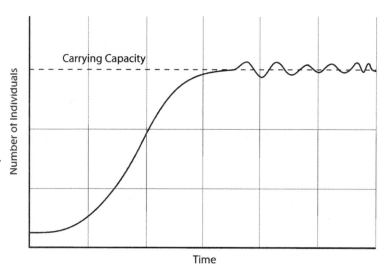

Figure 6.18 Carrying Capacity Curve

the number of deaths will *increase*, thus bringing the population back down to the carrying capacity. This type of growth curve is known as **logistic growth**. Logistic growth is sometimes called an **S-shaped curve** because it levels out at a certain point.

Figure 6.19 Frogs

For example, a specific pond has a carrying capacity of 40 frogs. If more than 40 frogs are in the pond, then food and space become limited, and some frogs will likely move to another pond or die. If fewer than 40 frogs are present in the pond, then some frogs may move into the pond or more offspring will survive.

A decrease in environmental quality will decrease the carrying capacity of that environment. For example, if the pond becomes polluted, it is less likely that it will support 40 frogs. Lack of oxygen and nutrients will cut the frog population to less than 40.

An increase in the environmental quality will increase the environmental carrying capacity. For instance, if the pond is cleared of some or all of its pollution, it will be able to support more than 40 frogs.

REGULATION OF POPULATION SIZE

Availability of resources is not the only factor that limits population growth. A **limiting factor** is anything in a population that restricts the population size. Remember that resources in an ecosystem are limited, and the availability of matter, space and energy is finite. There are two main categories of limiting factors: **density-dependent factors** and **density-independent factors**. Density-independent factors are limiting no matter the size of the population and include unusual weather, natural disasters and seasonal cycles. Density-dependent factors are phenomenon, such as competition, disease and predation, which only become limiting when a population in a given area reaches a certain size. Density-dependent factors usually only affect large, dense populations.

SUCCESSION

Over time, an ecosystem goes through a series of changes known as **ecological succession**. Succession occurs when one community slowly replaces another as the environment changes. There are two types of succession: primary succession and secondary succession.

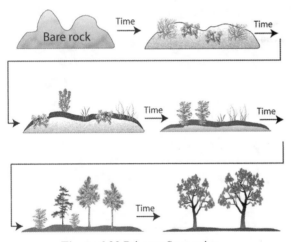

Figure 6.20 Primary Succession

Primary succession occurs in areas that are barren of life because of a complete lack of soil. Examples are new volcanic islands and areas of lava flows such as those on the islands of Hawaii. Areas of rock left behind by retreating glaciers are another site for primary succession. In these areas, there is a natural reintroduction of progressively more complex organisms. Usually, lichens are the first organisms to begin to grow in the barren area. Lichens hold onto moisture and help to erode rock into soil components. The second group of organisms to move into an area include: bacteria, protists, mosses and fungi. They continue the erosion process. Once there is a sufficient number of organisms to support them, the insects and other arthropods inhabit the area. Grasses, herbs and weeds begin to grow once there is a sufficient amount of soil; eventually, trees and shrubs can be supported by the newly formed soil.

In habitats where the community of living things has been partially or completely destroyed, **secondary succession** occurs. In these areas, soil and seeds are already present. For example, at one time prairie grasslands were cleared and crops planted. When those farmlands were abandoned, they once again became inhabited by the native plants. Trees grew where there were once roads. Animals returned to the area and reclaimed their natural living spaces. Eventually, there was very little evidence that farms ever existed in those parts of the prairies.

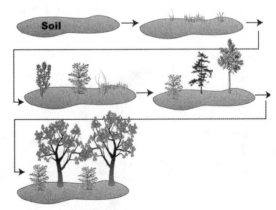

Figure 6.21 Secondary Succession

Section Review 4: Population Dynamics

A. Define the following terms.

growth rate   carrying capacity   density-independent factor

immigration   logistic growth   ecological succession

emigration   limiting factor   primary succession

exponential growth   density-dependent factor   secondary succession

population

B. Choose the best answer.

1. A density-dependent factor

    A.   limits a population in a given area regardless of size.

    B.   limits the population when the population reaches a certain size.

    C.   may include weather or a natural disaster.

    D.   often affects small, sparse populations.

2. Anything that restricts a population is called a

    A.   distribution factor.   C.   logistic factor.

    B.   restricting factor.   D.   limiting factor.

3. A population will tend to grow if

    A. it has no environmental limitations.

    B. the number of births exceeds the number of deaths.

    C. the immigration rate exceeds the emigration rate.

    D. all of the above.

4. An active volcano under the ocean erupts, and the build-up of cooled lava eventually forms a new island. What type of succession will take place immediately following this event?

    A.   primary succession

    B.   secondary succession

    C.   both primary and secondary succession

    D.   no succession

C. Answer the following questions.

1. How is the carrying capacity of a population determined?

2. Why do you think it is important for a population to have limiting factors?

ENERGY FLOW THROUGH THE ECOSYSTEM

Matter within an ecosystem is constantly recycled over and over again. Earth has the same amount of abiotic matter today as it did one hundred years ago. Elements, chemical compounds and other sources of matter pass from one state to another through the ecosystem.

As a deer eats grass, the nutrients contained in the grass are broken down into their chemical components and then rearranged to become living deer tissues. Waste products are produced in the deer's digestive system and pass from the deer's body back into the ecosystem. Organisms break down this waste into simpler chemical components. The grass growing close by is able to take up those components and rearrange them back into grass tissues. Then the energy cycle begins again.

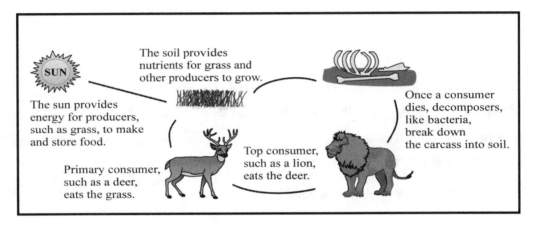

The soil provides nutrients for grass and other producers to grow.

The sun provides energy for producers, such as grass, to make and store food.

Primary consumer, such as a deer, eats the grass.

Top consumer, such as a lion, eats the deer.

Once a consumer dies, decomposers, like bacteria, break down the carcass into soil.

Figure 6.22 Energy Cycle

Energy can be added, stored, transferred and lost throughout an ecosystem. **Energy flow** is the transfer of energy within an ecosystem. Inorganic nutrients are recycled through the ecosystem, but energy cannot be recycled. Ultimately, energy is lost as heat. Remember, however, that energy cannot be destroyed; although it may be lost from one system as heat, it is gained somewhere else. In this way, energy is conserved.

FOOD CHAINS AND FOOD WEBS

The producers, consumers, and decomposers of each ecosystem make up a **food chain**. Energy flow through an ecosystem occurs in food chains, with energy passing from one organism to another. There can be many food chains in an ecosystem.

The **producers** of an ecosystem use **abiotic** (not living) factors to obtain and store energy for themselves or the consumers that eat the producers. In a forest ecosystem, the producers are trees, bushes, shrubs, small plants, grass and moss.

The **consumers** are members of the ecosystem that depend on other members for food. Each time a plant or animal consumes another organism, energy transfers to the consumer. Deer, foxes, rabbits, raccoons, owls, hawks, snakes, mice, spiders and insects are examples of consumers in a forest ecosystem. There are three types of consumers: **herbivores**, **carnivores** and **omnivores**. Table 6.1 lists characteristics of the three different types of consumers.

The **decomposers** are members of the ecosystem that live on dead or decaying organisms and reduce them to their simplest forms. They use the decomposition products as a source of energy. Decomposers include fungi and bacteria. They are also called **saprophytes**.

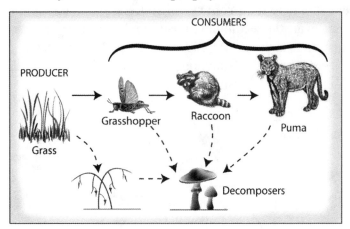

Figure 6.23 A Food Chain

Table 6.1 Types of Consumers

Consumer	Food Supply
Herbivore	animals that eat only plants
Omnivore	animals that eat both plants and other animals.
Carnivore	animals that eat only other animals.
Saprophytes	organisms that obtain food from dead organisms or from the waste products of living organisms

The interaction of many food chains is a **food web**. Most producers and consumers interact with many others forming a complex food web out of several simple food chains. Figure 6.24 shows the more complex food web.

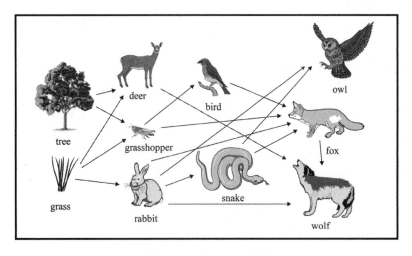

Figure 6.24 A Food Web

A **trophic level** is the position occupied by an organism in a food chain. Organisms that share a trophic level get their energy from the same source. Producers are found at the base of the energy pyramid and comprise the first trophic level of the food chain. Producers capture energy as sunlight and convert it into usable forms. Above them are the **primary consumers** that make up the second trophic level. Above the primary consumers are the **secondary consumers** that occupy the third trophic level. Finally, there are the **tertiary consumers** at the top trophic level. The tertiary consumers are the so-called "top" of the food chain. They are generally omnivores, like humans or carnivores, like lions. Different ecosystems will have different tertiary consumers.

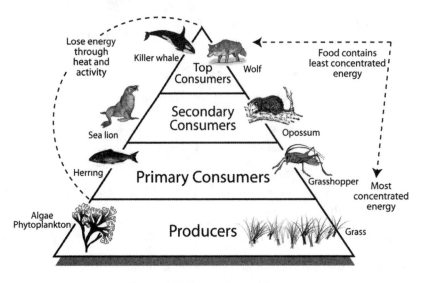

Figure 6.25 Energy Pyramid

Activity

Using the food chain diagram in Figure 6.23, assemble two food chains, choosing your own plants and animals. Use at least four organisms in your food chains.

Activity

Construct a food web like the one above using these organisms: dragonfly, spider, bird, frog, hawk, mouse, snake and some plants.

Activity

Select a biome described in section 1 of this chapter. Design a food web for your biome. Include as many animals as you can.

Section Review 5: Food Chains and Food Webs

A. Define the following terms.

food chain	decomposer	carnivore	trophic level	omnivore
producer	herbivore	food web	consumer	saprophytes

B. Choose the best answer.

1. Organisms that share a trophic level are

   A.   elephants and lions.

   B.   cheetahs and giraffes.

   C.   chipmunks and squirrels.

   D.   wolves and sparrows.

2. The owl is a nocturnal hunter of small mammals, insects and other birds. An owl is an example of a/an

   A.   producer.   B.   omnivore.   C.   carnivore.   D.   decomposer.

3. Which food would an herbivore always avoid?

   A. worms   B. clover   C. pine nuts   D. grass

4. Emperor penguins feed mostly on crustaceans, such as krill. They are prey to orca whales and leopard seals. What ecological role does the Emperor penguin play? (HINT: Krill are zooplankton, tiny sea organisms that feed on plankton.)

   A. It is a producer.

   B. It is a primary consumer.

   C. It is a secondary consumer.

   D. It is a top consumer.

5. _____ are to food webs like words are to sentences.

   A.   food chains

   B.   animals

   C.   plants

   D.   sunlight

C. Fill in the blanks.

1. Animals that eat both plants and other animals are called _____.

2. Organisms that obtain food from dead organisms or waste material are called _____.

THE NUTRIENT CYCLES

The process of recycling substances necessary for life is called the **nutrient cycle**. Nutrient cycles include the **carbon cycle**, the **nitrogen cycle**, the **phosphorous cycle** and the **water cycle**.

CARBON CYCLE

The **carbon cycle** is the cycling of carbon through the environment. Scientists usually separate carbon compounds into the **organic** and **inorganic** categories. Organic carbon compounds are part of living structures, like animals, trees and fungi. They consist mainly of carbon and hydrogen; an example is methane (CH_4). Inorganic carbon compunds are not part of living cellular mass, but may be a by-product of cellular processes. These compounds consist of carbon and hydrogen, oxygen, nitrogen, chlorine and other elements in a variety of forms. Inorganic carbon makes up 0.03% of the atmosphere as carbon dioxide (CO_2). Plants use carbon dioxide and energy from the Sun to perform photosynthesis. When animals eat plants, carbon passes into their tissues. Through food chains, carbon passes from one organism to another, as shown in Figure 6.26. It returns to Earth through respiration, excretion, or decomposition after death. Some animals do not decompose after death; instead, their bodies become buried and compressed underground. Over long periods of time, fossil fuels such as coal, oil and gas develop from decomposing organic matter. When fossil fuels burn, carbon dioxide returns to the atmosphere.

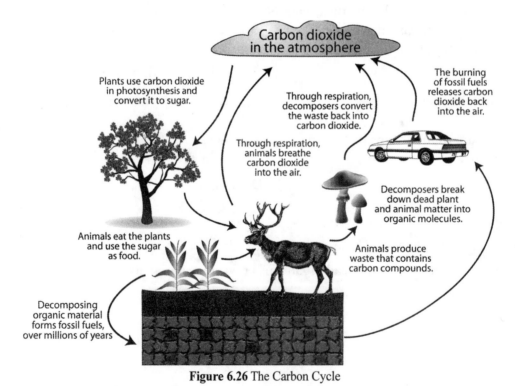

Figure 6.26 The Carbon Cycle

NITROGEN CYCLE

Nitrogen is the most abundant atmospheric gas, comprising 78% of the Earth's atmosphere. However, nitrogen gas is not in a form that is usable by most organisms. The **nitrogen cycle** transforms nitrogen into ammonia, nitrite, and finally nitrate so that it is usable by plants and animals. Refer to Figure 6.27 below to see the nitrogen cycle.

Nitrogen fixation is the conversion of nitrogen gas into nitrate by several types of bacteria. Nitrogen fixation occurs in three major steps. First, nitrogen is converted into ammonia (NH_3) by bacteria called **nitrogen fixers**. Some plants can use ammonia directly, but most require nitrate. **Nitrifying bacteria** convert ammonia into nitrite (NO_2^-) and finally into nitrate (NO_3^-). The nitrogen-fixing bacteria live on the roots of **legumes** (pea and bean plants). This process increases the amount of usable nitrogen in soil. The plants use the nitrogen, in the form of nitrate, to synthesize nucleic acids and proteins. The nitrogen passes along through food chains. Decomposers release ammonia as they break down plant and animal remains, which may then undergo the conversion into nitrite and nitrate by nitrifying bacteria. Other types of bacteria convert nitrate and nitrite into nitrogen gas that then returns to the atmosphere. The nitrogen cycle keeps the level of usable nitrogen in the soil fairly constant. A small amount of nitrate cycles through the atmosphere; this is created when lightning converts atmospheric nitrogen into nitrate.

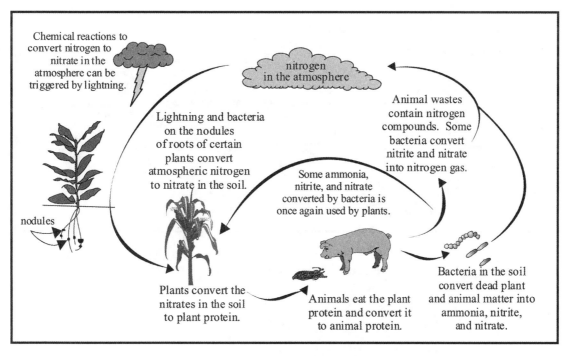

Figure 6.27 The Nitrogen Cycle

PHOSPHOROUS CYCLE

Phosphorous is an element that is essential to life. Unlike nitrogen and carbon, phosphorous is not found in the atmosphere. Phosphorous exists only as part of an organism, dissolved in water, or as an element in rock. Phosphorous, like nitrogen, is a water pollutant in excess quantities. The **phosphorous cycle** begins with the introduction of phosphates (PO_4) into the soil from weathering, or breakdown, of sedimentary rocks. Plants then absorb phosphate ions from the soil, which introduces phosphorous into living ecosystems. Fungi can also directly absorb phosphates from the soil. All other organisms obtain phosphorous through the consumption of the fungi or plant producers. The phosphorous then passes to the consumers of the plants before returning to the soil as waste or decomposed material. Figure 6.28 diagrams the phosphorous cycle.

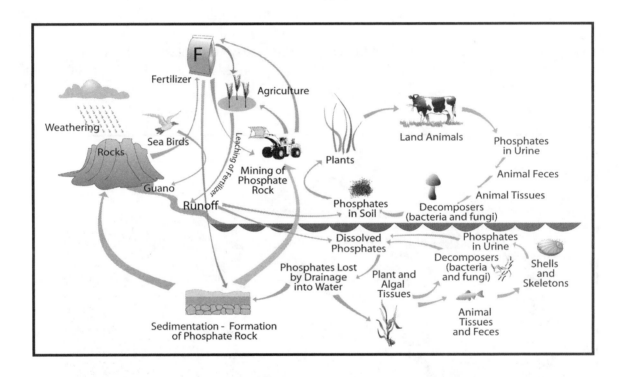

Figure 6.28 The Phosphorous Cycle

WATER CYCLE

The **water cycle** circulates fresh water between the atmosphere and the Earth as seen in Figure 6.29 on the following page. Even though water covers the majority of Earth, about 95% of it is salt water. Most of the fresh water is in the form of glaciers, leaving a very small amount of fresh water available for land organisms. Fresh water is vital for carrying out metabolic processes; the water cycle ensures that the supply is replenished. **Precipitation** in the form of rain, ice, snow, hail or dew falls to the earth and ends up in lakes, rivers and oceans through the precipitation itself or through **runoff.** The Sun provides energy in the form of heat, thus driving **evaporation** that sends water vapor into the atmosphere from bodies of water. Energy from the sun also powers winds and ocean currents. **Respiration** from people and animals and **transpiration** from plants also send water vapor to the atmosphere. The water vapor cools to form clouds. The clouds cool and become saturated with water. The water vapor condenses to form precipitation. Without this cycle of precipitation, runoff, evaporation and **condensation**, a fresh water supply would not be available.

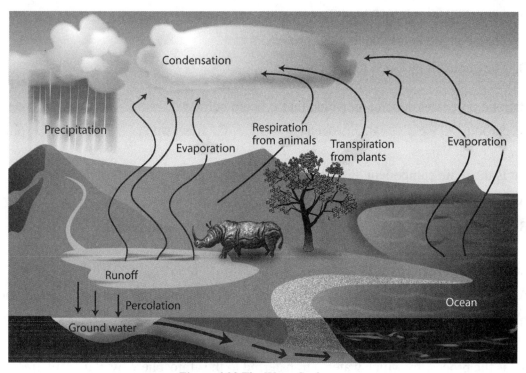

Figure 6.29 The Water Cycle

Section Review 6:   The Nutrient Cycles

A. Define the following terms.

nutrient cycle	nitrogen cycle	nitrogen fixers	phosphorous cycle
carbon cycle	nitrogen fixation	nitrifying bacteria	water cycle
precipitation	evaporation	condensation	respiration
inorganic	organic	runoff	transpiration

B. Choose the best answer.

1. Nitrogen-fixing bacteria perform which task?

    A. They convert nitrogen to ammonia.

    B. They convert nitrogen to animal protein.

    C. They convert ammonia to plant protein.

    D. They convert nitrogen to plant protein.

2. Metabolic processes depend on which factor listed below?

    A. carbon   B. nitrogen   C. fresh water   D. phosphorous

3. What is the main component of organic molecules?

    A. hydrogen   C. oxygen

    B. carbon   D. carbon dioxide

4. How do plants use nitrogen?

    A. to make sugar   C. to make proteins and nucleic acids

    B. to attract pollinators   D. to transport water to their leaves

5. What is the process by which water is transferred to the atmosphere by plants and trees called?

    A. evaporation   B. respiration   C. condensation   D. transpiration

6. Which of the following compounds is classified as an organic compound?

    A. CO_2 B. CH_4 C. NO_3^- D. H_2O

HUMANS AND THE ENVIRONMENT

Humans are, perhaps, the single most influential force affecting planet Earth today. Humans have the ability to change climate patterns, cause droughts and extinctions and alter the flow of energy through ecosystems. The global human population is growing exponentially, and shows no signs of slowing. Humans, along with a select few other animals, have the ability to modify their environment to suit their own needs. Humans modify and change the environment in many different ways. Four areas where human environmental impact is often studied are global warming, population growth, pesticide use and water and power consumption.

Humans often impact the environment in negative ways. Humans have the ability to arrest environmental degradation or cause further harm. We must work hard to stop environmental threats, after all we only have *one* planet Earth!

GLOBAL WARMING

No doubt global warming, or global climate change, is something you've heard before. From print news to television media, global warming is something many people talk about today. What most people neglect to mention is that global warming is part of a natural Earth warming process. This process is called the greenhouse effect.

The **greenhouse effect** traps solar heat within the Earth's atmosphere. Electromagnetic radiant energy provided by the Sun travels to the Earth through space. Some of this energy is trapped by bodies of water and land masses and some of this energy is reflected back into the atmosphere. Some reflected heat is lost back into space but most is trapped by atmospheric gasses. Gases like water vapor, carbon dioxide, methane and chlorofluorocarbons tend to trap more heat than other types of gases. Without this heat trapping processes, the average global temperature would be around -20°C. However, like many other natural cycles, humans have altered this natural warming cycle as well.

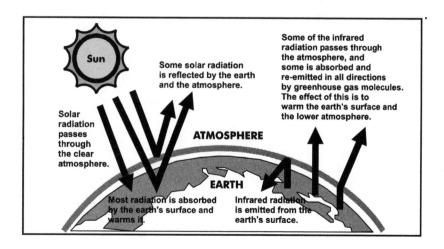

Figure 6.30 The Greenhouse Effect

Global warming is a term people use to describe the changes humans have made to the Earth's overall climate. Often, these changes include an increase in average global temperature. The scientific community is in agreement that humans are changing the planet in many ways. Some would argue that humans have not impacted the global climate and that to propose such theories is an alarmist, extreme point of view. This is where you, the science student, must use your skills to examine the facts and determine the most likely scenario. Here are some facts about recent changes in planet Earth.

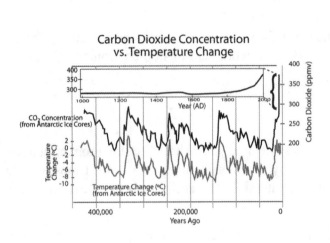

Figure 6.31 CO_2 Continent and Global Temp

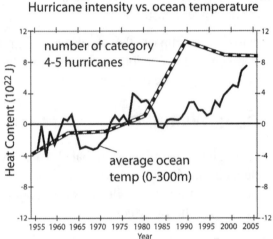

Figure 6.32 Ocean Temp and Hurricane Frequency

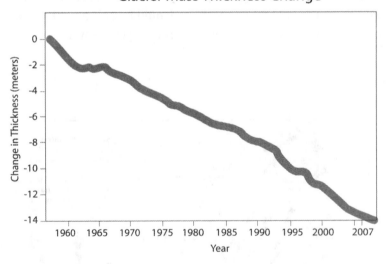

Figure 6.33 Average Global Glacier Mass Thickness

Figure 6.34 Arctic Ice Minimum 1979

Figure 6.36 Grinnell Glacier 1938   Figure 6.37 Grinnell Glacier 2005

Figure 6.35 Arctic Ice Minimum 2005

Other facts associated with global warming include average global temperature increase of 1°C and average polar temperature increase of 5°C. These warming trends have contributed to an increased incidence of regular tidal flooding. This has effected the geography and economy of many areas, in particular the Polynesian Island nation of Tuvalu. In recent years, Tuvalu has been nearly swallowed by the surrounding ocean. Its highest elevation is now 5 meters above sea level.

Recall that inferring and concluding are two important aspects in scientific inquiry. The information displayed above can be interpreted in several different ways by several different people. The observations listed above are plugged into advanced weather forecasting computer models. As more data is collected, the computer models become more accurate at forecasting future events. Based on the observations and computer models many scientific minds the world over agree that human caused climate change is a real threat to the Earth. The release of CO_2, pollution and other harmful chemicals into the atmosphere is increasing the overall Earth's temperature and melting the polar ice sheets faster than ever thought possible. One reason for the accelerated melting is the fact that water absorbs more heat than ice, and as a result causes more ice to melt, in an ever accelerating process. Scientists expect to see increased temperatures, frequent intense storms and rising sea levels to impact human populations in the near future. Ironically, global warming now will lead to massive global cooling later. It is theorized that as polar ice melts, ocean currents will slow, causing a dramatic drop in global temperatures and thus beginning the next ice age. After examining the facts above and reading this section, what can you infer about global warming? The Earth will survive the next ice age, will we?

HUMAN POPULATION GROWTH

In the past decade, the **human population** reached 6 billion. The positive growth rate has continued unabated since the Industrial Revolution in the early 1900s. In fact, the human population is experiencing an explosive exponential growth curve. Advancements in agriculture, medicine and sanitation have allowed the human population to grow so quickly. Along with this explosive growth comes increased pressure on the environment. Humans use lots of space for housing and food production. Examine Figure 6.38 showing the human population for the past 10,000 years.

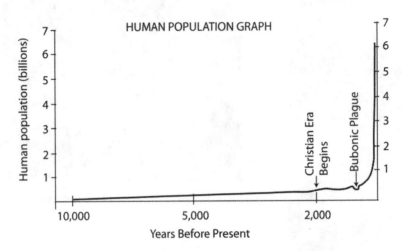

Figure 6.38 Human Population Graph

Since the Industrial Revolution changed the face of both industry and agriculture, the world population has been able to expand at an increasing rate. The British economist **Thomas Malthus** (1766–1834), predicted that the human species, growing exponentially, and the food supply, growing linearly, would lead to massive starvation worldwide at some future point. Over the centuries since, however, the opposite has proved to be the case: increases in agricultural efficiency and overall food supply has, since the industrial revolution, far exceeded the growth in population worldwide. However, certain problems remain between population and food supply. For example, food is not distributed evenly worldwide. While food is abundant in the U.S., the food supply is below the needs of the people in Somalia. These situations lead to famines, especially when wars and lack of infrastructure such as roads do not allow food to reach these populations in crisis.

A new problem related to belief in the theories of Malthus has occurred in population changes. Because many world governments believed Malthus was correct, they aggressively encouraged population control methods, both voluntary (Western nations) and forced (China's One Child policy) among their people. However, this promotion has led to a new, emerging problem, particularly in Europe at this point: underpopulation, especially of the youth. As a result of falling birthrates, an aging and retiring workforce has fewer youth and working age populations to support the elderly in the population. European governments are finding it increasingly difficult to support the masses of elderly given the current workforce available.

The UN currently projects the population to grow to 9.1 billion by 2050, but also shows the growth in population as declining. Both government promotion of population control and voluntary changes on an individual basis have changed the level of the growth, for better or worse. For example, as people gain education and socioeconomic status, they often wait until they have completed their education and establish their careers before starting a family, which reduces the number of children possible for a family. Projections of worldwide populations have been revised downward every decade since the UN began tracking growth rates. This is a very complicated issue. You should research the topic objectively before determining your position.

Activity
Divide the class in half and debate the validity of the global warming issue or government sponsored population controls (like China's One Child policy).

PESTICIDE USE

Figure 6.39 Crop Dusting Plane

Humans use pesticides for many reasons. A **pesticide** is a chemical agent used to kill damaging or harmful organisms, usually animals. Examples of organisms controlled using pesticides include termites, fire ants, grasshoppers, snails, beetles, snakes and even other mammals. Pesticides are used on a commercial scale in agriculture. Many homeowners also use pesticides to keep animals out of their home and off their lawn.

When a pesticide is applied to an area a certain percentage, usually 95–99%, of the target organism is killed, along with other non-target organisms. Only a small fraction of the original population is left intact. However, this small surviving fraction of the population passes along its immunity to future generations. Let's say for example a tomato farmer has a problem with snails. He estimates his field has a population of about 1,000,000 snails. He applies metaldehyde, a type of mollusk pesticide, to his field. This chemical is 97.1% effective, and kills 971,000 of the snails on his field. The remaining 29,000 snails have a resistance to the pesticide, these snails reproduce passing along their resistance to the next generation. Over time, more potent chemicals, and more volumes of chemicals, are necessary to control the same percentage of organisms. Examine Figure 6.40 showing five hypothetical years on the tomato farm.

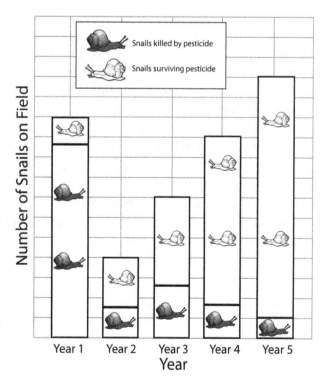

Figure 6.40 Snails

A pesticide is a poison and after it is applied to a farmer's field it often washes into watersheds. Sometimes pesticides persist in the soil for decades after application. Toxic levels of chemicals are found in virtually every watershed in the United States. These chemicals are dangerous to amphibians (natural insect controllers), birds, fish, reptiles and humans. Sometimes the mixing of non-harmful chemicals leads to other deadly chemical cocktails. Pesticide residue is often found on foods and even penetrates the skins of many fruits and vegetables. Some people suffer from chemical toxicity disorders where they have increased sensitivity to *any* chemical agent in the environment. Pesticides have been linked to many cancers, endocrine system disorders, infertility, personality disorders, skin conditions, memory disorders and birth defects.

HUMAN CONSUMPTION

Figure 6.41 Water Consumption

As human technology has advanced, so too has our ability to modify our environment to suit our needs. Humans need **natural resources** such as water, soil and air for survival. Humans dam rivers to prevent flooding and provide a consistent, reliable source of fresh water. Dams create lakes and increase the rate at which water evaporates, thereby speeding up the water cycle. Careless water consumption like running the water while you brush your teeth or having leaky pipes further increases the rate at which this precious natural resource is used.

Along with the need for natural resources, humans also have a need for power and lots of it. Humans use power to heat and cool homes, store and prepare foods and run electronic equipment. Humans can obtain power from natural resources like fossil fuels, water, sunlight and wind. The growing human population places increased demands on ecosystems to produce energy at ever increasing rates. In reality, humans are using up many natural resources much faster than they are recycled by ecosystems. Fossil fuels, a nonrenewable energy source, produce over 60% of the electrical power used in the

Figure 6.42 Power Production

United States. Careless power consumption, like leaving lights or television sets turned on when not in use, reduces the amount of energy available in the future and increase the amount of carbon released into the atmosphere (accelerating global warming trends). Non-renewable resources are finite and are in limited supply on Earth. Once used, fossil fuels cannot be replaced in a human lifetime.

Activity

Think of activities you do to consume power and water in your home. Come up with ways to reduce your consumption of these resources, and begin using one or two each week. Record your experiences while attempting to implement your plan. After a month write a paper or put on a play about your most meaningful moment during the consumption reduction month.

Section Review 7: Pesticide Use and Human Consumption

A. Define the following terms.

greenhouse effect   human population   natural resource

global warming   pesticide

B. Choose the best answer.

1. Why do humans need more potent pesticides over time?

    A.   because the target population soon develops a resistance to the chemical

    B.   because pesticide salesman need to make more money

    C.   because humans want to constantly develop newer and better chemicals

    D.   because the explosive growth of the human population places increased demands on current farmers

2. Which of the following is an environmentally responsible water consumption technique?

    A.   washing your favorite outfit by itself in the washing machine

    B.   watering your garden before 10 am

    C.   leaving the hose running the entire time you wash your car

    D.   taking 2 showers/baths a day

3. What factors listed below have NOT contributed to the explosive human growth seen in the last 100 years?

    A.   advances in medicine   C.   more available jobs

    B.   improved sanitation   D.   improved food production techniques

4. Which factor listed below is NOT considered scientific evidence for global warming?

    A.   data from retreating glaciers   C.   increase in storm intensities

    B.   average increase in global temperatures   D.   increased rate of extinctions

5. What is the carrying capacity for humans on planet Earth?

    A.   1 million   C.   100 billion

    B.   6 billion   D.   unknown

CHAPTER 6 REVIEW

A. Choose the best answer.

1. The biotic factors are
   A. living.
   B. lipids.
   C. non-living.
   D. always unicellular.

2. The abiotic factors are
   A. decomposers.
   B. living.
   C. non-living.
   D. photosynthetic.

3. The place where a member of a community lives and finds food is called its
   A. pond.
   B. biome.
   C. habitat.
   D. residence.

4. Brim fish in a pond are _____ of that community.
   A. producers
   B. a population
   C. unnecessary elements
   D. the habitat

5. The interactions of plants, animals and microorganisms with each other and with their environment constitutes a(n)
   A. food chain.
   B. ecosystem.
   C. trophic level.
   D. symbiotic relationship.

6. Unusual weather will
   A. affect all individuals within a population.
   B. only affect small populations of organisms.
   C. only affect large populations of organisms.
   D. have no effect on populations.

7. Which terrestrial ecological system has the greatest diversity of plants and animals?
   A. tundra
   B. grassland
   C. rain forest
   D. deciduous forest

8. What type of ecological system can include rivers, lakes, streams, marshes and swamps?
   A. freshwater
   B. estuary
   C. marine
   D. ocean

9. Lions are carnivores and are considered a _____ in the energy cycle.
   A. primary consumer
   B. top consumer
   C. provider
   D. decomposer

10. Photosynthesis is performed by

A. omnivores. C. secondary consumers.

B. producers. D. primary consumers.

11. Which of the following most likely would be a part of the first community on a newly formed volcanic island?

A. pine trees B. oak trees C. lichen D. sea gulls

12. Many types of bacteria obtain their nutrition from dead plants and animals and, in turn, recycle elements such as carbon and nitrogen. These bacteria are

A. decomposers. C. carnivores.

B. producers. D. viruses.

13. In the nutrient cycle, producers use carbon dioxide in the process of

A. respiration. C. decomposition.

B. recycling. D. photosynthesis.

14. During the nitrogen cycle, a plant converts the nitrates in the soil to

A. plant protein. C. fertilizer.

B. fat. D. carbohydrates.

B. For questions 15 – 17 examine the diagram to the right:

15. This graph shows _____ growth for the population.

A. exponential C. logistic

B. J-shaped D. M-shaped

16. The carrying capacity for elk in this environment is around

A. 65. C. 75,000.

B. 6,500. D. 65,000.

17. If a large oil company enters this environment and begins drilling for oil, building structures, and polluting the land, what will probably happen to the carrying capacity of the elk?

A. It will be more than 65,000. C. Nothing; it will remain the same.

B. It will be less than 65,000. D. The elk will all leave and move into a new environment.

Carrying Capacity of Elk in Alaska

Copyright © American Book Company. DO NOT DUPLICATE. 1-888-264-5877.

18. A symbiotic relationship means
    A. the energy cycle is not involved.
    B. no one benefits.
    C. the solar system is involved.
    D. one or both parties benefit.

19. Man-of-war fish cluster around the venomous tentacles of jellyfish to escape larger predators. The presence of the man-of-war fish does not harm or benefit the jellyfish. This type of relationship is called
    A. parasitism.
    B. commensalism.
    C. succession.
    D. mutualism.

20. The greenhouse effect is responsible for which factor listed below?
    A. global warming
    B. thermal pollution
    C. photosynthesis
    D. clear cutting of rain forests

21. Which of the following activities is an environmentally responsible use of power?
    A. leaving your TV on when you are not home
    B. run your furnace at 72°F year round
    C. leaving doors and windows open with the heat or air on
    D. turning off lights as you leave a room

22. What will happen when the global carrying capacity for humans is reached?
    A. Animals will go extinct.
    B. Humans will go extinct.
    C. Humans will not continue reproducing.
    D. Human populations will shrink.

23. A landscaper sprays a lawn with a pesticide that is 96% effective. If there are around 50 grasshoppers living on the lawn before the pesticide application how many are likely to survive the pesticide?
    A. 1   B. 2   C. 3   D. 4

24. How can you combat global warming?
    A. compost kitchen scraps
    B. recycle
    C. avoid eating fish
    D. turn off lights when you leave a room

Chapter 7
Nuclear Processes

GA HSGT SCIENCE STANDARDS COVERED IN THIS CHAPTER INCLUDE:

SPS3 a – d	Students will distinguish the characteristics and components of radioactivity.

RADIOACTIVITY, FISSION AND FUSION

RADIOACTIVITY

As you know, **isotopes** are atoms of the same element with different numbers of neutrons. The nucleus of an atom can be unstable if there are too many neutrons for the number of protons. An unstable nucleus is **radioactive**, and unstable isotopes are called radioactive isotopes. All elements with atomic numbers greater than 83 are radioactive. Radioactive atoms give off radiation in the form of alpha particles, beta particles and gamma rays.

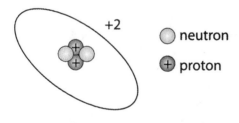

Figure 7.1 Model of an Alpha Particle

An **alpha particle** is equivalent to a helium nucleus, with 2 protons and 2 neutrons, as shown in Figure 7.1. When an alpha particle is released from the nucleus of an atom, the atomic number of the parent nucleus is reduced by two. Alpha particles cannot penetrate a piece of paper or even a thin layer of cloth. However, if ingested, they will do more damage to internal tissue than other forms of radiation.

Beta particles are electrons emitted by an unstable atom. Beta particles are more able to penetrate matter than alpha particles; however, lead is capable of stopping them. **Gamma rays** are high energy X-rays and only thick lead or concrete can stop them.

Table 7.1 Radioactive Particles

Radiation	Symbol	Particles/Waves	Electric Charge	Energy	Energy stopped by
Alpha particle	α	2 protons, 2 neutrons	positive	low	a piece of paper
Beta particle	β	1 electron	negative	medium	lead 1 cm thick
Gamma rays	γ	wave of energy	no charge	high	thick lead or concrete

A radioactive atom that emits an alpha particle, beta particle or gamma ray is going through a process of **radioactive decay**. Radioactive decay causes an atom of one element to become a different element by reducing its atomic number.

Each isotope decays in its own characteristic way. It will emit α particles, β particles and/or γ rays in a particular order, over a particular period of time. The amount of time that it takes for ½ of the atoms of a radioactive sample to decay is called the **half life** of the isotope. For instance, radium-226 has a half-life of 1,602 years. Let's say a sample of 10 grams of ^{226}Ra is placed in a weighing dish and left in a locked vault. After 1,602 years, the vault is opened. How much ^{226}Ra is in the weighing dish now? That's right, only 5 grams remains. One half of the sample has decayed to something else. But what? That is where it becomes important to know *how* the isotope decayed.

Radium-226 decays by alpha particle emission, as shown in the following equation.

$$\,^{226}_{88}\text{Ra} \longrightarrow \,^{222}_{86}\text{Rn} + \,^{4}_{2}\alpha$$

By releasing an alpha particle, the radium-226 atom has lowered its energy and transformed itself into a radon-222 atom.

So, you have seen that unstable nuclei can emit an α particle, β particle or γ ray to become more stable. However, there is another way for an unstable nucleus to lower its energy: the process of nuclear fission.

FISSION

Fission occurs when the nucleus of an atom that has many protons and neutrons becomes so unstable that it splits into two smaller atoms. Fission may be spontaneous or induced.

Spontaneous fission is a natural process that occurs mostly in the transactinide elements, like rutherfordium (Rf). However, some of the actinides (which are a little bit lighter than the transactinides) decay partially by spontaneous fission, including isotopes of uranium (U) and plutonium (Pu). For example, a ^{235}U atom has 92 protons and 143 neutrons. When fission occurs, it may split into a krypton atom and a barium atom, plus 2 neutrons, as shown in the following equation and in Figure 5.2.

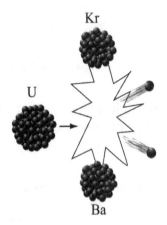

$$\,^{235}_{92}\text{U} \longrightarrow \,^{94}_{36}\text{Kr} + \,^{139}_{56}\text{Ba} + 2\,^{1}_{0}\text{n}$$

Figure 7.2 Spontaneous Fission

The process of spontaneous fission wasn't well-known or understood until fairly recently. In fact, it was only discovered as a by-product of the investigation into induced fission. **Induced fission** is the process of firing neutrons at heavy atoms, to induce them to split. It was first investigated by **Enrico Fermi** in the 1930s. The theory was proven in 1939, with the discovery by **Lise Meitner** and **Otto Frisch** that the use of neutron projectiles had actually caused a uranium nucleus to split into two pieces, as shown in Figure 7.3 (except that more neutrons were emitted). Meitner and Frisch named the process nuclear fission. Fermi proceeded to co-invent the first nuclear reactor. This design led to the invention of nuclear reactors found in nuclear power plants, as well as nuclear bombs.

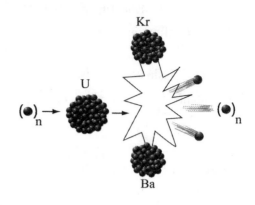

Figure 7.3 Induced Fission

FUSION

During this time, another nuclear process was being investigated: nuclear fusion. **Fusion** is the exact opposite of fission, involving the joining (fusing) of two small atoms to form one larger atom. Fusion reactions occur in the Sun (and other stars), where extremely high temperatures allow hydrogen isotopes to collide and fuse, releasing energy. In 1939, **Hans Bethe** put forth the first quantitative theory (mathematical model) explaining fusion, for which he later won the Nobel Prize.

The most commonly-cited fusion reaction is the fusion of hydrogen's two isotopes, deuterium (^{2}H) and tritium (^{3}H), to form a helium nucleus and a neutron. This is shown in Figure 7.4.

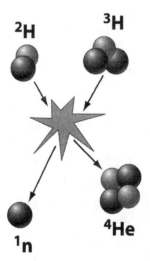

Figure 7.4 Fusion

Section Review 1: Radioactivity, Fission and Fusion

A. Define the following terms.

induced fission	isotope	alpha particle	half-life
spontaneous fission	radioactive	beta particle	fission
	gamma ray	radioactive decay	fusion

B. Choose the best answer.

1. Where would you find a nuclear fusion reaction occurring?

    A.   in a nuclear power reactor   C.   in an X-ray machine

    B.   in the Sun   D.   in a microwave oven

2. Palladium-100 has a half-life of 4 days. If you started with 20 grams of palladium-100, how much would remain after 12 days?

    A.   10 grams   B.   0 grams   C.   5 grams   D.   2.5 grams

3. Which of the following would you use to induce the fission of a radioactive isotope?

    A.   proton   B.   neutron   C.   alpha particle   D.   beta particle

C. Answer the following questions.

1. Describe the contributions of the following people to the development of our nuclear understanding and technology.

    A.   Lise Meitner and Otto Frisch   B.   Enrico Fermi

2. What is the difference between induced fission and spontaneous fission?

3. Would it be a good idea to build a nuclear power reactor that utilized spontaneous fission? Why or why not?

Use the figure to answer questions 4 and 5.

4. Does carbon decay by α-particle emission?

5. An initial sample of 30 grams of ^{14}C is allowed to decay for 11,460 years. How much does the sample weigh at that time?

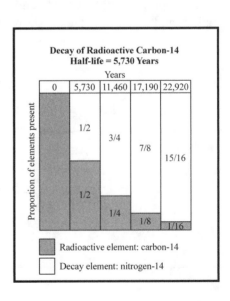

INDUCED FISSION

Induced fission is the process of bombarding radioactive atoms with neutrons to cause them to split apart. What are the products of these processes? There are several, including fission fragments, neutrons and energy. First, let's look at the fission fragments and neutrons.

FISSION FRAGMENTS AND NEUTRONS

Look back at Figures 7.2 and 7.3. The illustrations simplify the fission process and depict an atom of uranium always splitting into krypton and barium. In actuality, however, the nuclear products are much more diverse, as shown in Figure 7.5.

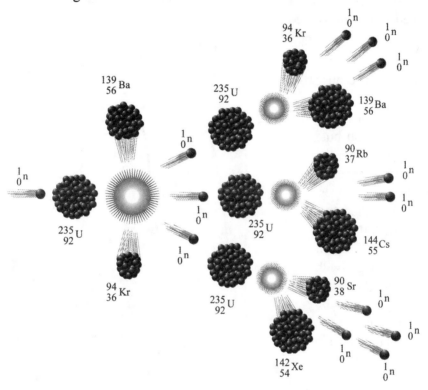

Figure 7.5 Production of Fission Fragments

Besides barium and krypton, rubidium, cesium, strontium and xenon are also produced. These **fission fragments** are the products of an atom split by neutron bombardment. The average mass of ^{235}U fission fragments is 118, but as Figure 7.6 indicates, a fragment of mass 118 is rarely detected. Instead, ^{235}U tends to split into uneven fragment masses around 95 and 137. To see this in another way, look again at the mass numbers and atomic numbers of the fragments shown in Figure 7.5.

Each of the fission fragments is an isotope with a half-life of its own, which may range from seconds to millions of years. As the half-life of each isotope passes, the isotope decays by emitting one or more forms of radiation, like alpha and beta particles or gamma rays. The result is a new isotope called a **daughter**, which may or may not be **stable**. If the atom is **unstable** (meaning that it is still radioactive), it will decay to yet another isotope. If the atom is stable, it will remain as it is, with no further transformation. The succession of decays is called a **decay chain**.

One common pair of fragments is xenon and strontium. The fission is illustrated by the following reaction.

$$^{235}U + n \longrightarrow {}^{236}U^* \longrightarrow {}^{140}Xe + {}^{94}Sr + 2n$$

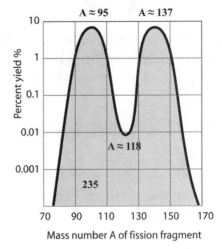

Figure 7.6 Fission Fragment Mass Distribution

U-236 has an asterisk (*) because it only lasts a moment after absorbing the neutron. The forces within the nucleus redistribute themselves allowing for the fission decay, in this case to xenon and strontium isotopes. Xenon-40 is a highly radioactive isotope with a half-life of 14 seconds. It undergoes a series of decays, finally ending with cerium-140. Strontium-94, with a half-life of 74 seconds, decays by beta emission to yttrium-94. Let's look at a partial decay chain of those isotopes, as in Figure 7.7.

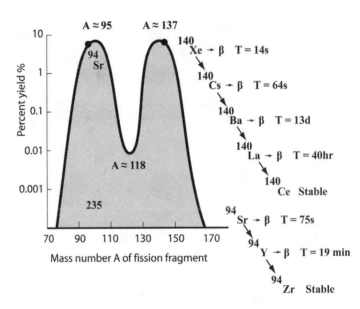

Figure 7.7 Decay Chain

These decay chains show only beta (β) emissions, but other fission fragments may have other types of radiative decay. Even different isotopes of xenon and strontium will decay differently. For instance, we have been looking at Xe-140 and Sr-94. Look back at Figure 7.5. See that the isotopes of strontium and xenon noted there are Xe-142 and Sr-90. The reaction that produces those fragments would be:

$$^{235}U + n \longrightarrow {}^{236}U^* \longrightarrow {}^{142}Xe + {}^{90}Sr + 4n$$

These isotopes will have a different decay chain than that illustrated by Figure 7.7. Try going to the Internet to find their decay chains. Surf around the Brookhaven National Lab's national nuclear database at http://www.nndc.bnl.gov.

Nuclear Energy

When a nucleus splits, or fissions, a great deal of energy is also released. In fact, the scientific world was surprised by how much energy was generated. **Neils Bohr**, the Danish physicist who first modeled the atom, wrote to Lise Meitner to comment on how unexpectedly large the energy release was. The energy release was much larger than calculations had predicted, it turns out. Up until this point, fission research had been performed simply to understand more about the atom. Now, though, the stakes began to rise: a new energy source had been found.

How much energy are we talking about, though? The **nuclear energy** produced by fission and fusion reactions requires only a small amount of matter. After all, an atom is a very small amount of matter. Einstein's famous **mass-energy equation**, $E = mc^2$, states this fact very simply. Einstein's equation, written in word form, is Energy = mass × speed of light × speed of light. Since the speed of light is 3×10^8 meters per second and this term is squared, we can still have a very small amount of matter and end up with a large amount of energy. A nuclear fission reaction, utilizing one U-235 atom, will produce 50 million times more energy than the combustion (burning) of a carbon atom.

Today we use nuclear reactors to harness this power for the production of electricity. Figure 7.8 shows the process. Fissile material, like uranium-235, is manufactured into pellets that are bound together into long rods, called **fuel rods**. Fuel rods are bundled together with **control rods** and placed in the reactor core. Here is what happens.

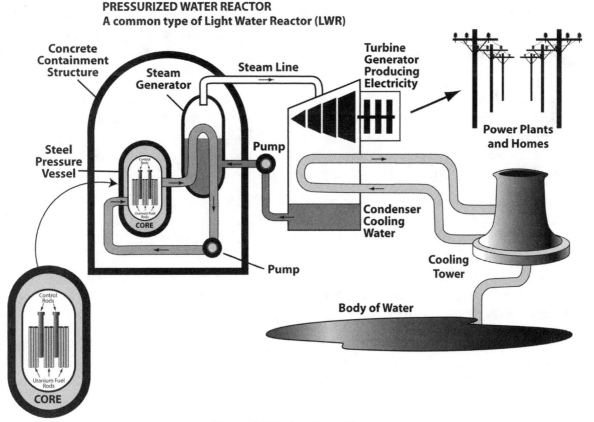

Figure 7.8 Nuclear Power Reactor

Every time a uranium atom fissions, it releases neutrons, which cause another atom to fission. This process is called a **chain reaction**, and it produces energy in the form of heat. The water surrounding the reactor core gets very hot. It is pumped through another water tank by way of a pipe. Note that the water from the core never touches any reactor component outside the core. The continuous pumping of the super-hot water from the reactor core heats the secondary tank water to produce a continuous supply of steam. The steam turns the turbines of a generator, which generates electricity. The steam is then diverted to a cooling tower.

Nuclear Power Plant
Figure 7.9 Cooling Tower

This structure, as shown in Figure 7.9, is commonly associated with nuclear power plants, though it actually has nothing to do with energy production. It is where the steam condenses and cools before its release into a body of water, like a river.

ENERGY AND ENVIRONMENTAL CONSEQUENCES

Nuclear power is a very attractive energy option because it is clean and cheap. However, as with every energy option, there are environmental consequences. The two that are the most important to prevent are **supercriticality** and **environmental contamination** from general operation.

SUPERCRITICALITY

Inside a nuclear power reactor, uranium fuel is used to create energy. Long fuel rods formed of small U-235 pellets are arranged into bundles and submerged in some coolant, usually water. In order for the reactor to work, the submerged bundles of rods must be *slightly* **supercritical**. This means that, left to its own devices, the uranium in the rods would eventually overheat and melt.

To prevent this, control rods are used. **Control rods** are made of a material, like cadmium, that absorbs neutrons. Inserted into the bundle of uranium, control rods allow operators to control the rate of the nuclear reaction. If more heat is needed, the rods are raised out of the uranium bundle. To lessen heat, the rods are lowered into the uranium bundle. The rods can also be lowered completely into the uranium bundle to shut the reactor down in the case of an accident or to change the fuel.

These control rods are the safeguard of the power plant. Without them, true supercriticality could be reached. Were this to happen, the uranium would melt the reactor core, causing a **breech** (a crack or hole) and subsequent release of radioactive isotopes, encased in superheated steam and melted metals. Depending on the scale of the breech, this could be an environmental disaster. The Three Mile Island accident in the US was not a disaster; very little radioactivity was released. It was a warning, however, for the U.S. to increase safety and maintenance precautions. The Chernobyl accident in the former Soviet Union was a disaster and one that the region has yet to recover from.

The issue of environmental impact must be studied whenever an effort to produce energy is planned. Drilling for oil, damming rivers and erecting windmills all have environmental impacts. These must be weighed against the value of the energy produced and the ultimate cost of failure.

ENVIRONMENTAL CONTAMINATION

We have noted that Sr-90 is one product of the induced fission of U-235. This isotope of strontium has an intermediate half-life of around 30 years. This is a difficult time span for environmental contaminants. If you are asking "why," consider this. A short half-life of minutes, days or weeks indicates that the contaminant will be gone (decay) quickly and not have a chance to do much damage, particularly in low concentrations. A long half-life of hundreds, thousands or even millions of years indicates that the isotope releases radioactive particles so infrequently that little damage is done. An intermediate half-life, however, can do great damage.

In addition, strontium mimics the properties of calcium. Look where it is on the Periodic Table — in the same group as calcium. This means that strontium is taken up by living organisms that utilize calcium; those organisms incorporate Sr-90 into their bones. There the Sr-90 decays, emitting radiation that can cause cancer. While strontium is *very unlikely* to enter the environment from a nuclear power reactor, it is one of several isotopes that would have a negative environmental effect if released. In addition to the normal security and operational controls of a nuclear power plant, the area surrounding the reactor must be continually monitored to ensure that no such release has occurred.

Another, more pressing, example of environmental contamination is the issue of radioactive waste. Remember that many different kinds of radioactive isotopes, each of which decays in a different way, are the result of the fission of ^{235}U. This occurs *within the core of the reactor*; during normal operation, no radioactive components come in contact with any other part of the facility. However, a reactor core does not last forever; periodically, fuel rods and control rods must be replaced to maintain optimal function of the reactor. The spent rods still contain a great deal of radioactive material, mostly from the still-decaying daughters of the fission fragments.

The processing of this waste, to separate and neutralize the individual components, is not always possible or feasible. At present, there is no ideal storage solution for this waste. In order to avoid contamination, it must be stored in a highly absorbing material and allowed to decay in a location that will remain secure for many years. **Yucca Mountain** (in Nevada) is the prospective site for nuclear waste storage in this country. Other countries, like France, almost completely reprocess their nuclear waste; this leaves little need for waste storage.

ONGOING RESEARCH

Three kinds of research are being performed that may revolutionize the way nuclear processes are used in power production.

1. New fission reactor designs are now under construction that make nuclear power even cheaper, safer and more efficient.

2. New waste re-processing technologies are being investigated to help us deal with dangerous and long-lived nuclear waste.

3. Fusion reactors are still being investigated. Fusion reactions, as described earlier in this section, produce a great deal of energy — potentially much more than fission reactions. They have fewer reactants, fewer products and produce little waste. Scientists are still trying to overcome the obstacle of the extremely high temperatures necessary for fusion to occur and sustain itself.

Keep an eye on these technologies, as well as other energy technologies. Remember, you will be paying the power bills one day soon.

Section Review 2:   More About Nuclear Energy

A. Define the following terms.

stable	unstable	decay chain	control rod
fission fragments	supercritical chain reaction	breech	fuel rod

B. Choose the best answer.

1. In the following reaction, how many neutrons are produced?

$$^{235}U + n \longrightarrow {}^{236}U^* \longrightarrow {}^{90}Rb + {}^{144}Cs + \underline{\hspace{1cm}}$$

    A.   1   B.   2   C.   3   D.   4

2. Which of the following is NOT a product of fission?
    A.   fission fragments   C.   protons
    B.   neutrons   D.   energy

C. Answer the following questions.

1. Describe the use of control rods in a nuclear power reactor.

2. Search the terms "Three Mile Island" and "Chernobyl" on the Internet. From what you find, describe what happened and what the difference was in the two accidents.

3. Describe the environmental impact of nuclear power plants.

4. It was noted in this chapter that many different fission fragments are produced during a fission process. Does this have an impact on the handling of nuclear waste?

5. Nuclear fission reactions are used to make nuclear energy. Name one advantage and one disadvantage of using nuclear fission as an energy source.

6. A nuclear reactor uses fission to produce harnessed energy that we can use. A nuclear bomb produces a nuclear explosion of unharnessed energy. What is the difference between these two nuclear devices?

7. Why would a fusion reactor be more desirable than a fission reactor? Why are fusion reactors not used?

8. How is nuclear fission similar to nuclear fusion? How are these two types of nuclear reactions different?

CHAPTER 7 REVIEW

Choose the best answer.

1. A scientist detected radiation escaping from a material encased in a thick block of concrete. Identify the type of radiation the scientist MOST likely detected.

   A. beta particles

   B. alpha particles

   C. gamma radiation

   D. radio nuclides

2. Given 100.0 g of a radioactive isotope that has a half-life of 25 years, identify the amount of that isotope that will remain after 100 years.

   A. 50.0 g   B. 25.0 g   C. 12.5 g   D. 6.3 g

3. The half-life of an isotope is the time required for half of the nuclei in the sample to undergo

   A. induced fission.

   B. spontaneous fission.

   C. fusion.

   D. radioactive decay.

4. Which of the following radioactive emissions is the MOST dangerous if ingested?

   A. α-particle

   B. β-particle

   C. X-ray

   D. microwave

5. Identify the element that *cannot* participate in nuclear fission reactions.

   A. plutonium

   B. hydrogen

   C. uranium

   D. thorium

6. Identify the issue that has NOT been a factor in any new nuclear power plants having been built in over twenty years.

   A. construction costs

   B. political opposition

   C. availability of nuclear fuel

   D. disposal of radioactive by-products

7. Describe the reaction illustrated by:

$$^{1}H + {}^{2}H \longrightarrow {}^{3}He$$

   A. spontaneous fission

   B. induced fission

   C. decay

   D. fusion

8. Which of the following is an appropriate material to use in making control rods?

   A. hydrogen   B. cadmium   C. plutonium   D. uranium

9. The following reaction shows the alpha decay of uranium-238 to thorium-234. The nuclear mass, in grams, is written beneath each nuclide symbol. What is the change in mass (Δm) for this reaction?

$$^{238}U \longrightarrow {}^{234}Th + {}^{4}He$$
$$238.0003 \quad 233.9942 \quad 4.00150$$

   A.   −0.0046 g   B.   0.0046 g   C.   8.0076 g   D.   −8.0076 g

10. Every mass has an associated energy, and every energy has an associated mass. This is described by Einstein's equation $E=mc^2$. When the mass of a product set is different than the mass of a reactant set, what has happened to the mass?

   A.   It has been eliminated.

   B.   It has been converted to energy.

   C.   It has been accelerated to the speed of light.

   D.   It has been accelerated to the speed of light, squared.

11. Complete the following equation. What nuclei belongs in the first blank and how many neutrons are produced (second blank)?

$$^{1}n + {}^{235}U \longrightarrow {}^{136}I + \underline{\quad} + \underline{\quad} {}^{1}n$$

   A. $^{96}\gamma$, 3   B. ^{94}Sr, 4   C. $^{96}\gamma$, 4   D. ^{94}Sr, 3

12. A decay chain ends when

   A.   the product nucleus decays to zero grams.

   B.   the product nucleus undergoes fission.

   C.   the product nucleus is stable.

   D.   the product nucleus undergoes fusion.

13. When a reaction is supercritical,

   A.   small amounts of neutrons are being produced.

   B.   large amounts of neutrons are being produced.

   C.   all the fission fragments in the core are unstable.

   D.   all of the fission fragments in the core are stable.

14. Which of the following is NOT an isotope of hydrogen?
   A. ^{1}H B. ^{2}H C. ^{3}H D. ^{4}H

Chapter 8
Structure, Properties and Bonding of Elements

GA HSGT SCIENCE STANDARDS COVERED IN THIS CHAPTER INCLUDE:

GPS Standards	
SPS1 a – b	Students will investigate our current understanding of the atom.
SPS2 b – e	Students will explore the nature of matter, its classifications, and its system for naming types of matter.
SPS4 a – b	Students will investigate the arrangement of the Periodic Table.

THE STRUCTURE OF ATOMS

ATOMIC STRUCTURE

Atoms are made up of **subatomic particles**. These particles include protons neutrons, and electrons. **Protons** have a positive charge, and **electrons** have a negative charge. **Neutrons** have neither a positive nor negative charge, they are neutral. The SI unit of electrical charge is the **Coulomb** (C). The properties of each subatomic particle are shown in Table 8.1.

Table 8.1 Comparison of Subatomic Particles

Subatomic Particle	Mass	Charge
Proton	1.673×10^{-27} kg	1.602×10^{-19} C
Neutron	1.675×10^{-27} kg	0 C
Electron	9.109×10^{-31} kg	-1.602×10^{-19} C

As you can see, the proton and neutron are bigger than the electron. Can you tell how much bigger? Divide the mass of the proton by the mass of the electron and you will see that the proton is about 1,837 times larger than the electron. For comparison, a commercial airliner like the Boeing 767, when empty of cargo and passengers, weighs about 1,867 times what you do (give or take a few pounds).

You know from the last chapter that protons and neutrons are located together inside the nucleus of the atom. In this chapter, we will look at the arrangement of the atom outside of the nucleus — that means electrons.

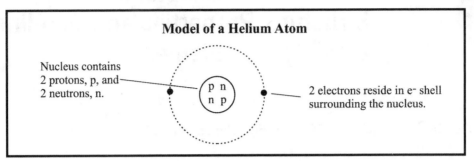

Figure 8.1 Model of a Helium Atom

The negatively charged electrons are electrically attracted to their oppositely charged counterparts, the protons. This attraction holds the electrons in orbit around the nucleus. The area that they occupy is called an **orbital**. An orbital is an area where an electron of a particular energy level is likely to be found. Keep in mind that an orbital is *not* a specifically defined area, like a yard that has been fenced off. An orbital is an area of probability, and it is a little vague. An electron may be found at any point within the space of an orbital (and sometimes even outside of the orbital space!). These orbitals are designated s, p, d and f, each of which has a different shape. When associated with their quantum mechanical **energy level** (1, 2, 3…), these orbitals define the electron distribution of an atom. The s orbital is found closest to the nucleus; it can be imagined as a sphere around the nucleus. The smallest atom, hydrogen (H), consists of 1 proton and 1 electron. The proton is in the nucleus (in fact, for hydrogen, the proton essentially *is* the nucleus) and the electron orbits the nucleus in the 1s orbital. The next largest atom is helium (He), which consists of 2 protons, 2 neutrons and 2 electrons. As shown in Figure 8.1, the 4 protons and neutrons of the helium atom are held together in the nucleus, while the 2 electrons orbit the nucleus in the 1s orbital.

An s orbital will only hold two electrons, however. The next element in the Periodic Table is lithium (Li), which has 3 protons, 4 neutrons and 3 electrons. Two of lithium's electrons will go into the 1s orbital, and the third will go into the 2s orbital, as shown in Figure 8.2. While having the same orbital designation (s) as the 1s orbital, the 2s orbital has a higher quantum number (2), and is thus a higher energy orbital, located farther from the nucleus. The greater the distance between two charged particles, the weaker the electrostatic force that holds them together. Therefore, since the lithium electron in the 2s

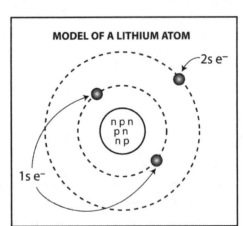

Figure 8.2 Lithium Atom Model Including Electron Shells

orbital spends most of its time farther away from the nucleus than the atom's 1s electrons, it is less tightly bound to the nucleus.

Even without explicitly addressing the quantum mechanical considerations necessary to examine larger atoms, we can still understand a bit about how those atoms are put together. The quantum number and orbital designation of each electron can be accounted for in an atom's **electron configuration**. This is the organizational concept behind the Periodic Table, and will be discussed in the next section. For now, it is sufficient to recognize that electrons sequentially fill various quantum energy levels (1,2,3, etc…), and the various orbitals (sometimes called **shells**) within those energy levels. As each energy level becomes full, electrons begin to fill the next highest level. The highest energy level orbital containing electrons is the atom's **valence shell**; it contains the electrons that exist farthest away from, and thus the least tightly bound to, the nucleus of the atom. These "outer electrons" are called **valence electrons**, and are free to participate in bonding with other atoms. Table 8.2 shows the electron configuration for sulfur, which has 16 electrons. It has four valence electrons in the 3p orbital. Note that the p orbital consists of three sub-orbitals — p_x, p_y and p_z — each of with holds a maximum of two electrons, for a total of six.

Table 8.2 Electron Configuration of Sulfur

Number of Electrons to fill the Energy Level
$1s_2$ $2s_2, 2p_{x2,} 2p_{y2}, 2p_{z2}$ $3s_2, 3p_{x2,} 3p_{y1}, 3p_{z1}$

Section Review 1: The Structure of Atoms

A. Define the following terms.

subatomic particles	electron	neutron	orbital
electron configuration	atom	proton	energy level
valence electron	Coulomb		
valence shell			

B. Choose the best answer.

1. Which of the following parts of an atom has a positive charge?

    A.   protons   B.   neutrons   C.   electrons   D.   electron shells

2. Which of the following parts of an atom has a negative charge?

    A.   protons   B.   neutrons   C.   electrons   D.   the nucleus

3. Which of the following parts of an atom has no charge?

    A.   protons   B.   neutrons   C.   electrons   D.   the nucleus

4. Which subatomic particles are found in the nucleus of an atom?

    A.   protons and electrons   C.   protons and neutrons

    B.   electrons and neutrons   D.   protons, neutrons, and electrons

5. What is the maximum number of electrons that are contained in an s orbital?

    A. 1   B. 2   C. 3   D. 4

C. Answer the following questions.

1. Compare and contrast protons, neutrons and electrons.

2. What is a valence electron?

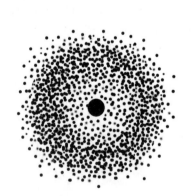

3. The diagram at left shows a typical electron distribution pattern in a 1s orbital. You know, however, that a 1s orbital can contain, at most, only 2 electrons. What is your interpretation of the meaning of the large dot in the center of the diagram, and of many dots shown as a cluster around it? (HINT: Think of this figure as the result of adding a series of snapshots together.)

ORGANIZATION OF THE PERIODIC TABLE

ATOMIC NUMBER AND ATOMIC MASS

Elements are substances that cannot be further broken down by simple chemical means. An element is composed of atoms with the same number of protons. Each element has its own symbol, atomic number, atomic mass and electron shell arrangement (electron configuration). The atomic number represents the number of protons found in a given atom.

The mass of an atom, referred to as **atomic mass**, is related to the number of protons, electrons and neutrons in the atom. Protons and neutrons account for the majority of the atom's mass. The unit of atomic mass, as expressed in the Periodic Table, is called an **atomic mass unit (amu)**. One atomic mass unit is defined as a mass equal to one-twelfth the mass of one atom of carbon-12. The amu is also known as the **dalton (Da)**.

To find the number of neutrons most commonly found in an element, subtract the atomic number from the atomic mass, and round to the nearest whole number.

Carbon is represented in the Periodic Table as follows:

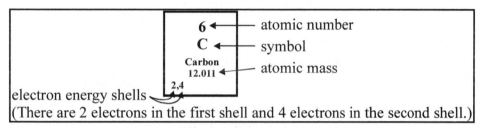

Figure 8.3 Periodic Table Information for Carbon

To find the number of neutrons most commonly found in an atom of carbon, subtract the atomic number, 6, from the atomic mass, 12.011, to get 6.011. Round to the nearest whole number to get 6. Carbon atoms most often have 6 neutrons in their nuclei.

PERIODIC TABLE

Look at Figure 8.5. As you already know, this is called the **Periodic Table**. The Periodic Table arranges all known elements by atomic number, starting with atomic number 1 (hydrogen) and "ending" with atomic number 111 (roentgenium). However, if the Periodic Table were only organized by atomic number, it would not be very useful. It also organizes the elements by their properties. The horizontal rows of the table are called **periods**. By moving across the periods from left to right, one can determine two things: how many valence electrons a given element has and the order in which their orbitals fill (called the **electron configuration**). The vertical columns of the Periodic Table are called **groups** (or, sometimes, **families**); all members of any vertical Group have the same number of valence electrons in the same orbital. An element's placement in the rows and columns of the table has meaning, and enables the observer to understand many properties of that element.

Figure 8.4 shows a portion of the Periodic Table. Notice the pattern of electrons in the outer shells of elements in the same period versus elements in the same group. For instance, lithium (Li) and beryllium (Be) are both in Period 2, but they are in different Groups.

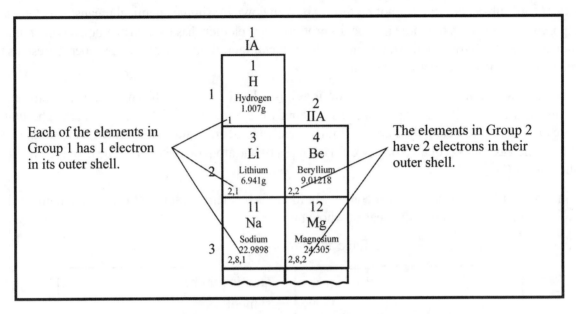

Figure 8.4 Groups 1 and 2 of the Periodic Table

Challenge Activity

The lines point to the number of valence electrons in each group: 1 valence electron in each Group 1 element and 2 in each Group 2 element. Can you figure out what the other numbers are? (HINT: look back at Table 8.2.)

Figure 8.5 The Periodic Table

THE PERIODIC TABLE OF THE ELEMENTS

																	Noble Gases
1 IA																	18 VIIIA
1 H Hydrogen 1.007g	2 IIA											13 IIIA	14 IVA	15 VA	16 VIA	17 VIIA	2 He Helium 4.0026
3 Li Lithium 6.941g	4 Be Beryllium 9.01218											5 B Boron 10.81	6 C Carbon 12.011	7 N Nitrogen 14.0067	8 O Oxygen 15.9994	9 F Fluorine 18.998403	10 Ne Neon 20.179
11 Na Sodium 22.9898	12 Mg Magnesium 24.305	3 IIIB	4 IVB	5 VB	6 VIB	7 VIIB	8 VIIIB	9 VIIIB	10 VIIIB	11 IB	12 IIB	13 Al Aluminum 26.98154	14 Si Silicon 28.0855	15 P Phosphorus 30.97376	16 S Sulfur 32.06	17 Cl Chlorine 35.453	18 Ar Argon 39.948
19 K Potassium 39.0983	20 Ca Calcium 40.08	21 Sc Scandium 44.9559	22 Ti Titanium 47.90	23 V Vanadium 50.9415	24 Cr Chromium 51.996	25 Mn Manganese 54.9381	26 Fe Iron 55.847	27 Co Cobalt 58.9332	28 Ni Nickel 58.69	29 Cu Copper 63.546	30 Zn Zinc 65.38	31 Ga Gallium 69.723	32 Ge Germanium 72.61	33 As Arsenic 74.9216	34 Se Selenium 78.96	35 Br Bromine 79.904	36 Kr Krypton 83.80
37 Rb Rubidium 85.4678	38 Sr Strontium 87.62	39 Y Yttrium 88.9059	40 Zr Zirconium 91.22	41 Nb Niobium 92.9064	42 Mo Molybdenum 95.94	43 Tc Technetium 97.91	44 Ru Ruthenium 101.07	45 Rh Rhodium 102.9055	46 Pd Palladium 106.4	47 Ag Silver 107.868	48 Cd Cadmium 112.41	49 In Indium 114.82	50 Sn Tin 118.71	51 Sb Antimony 121.75	52 Te Tellurium 127.60	53 I Iodine 126.9045	54 Xe Xenon 131.30
55 Cs Cesium 132.9054	56 Ba Barium 137.33	57 La Lanthanum 138.9055	72 Hf Hafnium 178.49	73 Ta Tantalum 180.9479	74 W Tungsten 183.84	75 Re Rhenium 186.2	76 Os Osmium 190.2	77 Ir Iridium 192.22	78 Pt Platinum 195.09	79 Au Gold 196.9665	80 Hg Mercury 200.59	81 Tl Thallium 204.383	82 Pb Lead 207.2	83 Bi Bismuth 208.9808	84 Po Polonium 208.98244	85 At Astatine 209.98704	86 Rn Radon 222.02
87 Fr Francium 223.01976	88 Ra Radium 226.0254	89 Ac Actinium 227.02779	104 Rf Rutherfordium 261.1	105 Db Dubnium 262.11	106 Sg Seaborgium 263.12	107 Bh Bohrium 262.12	108 Hs Hassium 264.13	109 Mt Meitnerium 266.14	110 Ds Darmstadtium 271	111 Rg Roentgenium 272	112	113	114	115	116	117	118

Lanthanide Series

57 La Lanthanum 138.9055	58 Ce Cerium 140.12	59 Pr Praseodymium 140.9077	60 Nd Neodymium 144.24	61 Pm Promethium 144.91279	62 Sm Samarium 150.4	63 Eu Europium 151.96	64 Gd Gadolinium 157.25	65 Tb Terbium 158.9254	66 Dy Dysprosium 162.50	67 Ho Holmium 164.9304	68 Er Erbium 167.26	69 Tm Thulium 168.9342	70 Yb Ytterbium 173.04	71 Lu Lutetium 174.967

Actinide Series

89 Ac Actinium 227.02779	90 Th Thorium 232.0381	91 Pa Protactinium 231.0359	92 U Uranium 238.029	93 Np Neptunium 234.0482	94 Pu Plutonium 244.06424	95 Am Americium 243.06139	96 Cm Curium 247.07035	97 Bk Berkelium 247.07030	98 Cf Californium 251.0796	99 Es Einsteinium 252.08	100 Fm Fermium 257.09515	101 Md Mendelevium 258.1	102 No Nobelium 259.100	103 Lr Lawrencium 262.11

Atomic Number → 36
Symbol → Kr
Name → Krypton
Atomic Mass → 83.80

ELEMENTAL CLASSIFICATION

Elements can all be classified as metals, nonmetals or metalloids depending on where they are located in the Periodic Table.

Metals make up the majority of the elements on the Periodic Table, more than 75%! They are located on the left side of the Table and in the center. Group 1 metals are called *alkali metals*. (Hydrogen is the only exception — it is a gas at room temperature and considered a nonmetal.) Group 2 metals are called *alkaline earth metals*. The block of elements in the center of the Table (Groups 3 – 12) is called the *transition metals*. Here are a few important properties of metals:

- They have metallic shine, or **luster**.

- They are usually solids at room temperature.

- They are **malleable**, meaning that they can be hammered, pounded, or pressed into different shapes without breaking.

- They are **ductile,** meaning that they can be drawn into thin sheets or wires without breaking.

- They are good **conductors** of heat and electricity, which means thermal and electrical energy flow through them easily.

Nonmetals are on the right side of the Periodic Table in Groups 14 – 18. There are only 18 elements that fall into this category. Nonmetals are usually gases or dull, brittle solids at room temperature. Some examples of nonmetals are hydrogen, helium, carbon, nitrogen, oxygen, fluorine and neon. Here are a few important properties of nonmetals:

- They rarely have metallic luster.

- They are usually gases at room temperature.

- Nonmetallic solids are neither malleable nor ductile.

- They are poor conductors of heat and electricity.

The *halogens* are a group of elements that are all non-metals. They are found in Group 17. The halogens react easily with the alkali metals to form salts like NaCl (sodium chloride). Group 18 also contains non-metals. This group is called the *noble gases*. They do not usually react with any other elements.

The elements diagonally between the metals and the nonmetals are called **metalloids**. There are 7 elements that fall into this category. These are boron (B), silicon (Sc), germanium (Ge), arsenic (As), antimony (Sb), tellurium (Te) and polonium (Po). Metalloids have properties of both metals and nonmetals. One important property is that most metalloids are **semiconductors**. This means that, at certain temperatures, they conduct electricity very well; at other temperatures, they do not. Metalloids are frequently used in computer chips.

These are general categories that allow us to group elements by their physical properties. The Periodic Table may also be used to discover important information about the chemical properties of the elements. It tells us how the elements "like" to combine with other elements! This combining of atoms is called **bonding**. The process of reorganizing atoms into different bonded clusters (called *molecules*) is what happens in a *chemical reaction*. The number of protons and neutrons in a chemical reaction does not change, but the number of electrons does. We will look at chemical reactions in the next few sections of this chapter.

Section Review 2:   Organization of the Periodic Table

A. Define the following terms.

atomic mass	period	metal	metalloid
Periodic Table	family/group	nonmetal	luster
element	dalton/amu	semiconductors	malleable
		conductor	ductile

B. Choose the best answer.

1. Which element has two electrons in its 2p orbital?

   A.   He   B.   C   C.   Be   D.   O

2. Lithium and sodium are in the same group of elements in the Periodic Table. Which of the following statements is true regarding these two elements?

   A.   They have the same number of electrons in their valance shell.

   B.   They have the same number of protons in their nucleus.

   C.   They are both noble gases.

   D.   They have different chemical properties.

3. Which of the following is NOT a property of most metals?

   A.   solid at room temperature   C.   conduct heat and electricity well

   B.   have luster   D.   do not react readily with any other elements

4. Where might you find a metalloid element used?

   A.   computer motherboard   C.   electrical power lines

   B.   kitchen potholder/oven mitt   D.   atmospheric gas mixture

5. The current Periodic Table is arranged in what order?

   A.   increasing atomic weight   C.   increasing number of electrons

   B.   increasing atomic mass   D.   increasing atomic number

C. Answer the following questions.

1. What do elements in the same group have in common?

2. Name two physical properties of nonmetals.

3. Name two physical properties of metals.

4. Which group of elements is very stable and does not react readily?

REACTIVITY OF ELEMENTS IN THE PERIODIC TABLE

In general, an element is most stable when its valance shell is full. Recall that the valance shell is the highest energy level containing electrons. Period 1 elements (hydrogen and helium) have the valence shell 1s, which can only contain 2 electrons. Period 2 elements (lithium through neon) may have a 2s or 2s, 2p valence shell configuration that can hold up to 8 electrons. The 2s orbital can contain up to 2 electrons, and the 2p orbital can contain up to 6 (two in each of the sub-orbitals p_x, p_y and p_z) for a total of 8. Look at the Periodic Table in Figure 8.5 and count this out.

You will learn more about electron configurations and energy levels in AP Chemistry or college chemistry, but for now it is important to realize that bonding between elements occurs primarily because of the placement of electrons in the valence shell, particularly the unfilled orbital of the valence shell. Remember this: *Bonding is all about energy!*

For instance, the energy needed to remove an electron from an atom is called the **ionization energy.** Another term is directly related to ionization energy: **electronegativity.** The electronegativity of an atom is a description of the atom's energetic "need" for another electron. An atom with a high electronegativity "wants" another electron; it would be very difficult to remove an electron from an atom that already wants another electron. Therefore, the ionization energy of that atom would also be high. Elements in the same family tend to have similar chemical reactivity based on their willingness to lose or gain electrons. We will look at some of these trends in the following section.

ELEMENTAL GROUPS

Group 1 (or IA) elements, with the exception of hydrogen, are called the **alkali metals.** All the elements in Group 1 (or IA) are very reactive. Since they only have one electron in their valance shell, they will give up that one electron to another element in order to become more **stable.**

When an element loses or gains an electron, it forms an **ion.** An ion is an atom that has lost or gained electrons. Ions have either a positive or a negative charge. When the elements in Group 1 give up the one electron in their valence shell, they form positive ions (or **cations**) with a +1 charge. The positive +1 charge comes from having one more proton than electron. The alkali metals become more reactive as you move down the Periodic Table because the lone electron in the valence shell is further from the positive charge of the nucleus, and thus the electrical attraction is less. *Group 1 (or IA) elements form ions with a +1 charge.*

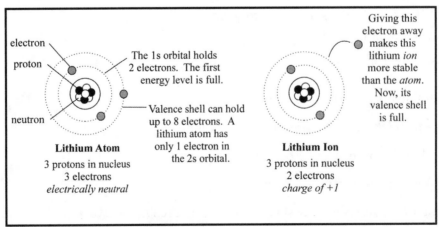

Figure 8.6 Lithium - Family IA

Group 2 (or IIA) elements are called the **alkaline earth metals**. They have 2 electrons out of a possible 8 in their valance shell. These metals are less reactive than the alkali metals but are still very reactive. The alkaline earth metals will give away both of their electrons in their valance shell in order to be more stable. Therefore, they form positive ions with a +2 charge. The +2 charge comes from having two more protons than electrons. The alkaline earth metals also become more reactive as you move down the Periodic Table. *Group 2 (or IIA) elements form ions with a charge of +2.*

Groups 1 – 2 are sometimes called the s-block because their valence electrons are found in the s orbital.

Groups 3 – 12 (IIIB-IIB) elements in the middle of the Periodic Table are called **transition metals**. Sometimes this is called the d-block, because these elements all have electrons in the d orbital. In general, the reactivity of these metals increases as you go down the Periodic Table and from right to left.

Groups 13, 14 and 15 contain both metals and non-metals. In Group 13, boron is a metalloid; going down the column, all other elements are metals. Group 13 elements form oxides with the general formula R_2O_3. (R is a place holder in this formula.) Group 14 is headed by carbon, a prominent nonmetal; going down the column, there are both metalloids (silicon and germanium) and metals. Group 14 elements form oxides with the general formula RO_2. Having four valence electrons (a half-full valence shell) lends these elements a special stability. Group 15 also shows the variation from nonmetal (nitrogen and phosphorous) to metalloid (arsenic and antimony) to metal (bismuth). These elements generally form oxides of the formula R_2O_3 or R_2O_5. *Group 13 elements form +3 cations and Group 15 elements form negatively charged, −3 ions (or anions). Group 14 elements are generally too stable to ionize.*

Group 16 elements have 6 out of a possible 8 electrons in their valence shell. These elements want to gain two electrons to fill the valence shell. Said another way, Group 16 elements have a high electron affinity, particularly oxygen. *Group 16 elements form anions with a −2 charge.*

Group 17 elements are called the halogens. They have seven electrons in their valence shell, and only require one more to achieve a full valence shell. They have a very high electronegativity and are the most reactive nonmetal elements. They are generally designated with the symbol X and exist in the form X_2, as in Cl_2 gas. They also react with hydrogen, as in HC1. *Group 17 elements form ions with a −1 charge.*

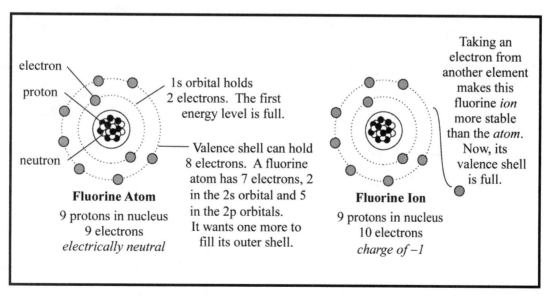

Figure 8.7 Fluorine - Group 17

Group 18 is the **noble gases**. The noble gases have 8 electrons in their outer shells with the exception of helium, which fills its first energy level with only 2. (Remember, the first energy level will only hold 2 electrons.) The noble gases are very stable elements because their outermost electron shell is completely filled. They will not react readily with any other elements. They are **inert**.

Groups 13 - 18 are sometimes called the p-block, as their valence electrons are located in p orbitals.

SUMMARY OF PERIODIC TRENDS OF ELEMENTS

- Reactivity of metals increases down the Periodic Table.

- Reactivity of non-metals increases up the Periodic Table.

- In general, atomic radius increases down the Periodic Table.

- Atomic radius decreases left to right across the Periodic Table. This trend may seem opposite from what you would guess. Since the atoms increase in number of protons, neutrons, and electrons, you may think the atomic radius would also get larger. However, the opposite is true. Since the atoms have an increasing number of protons, the positive charge in the nucleus increases. The greater the positive charge in the nucleus, the closer the electrons are held to the nucleus due to the electrical force between them. So, in general, the atomic radius decreases from left to right on the Periodic Table.

- In general, ionization energies increase left to right across the Periodic Table and decrease down the Periodic Table. Ionization energy is a measure of how tightly an electron is bound to an atom, or how much energy is required to remove the electron.

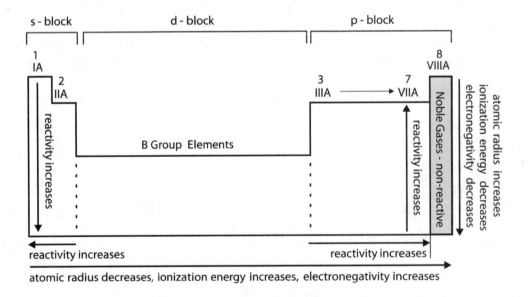

Figure 8.8 Trends of the Elements in the Periodic Table

Section Review 3: Reactivity of Elements in the Periodic Table

A. Define the following terms.

valence electron	alkali metal	alkaline earth metal	halogen
ionization energy	ion	transition metals	noble gas
electronegativity	cation	anion	inert
stable			

B. Choose the best answer.

1. Choose the **valence** shell configuration of sulfur (S).

   A. $3s_2, 3p_{x2}, 3p_{y1}, 3p_{z1}$

   B. $3s_2, 3p_{x2}, 3p_{y2}, 3p_{z1}$

   C. $3s_2, 3p_{x1}, 3p_{y1}, 3p_{z1}$

   D. $3s_2, 3p_{x2}, 3p_{y2}, 3p_{z2}$

2. Given the following set of elements as found in the Periodic Table, which 2 elements would have the most similar chemical properties?

3 Li Lithium 6.941g 2,1	4 Be Beryllium 9.01218 2,2
11 Na Sodium 22.9898 2,8,1	12 Mg Magnesium 24.305 2,8,2

   A. lithium and beryllium

   B. lithium and sodium

   C. sodium and beryllium

   D. sodium and magnesium

3. Which of the following statements is **not** true of noble gases?

   A. They have a full valence shell.

   B. They do not react readily with other elements.

   C. They usually exist as ions.

   D. They are in Group 18 (or VIIIA).

C. Answer the following questions.

1. What does an atom become when it gains or loses an electron?

2. Which Group of elements is the most stable? Why?

3. If an atom gains two electrons, what is the charge of the resulting ion?

4. What chemical characteristic do elements in a group share?

5. Why do alkali metals become more reactive as you move down the Periodic Table?

6. Consider what you learned about electronegativity in this section. Circle the element in each series that has the highest electronegativity:

   (a) lithium (Li), boron (B), helium (He), oxygen (O)

   (b) carbon (C), hydrogen (H), chlorine (Cl), silicon (Si)

   (c) fluorine (F), chlorine (Cl), oxygen (O), hydrogen (H)

   (d) boron (B), aluminum (Al), nitrogen (N), phosphorous (P)

BONDING OF ATOMS

An element is a substance composed of identical atoms. A **compound** is a substance composed of identical molecules. A **molecule** is the product of two or more atoms joined by chemical bonds. Atoms of different elements can combine chemically to form molecules by sharing or by transferring **valence electrons**. Valence electrons are either lost, gained, or shared when bonds are formed.

IONIC BONDS

An **ion** is an atom with a charge. It is formed by the *transfer* of electrons. When one atom "takes" electrons from another atom both are left with a charge. The atom that took electrons has a negative charge. (Recall that electrons have a negative charge). The atom that "gave" electrons has a positive charge. The bond formed by this transfer is called an **ionic bond**. Ionic bonds are very strong. Ionic compounds have high melting points and high boiling points. These compounds tend to have ordered crystal structures and are usually solids at room temperature. Ionic compounds will usually dissolve in water, and they have the ability to conduct electricity in an aqueous (dissolved in water) or a molten state.

Aluminum oxide is an example of a compound with an ionic bond. In aluminum oxide, two atoms of aluminum react with three atoms of oxygen. The two aluminum atoms give up three electrons each to form positive ions with +3 charges. The three oxygen atoms gain two each of the six electrons given up by the two aluminum atoms to form negative ions with –2 charges. Figure 8.9 illustrates this electron transfer. Note that the orbital shape (circular) has been simplified for clarity.

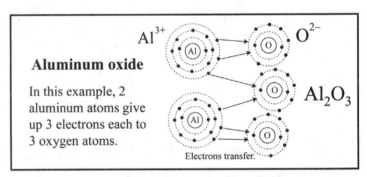

Aluminum oxide

In this example, 2 aluminum atoms give up 3 electrons each to 3 oxygen atoms.

Electrons transfer.

Figure 8.9 Ionic Bonding in Aluminum Oxide

COVALENT BONDS

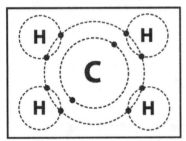

Figure 8.10 Methane Molecule (CH_4)

Covalent bonds are formed when two or more elements *share* valence electrons in such a way that their valence electron orbital is filled. The sharing arrangement creates a more stable outer electron structure in the bound elements than was present in their elemental state. In general, there are two rules about which elements form covalent bonds:

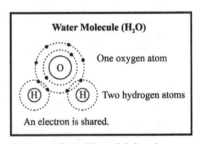

Water Molecule (H_2O)

One oxygen atom

Two hydrogen atoms

An electron is shared.

Figure 8.11 Water Molecule

1. Elements with similar electronegativities form covalent bonds.

2. Non-metals form covalent bonds.

The compounds that result from covalent bonding have low melting points and low boiling points. In general, they do not conduct electricity well, although there are some exceptions to that rule. Let's look at two examples of covalent compounds.

Carbon and hydrogen have very similar electronegativities and commonly form covalent bonds. Methane (CH_4) is a good example of a covalent compound. Each of the four hydrogen atoms shares one electron with a single carbon atom. Likewise, the carbon atom shares its four valence electrons-one is shared with each of the four hydrogen atoms. This arrangement gives the carbon atom a full octet of eight electrons and each hydrogen atom a full octet of two electrons (remember that hydrogen's valence orbital is the 1s orbital, which can only contain 2 electrons). Note how the valence orbitals of carbon and hydrogen are drawn in Figure 8.10; the overlap of orbitals represents shared electrons.

Water is another example of covalent bonding. Two hydrogen atoms and one oxygen atom combine to form one molecule of water. Figure 8.11 shows how the atoms in water share electrons. However, oxygen has a greater electronegativity than hydrogen; this means that it draws electrons away from hydrogen and toward itself. This lends an "ionic character" to the bond, which will be described in the next section.

POLAR COVALENT AND HYDROGEN BONDS

The covalent bond will sometimes have an "ionic character," depending on the identity of the atoms involved in the bonding. This means that one of the two atoms participating in the bond "wants" electrons more than the other, and thus pulls them closer; this atom has a partially negative charge, symbolically shown as $\delta-$. The other atom, which has allowed its electrons to be pulled away a bit, has a partially positive charge, symbolically shown as δ^+. These molecules are called **polar molecules**, and water is an excellent example. The oxygen atom in water pulls electrons toward it; the hydrogen atom is left with a partially positive charge.

The presence of these partial charges creates an electrical attraction between polar molecules: the partially positive end (that is, the hydrogen) lines up in such a way that it is close to the partially negative end (the oxygen) of another polar molecule. The resulting orientation is highly stabilizing, and powerful enough to be called a form of bonding: **hydrogen bonding**. Hydrogen bonds are not as powerful as covalent bonds, but are highly stabilizing and represent a significant organizing force.

Didn't we say that covalent compounds were generally poor conductors of electricity? Well, water is one of the exceptions to that rule. The electrical attraction between the polar water molecules makes a kind of path for electricity to flow through. Free hydrogen ions can also move through water to transport charge. When other compounds, like salt (NaCl), are dissolved in water, it becomes even more electrically conducting.

Section Review 4: Bonding of Atoms

A. Define the following terms.

ion   ionic bond   molecule

compound   covalent bond   hydrogen bond

valence electrons   polar molecule

B. Choose the best answer.

1. A covalent compound has which of the following characteristics?

    A. high melting and high boiling points   C. conducts electricity

    B. atoms share electrons to bond   D. all of the above

2. Hydrogen bonding takes place between

    A. polar molecules.   C. ionic compounds.

    B. protons.   D. valence electrons

3. What type of bond is formed when atoms transfer electrons?

    A. covalent   B. hydrogen   C. ionic   D. polar

4. Which of the following molecules is non-polar?

    A. NaCl   B. HF   C. CH_4 D. H_2O

5. Which of the following polar molecules could NOT exhibit hydrogen bonding?

    A. HCl   B. CCl_4 C. NH_4 D. HBr

6. Which of the following molecules is MOST likely to have a covalent bond?

    A. O_2 B. NaCl   C. MgO   D. Fe_2O_3

C. Answer the following questions.

1. Compare and contrast ionic, covalent and hydrogen bonds. What kind of bonding do you think is found in a crystal of table sale (NaCl)? How about octane (C_8H_{18}, a primary component of gasoline)? How about in ethanol (C_2H_5OH)?

2. Look at Figure 8.9. How many valence electrons do Al and O each have? How many total electrons?

We have discussed the characteristics of individual elements at the atomic level. It should be clear that the number of valence electrons that an atom of an element has is the primary factor in determining the kind of bonding arrangements that atom forms with atoms of other elements. Once bound together, individual atoms become a **molecule**. We will now examine these molecular arrangements and the chemical interaction between molecules.

UNDERSTANDING CHEMICAL FORMULAS

A **chemical formula** is a group of symbols that shows the makeup of a molecule. For example, the chemical formula for a molecule of water is H_2O. The **subscript**, or small number, after the elemental symbol indicates the number of atoms of the element present in the molecule. The chemical formula for water, H_2O, indicates that 2 atoms of hydrogen combine with 1 atom of oxygen. In aluminum oxide, Al_2O_3, 2 atoms of aluminum combine with 3 atoms of oxygen (look back to Figure 8.9 to see how). In sodium chloride, NaCl, 1 atom of sodium combines with 1 atom of chlorine.

Atoms bind together to form molecules like ammonia, NH_3, which is a gas. Notice that the NH_3 molecule is neutral, meaning that it has no charge. Does the fact that the molecule is neutral mean that it will not interact with other molecules? Nope! Ammonia may be neutral, but that does not mean that it is chemically unreactive. Remember that N and H have different electronegativities, so this will be a polar molecule. Watch what happens when gaseous ammonia is bubbled through a beaker of liquid water.

$$NH_3 + H_2O \longrightarrow NH_4^+ + OH^-$$

New molecules have formed, but these have a charge. Recall that atoms can be ionized by removing an electron from their valence shell. A similar thing has occurred in this situation: the electron arrangement of the ammonia and water molecules has been changed by their interaction with each other. The result is two charged molecules called **ions**.

Since opposite charges are drawn to each other by **electrostatic attraction**, the two new ions are usually written as a molecule, NH_4OH. A whole bunch of these molecules together are referred to as a compound. Where would you find a whole bunch of NH_4OH molecules? Well, if you look in the laundry cabinet at your house, you will probably see a jug containing this compound: ammonium hydroxide, or liquid bleach.

It is important to know that chemical formulas of individual ions are often written together as uncharged molecules. If you can tell when this has been done, you will know when an ionic bond is present. Recall that an ionic bond is a transfer of electrons. Sometimes a chemical formula clearly shows you what the ions are, by using parentheses, as aluminum nitrate $Al(NO_3)_3$. You can also use the formula to find the number of atoms of each element just multiply the subscript number inside the parentheses by the subscript number outside the parentheses.

Example 1: $Al(NO_3)_3$ has 1 atom of aluminum, 3 atoms of nitrogen and 9 atoms of oxygen.

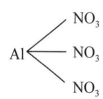

Now that we know what elements make up each of these chemical formulas, let's try to name them. The **International Union of Pure and Applied Chemistry (IUPAC)** has systematized the naming of all chemical compounds. We will just look at diatomic and binary compounds for now, but you can always go to www.iupac.org to see more.

DIATOMIC MOLECULES

Diatomic molecules consist of two atoms bound together into a molecule. A diatomic molecule may be **homonuclear** (two atoms of the same element, like O_2) or **heteronuclear** (two atoms of different elements, like HCl).

Oxygen, hydrogen and nitrogen, as well as all of the halogens, form homonuclear diatomic molecules as their most stable elemental state. Note that these are all gases, as indicated by the (g) in $O_2(g)$, $H_2(g)$ and $Cl_2(g)$. Even metals form homonuclear diatomic molecules when in a gaseous state. In this case, the molecule is just called by its elemental name.

Heteronuclear diatomic molecules, like NaCl, are a subclass of a larger category of molecules called binary compounds.

BINARY COMPOUNDS

A **binary compound** has two different elements that have reacted to form a molecule. Some examples are CCl_4, HBr, NaCl and $FeCl_3$. Note that HBr and NaCl are also heteronuclear diatomic molecules, which contain two atoms from two different elements. On the other hand, CCl_4 contains 5 atoms (one carbon atom and four chlorine atoms) from two different elements and $FeCl_3$ contains 4 atoms (one iron atom and three chlorine atoms) from two different elements. These two compounds are not diatomic but *multi*-atomic. However, all four compounds can correctly be called "binary," since they are made from two elements.

Also notice from these four examples that the bonding in a binary can be either ionic or covalent. In fact, the bonding arrangement must be known in order to correctly name the compound.

BINARY COVALENT COMPOUNDS

Covalent compounds are named using a few rules.

- Binary covalent compounds have two words in their name. Name them as their formulas are written, from left to right. The first word is simply the name of the element. For instance, in CCl_4, carbon (C) will be the first word.

- The second word is the name of the other atoms, with "ide" replacing the end of the element name. For instance, HBr would be called hydrogen bromide.

- Sometimes a prefix is needed to indicate how many of each element makes up the compound. Refer to Table 8.3 for the necessary prefixes. In CCl_4, carbon does not require the "mono" prefix; the only time that mono is used is when oxygen is being named. However, the four chlorides do require a prefix. The full, correct name is carbon tetrachloride.

- There are a few common molecules that are not named this way. Water is one of them. It is called water, rather than dihydrogen monoxide. Ammonia (NH_3) is another.

Number of Atoms	Prefix
1	mono- (use only for oxygen)
2	di-
3	tri-
4	tetra-
5	penta-
6	hexa-
7	hepta-
8	octa-

Table 8.3 Numerical Prefixes

BINARY IONIC COMPOUNDS

Binary ionic compounds are named similarly to binary covalent compounds.

- The first word is the name of the first element in the formula. This will always be the cation (+ charge ion). In NaCl, for instance, the cation is Na^+ and the first word in the compound's name is sodium.

- The second word is the name of the anion (– charge ion). Since we are naming binary compounds, the anion is a single element, like chlorine. When the anion is a halogen (F, Cl, Br, I, etc.), simply replace the –ine with an –ide. Halogen anions are then fluoride, chloride, bromide and iodide. So, NaCl is called sodium chloride. Sometimes the anion will be oxygen; in that case, use the anion name oxide.

- Some elements (particularly d and f-block elements) form cations that can have more than one possible charge. $FeCl_3$ and $FeCl_2$ are good examples. Iron in $FeCl_3$ has a +3 charge; iron in $FeCl_2$ has a +2 charge. At this point we would call both of them iron chloride. (Notice that they are named by charge of the ions, not by the number of atoms.) If more than one charge state is possible, then the charge must be specified in the name.

- If you determine that the compound you are naming has more than one charge state, a Roman numeral is used to specify the charge state by the following formula.

$$Roman\ numeral = -\frac{[(charge\ on\ anion) \times (number\ of\ anions)]}{(number\ of\ cations)}$$

To find out the charge on the anion, look back on pages 177 – 178 for the descriptions of the ions formed by various families in the p-block of elements, on the right side of the Periodic Table. It will be useful to remember that the halogens always form anions with a -1 charge; oxygen always forms anions with a -2 charge.

For $FeCl_3$, we get $-\frac{[(-1) \times (3)]}{(1)} = +3$, which means we use the Roman numeral (III).

The final name for $FeCl_3$ is then iron (III) chloride.

Section Review 5: Understanding Chemical Formulas and Equations

A. Define the following terms.

IUPAC	binary compound	crystal lattice
chemical formula	diatomic molecule	heteronuclear
lone pair	electrostatic attraction	homonuclear
subscript		

B. Choose the best answer.

1. One molecule of calcium carbonate, $CaCO_3$, has how many atoms of calcium, Ca?

   A. 0   B. 1   C. 2   D. 3

2. How many atoms of oxygen are present in one molecule of H_2SO_4?

   A. 1   B. 2   C. 4   D. 8

3. What is the ratio of atoms present in ammonia, NH_3?

   A. 1 atom of nitrogen to 3 atoms of hydrogen

   B. 3 atoms of nitrogen to 1 atom of hydrogen

   C. 1 atom of nitrogen to 1 atom of hydrogen

   D. the ratio varies

4. What kind of compound is $MgCl_2$?

   A. a homonuclear diatomic molecule   C. a binary ionic compound

   B. a heteronuclear diatomic molecule   D. a binary covalent compound

5. You have a weighing dish containing table salt. What is the correct way to describe it?

   A. as a sample of the NaCl molecule

   B. as a sample of NaCl atoms

   C. as a sample of the compound, NaCl

   D. as a sample of the binary covalent compound, NaCl

C. Answer the following questions.

1. Determine the names of CuO_2 and AgI using the rules for binary ionic compounds.

2. What is the name of the compound $N_2(g)$?

3. Determine the names of SF_6, CO_2 and H_2S using the rules for naming binary covalent compounds.

BASIC CHEMICAL EQUATIONS

A **chemical equation** expresses a chemical reaction. A **chemical reaction** is a process in which one or more elements or compounds (reactants) form new elements or compounds (products). The **reactants** are the starting substances. The **products** are the substances formed by the reaction. In a chemical equation, an arrow separates the reactants and the product. When reading a chemical equation aloud, you say that the reactants yield the products. The arrow represents the "yield" part of the equation. Many times, the chemical equation also contains information about the state of the reactants and products. The equation lists the physical states of the substances in parentheses. The right side of Figure 8.12 lists some of the common physical states and their abbreviations.

$NaOH(aq) + HCl(aq) \rightarrow NaCl(aq) + H_2O(l)$	(aq) aqueous (dissolved in water)
	(g) gas
	(l) liquid
reactants **yield** **products**	(s) solid; sometimes (cr) crystalline

Figure 8.12 Example of a Chemical Equation

BASIC CHEMICAL REACTIONS

All chemical reactions involve one or more reactants that interact to form one or more products. From the huge array of elements in the Periodic Table, we can assume that there is an equally wide variety of possible interactions between these elements. These interactions are divided into several different categories.

Synthesis reactions: Small molecules combine to form larger ones.

$$H_2(g) + Cl_2(g) \longrightarrow 2HCl(aq)$$

Decomposition reactions: The opposite of synthesis reactions. Large molecules break apart to form smaller molecules.

$$2H_2O_2(l) \longrightarrow 2H_2O(l) + O_2(g)$$

Single displacement reaction: When a pure element switches places with one of the elements in a compound.

$$Mg(s) + 2HCl(l) \longrightarrow MgCl_2(aq) + H_2(g)$$

Double displacement reaction: The components of ionic compounds switch places.

$$AgNO_3(aq) + NaCl(aq) \longrightarrow AgCl(s) + NaNO_3(aq)$$

Each of these is a **balanced equation**.

WRITING BALANCED CHEMICAL EQUATIONS

CONSERVATION OF MASS

Chemical equations must maintain balance. There must be the same number of atoms of each element on both sides of the equation. The **Law of Conservation of Matter** states that matter is conserved, which means that you can neither create nor destroy it. The amount of matter remains the same before and after a chemical reaction. An atom of hydrogen remains an atom of hydrogen, but it may chemically bond to form a different compound. The amount of mass is also conserved: if the reactants have a mass of 2 grams. The products will have a mass of 2 grams. This is sometimes called the **Law of Conservation of Mass**.

BALANCING CHEMICAL EQUATIONS

Look at the equation in Figure 8.13. On the side of the reactants, there is 1 atom of Na, 1 atom of O, 2 atoms of H and 1 atom of Cl. On the product side of the reaction, there is 1 atom of Na, 1 atom of Cl, 2 atoms of H and 1 atom of O. The number of atoms of each element is equal, so this is a balanced equation.

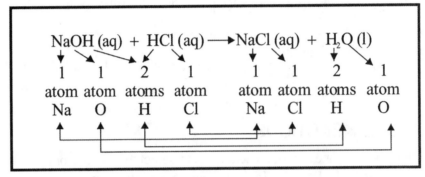

Figure 8.13 Example of a Balanced Equation

Now look at the following equation. There are 2 atoms of hydrogen reacting and 2 atoms of hydrogen as products, so the hydrogen in the equation is balanced. However, there are 2 atoms of oxygen reacting but only 1 atom of oxygen shown as products. This is not a balanced equation.

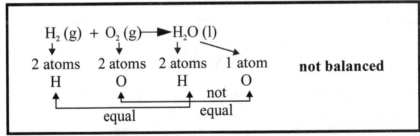

Figure 8.14 Example of an Unbalanced Equation

How can we balance the equation in Figure 8.14? We balance the equation by **inspection**. To do this, we compare the number of atoms of each element on the product side to that on the reactant side and then add where necessary to balance the sides.

Step 1: Put a 2 in front of the H_2O. Now, we have 2 atoms of oxygen to balance the oxygen, but the number of hydrogen atoms increases to 4.

Step 2: Put a 2 in front of the H_2. Now, we have 4 atoms of hydrogen on each side of the equation, and the equation is completely balanced.

Section Review 6: Chemical Equations

A. Define the following term.

Law of Conservation of Mass	chemical reaction	products
Law of Conservation of Matter	chemical equation	balanced equation
	reactants	inspection

B. Answer the following questions.

The following formula describes how iron and oxygen react to form iron oxide (rust). Use this equation to answer questions 1–4.

$$4Fe(s) + 3O_2(g) \rightarrow 2Fe_2O_3(s)$$

1. Write out the equation in words, and include the state of each substance.

2. Which substances are the reactants, and which ones are the products?

3. How many atoms of iron are in one molecule of rust?

4. What kind or kinds of reaction does the formula describe?

C. Balance the following equations.

1. $H_2O_{2(1)} \longrightarrow H_2O_{(1)} + O_{2(g)}$

2. $AgNO_3(aq) + NaCl(aq) \rightarrow AgCl(s) + NaNO_3(aq)$

3. $Na(s) + Cl_2(g) \rightarrow NaCl(s)$

4. $N_2(g) + H_2(g) \rightarrow NH_3(g)$

D. For each of the following, determine whether the chemical equation represents a synthesis, decomposition, single displacement or double displacement reaction.

1. $AgNO_3(aq) + KCl(aq) \rightarrow AgCl(aq) + KNO_3(aq)$_____

2. $N_2(g) + 3H_2(g) \rightarrow 2NH_3(g)$_____

3. $Cu(s) + AgNO_3(aq) \rightarrow CuNO_3(aq) + Ag(s)$ _____

4. $Zn(s) + H_2CO_3 \rightarrow H_2(g) + ZnCO_3(aq)$_____

5. $H_2CO_3(aq) \rightarrow H_2O(1) + CO_2(g)$_____

CHEMICAL AND PHYSICAL CHANGES

We have seen that elements and compounds have a distinct name and identity. That identity consists of all of the **chemical properties** of the element or compound. Many of the chemical properties of the element are indicated by its placement on the Periodic Table. This includes characteristics like electronegativity and preferred type of chemical bonding (ionic or covalent).

Other chemical properties are not summarized in the Periodic Table. So, how do you know what *all* the chemical properties of an element or compound are? Well, you are in luck: you can generally look them up in a chemical reference book, like the *CRC Handbook of Chemistry and Physics*. But every piece of information that you find on any substance is the result of someone doing an experiment (or many experiments) to see how that substance reacted when in the presence of other substances. The point is that chemical properties are determined by the interaction of substances, rather than their independent behavior. That is one reason why it is so important that you learn the possible chemical reactions. Let's go over the reaction types that we have seen in this chapter:

- Synthesis Reactions
- Decomposition Reactions
- Single Displacement Reactions
- Double Displacement Reactions

Each chemical reaction causes a chemical change. A **chemical change** produces a new substance that has entirely different chemical and physical properties. The physical evidence that a chemical change has occurred may be a change in smell, function, texture, color or temperature.

A chemical change is very different than a **physical change**, which results in the same substance with different physical properties. A physical change is the result of some physical act, such as cutting, grinding, mashing, compressing, dissolving, cooling, heating or drying. The product of the physical act is the same substance, but with a different appearance.

We will discuss physical changes more in the next chapter. Now let's look at our chemical reactions and the evidence that they have occurred.

EVIDENCE OF CHEMICAL CHANGE

Sometimes you cannot see the chemical change. For instance, you probably have a dark brown bottle of hydrogen peroxide at home. If you have had it for long enough, it may not be hydrogen peroxide anymore. Look at this decomposition reaction:

$$2H_2O_2 \,(l) \longrightarrow 2H_2O \,(l) + O_2(g)$$

So, how can you tell if your hydrogen peroxide has decomposed into water and oxygen? Hydrogen peroxide is a clear liquid just like water. Well, there is one thing: it will smell different. Water has no smell, but hydrogen peroxide definitely does. So, sniff the bottle (by wafting of course!). Another way to tell is more hands-on: the next time you get a scrape, pour the hydrogen peroxide on it. If you don't see any of the bubbling and foaming action that hydrogen peroxide normally produces upon contact with blood, then all you have is a bottle of water!

> **Evidence of the chemical change:** Change in smell and function.

Often, though, there is more direct visual evidence that a chemical reaction has occurred. For instance, you can see that rust has formed in the synthesis reaction of iron with oxygen. This chemical change is called **corrosion**. Other materials, especially metals, also corrode by oxidation. The tendency to corrode is a chemical property. If you have any gold or platinum jewelry, you will note that it does not corrode. A chemical property of those **noble metals** is that they are impervious to corrosion.

> **Evidence of the chemical change:** Change in color and texture of the metal, called corrosion.

Another chemical property is the tendency to burn. This is called **combustion**, and it is another example of a redox reaction. In this chemical process, a reactant combines with oxygen and gives off heat in the process. Organic (carbon-containing) substances will usually burn. For example, this chemical reaction shows the combustion of the organic compound CH_4 (commonly known as methane).

$$CH_4(g) + 2O_2(g) \longrightarrow CO_2(g) + 2H_2O(l) + heat$$

A chemical reaction that gives off heat is **exothermic**. One that absorbs heat is **endothermic**.

> **Evidence of the chemical change:** Production of energy in the form of heat and light, called combustion.

Solubility is another chemical property, one that we will discuss more fully in Chapter 9. Right now, let's look at solubility as evidence that a chemical reaction has occurred. Remember the examples of single and double displacement reactions in the last section? Here they are again:

Single Displacement Reaction: $Mg(s) + 2HCl(l) \longrightarrow MgCl_2(aq) + H_2(g)$
Double Displacement Reaction: $AgNO_3(aq) + NaCl(aq) \longrightarrow AgCl(s) + NaNO_3(aq)$

In the single displacement reaction, dissolving solid magnesium in hydrochloric acid gives magnesium chloride and gaseous hydrogen. The hydrogen gas will bubble out of the aqueous $MgCl_2$ solution. Evolution of the gas is evidence that a chemical reaction has taken place. Without seeing the gas, we might just assume that the solid magnesium had dissolved, and that is just a physical change.

> **Evidence of the chemical change:** Evolution of gas.

In the double displacement reaction, solid silver chloride is formed as a product. If you perform this reaction in a beaker in your laboratory, you will see solid AgCl begin to fall out of the solution and sit on the bottom of the beaker as it is formed. A chemical property of silver chloride is that it is insoluble. You have formed a **precipitate**!

> **Evidence of the chemical change:** Formation of a precipitate.

Section Review 7:   Chemical and Physical Changes

A. Define the following terms:

chemical properties	corrosion	precipitate
chemical change	noble metal	exothermic
physical change	combustion	endothermic

B. Choose the best answer.

1. Which of the following processes would result in a chemical change?

    A. boiling

    B. cutting

    C. dissolving

    D. burning

2. Rusting is an example of

    A. oxidation.

    B. combustion.

    C. a physical change.

    D. precipitation.

3. You heat 50 mL of salt water on a Bunsen burner until all the water has evaporated. NaCl crystals are left behind. Which statement describes the result of this action correctly?

    A. The water has undergone a chemical change.

    B. The salt has undergone a chemical change.

    C. The salt and water have decomposed.

    D. The salt and water have undergone a physical change.

4. A solid compound is poured into a beaker of liquid. You do not know the identity of either substance. Which of the following is NOT evidence that a chemical reaction has occurred between the two?

    A. The solid compound dissolves.

    B. Gas is evolved from the beaker.

    C. The beaker gets very hot.

    D. A strong smell wafts from the beaker.

5. A gaseous compound is bubbled through a tube into a beaker of liquid. You do not know the identity of either substance. Which of the following is NOT evidence that a chemical reaction has occurred between the two?

    A. A precipitate is formed.

    B. Gas is evolved from the beaker.

    C. The beaker gets very cold.

    D. A strong smell wafts from the beaker.

CHAPTER 8 REVIEW

Choose the best answer.

1. Look at the element of fluorine shown below as it appears in the Periodic Table. How many neutrons are in the nucleus of most fluorine isotopes?

9
F
Fluorine
18.998403
2,7

A. 9   C. 18

B. 10   D. 19

2. Why are Group 17 atoms extremely reactive?

A. They want to gain one electron to become stable.

B. They want to gain two electrons to become stable.

C. They want to lose one electron to become stable.

D. Their outer shell is full of electrons.

3. Look at the following blocks of elements as they appear in the Periodic Table. Which two elements would have the most similar chemical properties?

9 F Fluorine 18.998403 2,7	10 Ne Neon 20.179 2,8
17 Cl Chlorine 35.453 2,8,7	18 Ar Argon 39.948 2,8,8

A. fluorine and chlorine

B. fluorine and neon

C. fluorine and argon

D. chlorine and neon

4. Look at the following block of atoms as they appear in the Periodic Table. Which of the elements is most reactive?

A	**B**	**C**	**D**
15 P Phosphorus 30.97376 2,8,5	16 S Sulfur 32.06 2,8,6	17 Cl Chlorine 35.453 2,8,7	18 Ar Argon 39.948 2,8,8

5. Which family of elements contains 8 electrons in its valence shell?

A. noble gases   C. non metals

B. metals   D. metalloids

6. An ionic bond results from the transfer of electrons from
   A. one orbital to another within the same atom.
   B. a valence shell of one atom to a valence shell of another atom.
   C. the valence shell of one atom to the nucleus of another atom.
   D. the nucleus of one atom to the nucleus of another atom.

7. The element magnesium, Mg, has 12 electrons. In which energy level will its valence electrons be found?
   A. first   B. second   C. third   D. fourth

8. Which of the following statements correctly describes compounds containing covalent bonds?
   A. Covalent compounds have high melting points.
   B. Covalent compounds conduct electricity well.
   C. Covalent compounds have high boiling points.
   D. Covalent compounds tend to be brittle solids.

9. How many bonds does carbon usually form when part of an organic compound?
   A. 1   B. 2   C. 3   D. 4

10. Which of the following elements is a halogen?
    A. He (helium)   B. Cl (chlorine)   C. H (hydrogen)   D. O (oxygen)

11. What is the most common charge of an oxygen ion?
    A. +1   B. +2   C. −1   D. −2

12. The alkali earth metals are in Group 2. What is charge of a (Ca) calcium ion?
    A. +1   B. +2   C. −1   D. −2

13. Elements that "want" electrons, draw electrons close to them when they bond. This creates covalent bonds with an ionic character. Based on the component elements, which of the following bonds has the most ionic character?
    A. H-C (hydrogen-carbon)   C. H-Cl (hydrogen-chlorine)
    B. H-H (hydrogen-hydrogen)   D. H-O (hydrogen-oxygen)

14. Which of the following represents a balanced chemical reaction?

    A. $H_2 + O_2 \rightarrow H_2O$ C. $CH_4 + O_2 \rightarrow CO_2 + 2H_2O$

    B. $CO_2 + H_2O \rightarrow 2H_2CO_3$ D. $N_2 + 3H_2 \rightarrow 2NH_3$

15. Which of the following is NOT a binary compound?
    A. HCl   B. H_2O C. $MgSO_4$ D. CCl_4

16. The chemical formula for sugar is $C_6H_{12}O_6$. Sugar placed in a test tube and then heated over a Bunsen burner turns black and eventually disappears completely. Which of the following statements explains what happens to the sugar that causes it to disappear?

    A. The heat destroys the elements that make up the sugar.

    B. As the sugar burns, it combines with oxygen in the air to form water and carbon dioxide. Water vapor and carbon dioxide escape into the atmosphere.

    C. The sugar is converted to nitrogen gas and is released into the atmosphere.

    D. All of the sugar is converted to energy that cannot be seen.

17. In chemistry class, Mr. Smoak adds a small piece of sodium metal to a glass of water. The sodium reacts violently with the water, producing a flame. The end products are hydrogen gas and sodium hydroxide. Which of the following is the correct balanced chemical equation for the reaction described above?

    A. $2Na + 2H_2O \rightarrow 2NaOH + H_2$

    B. $Na + H_2O + O_2 \rightarrow 3NaOH + H_2$

    C. $H_2O_2 + 2Na \rightarrow 2NaOH + H_2$

    D. $2NaOH + H_2 \rightarrow 2Na + 2H_2O$

18. What type of reaction can be represented by the following general chemical equation?

$$AX + BY \rightarrow BX + AY$$

    A. synthesis

    B. decomposition

    C. single displacement

    D. double displacement

19. Which of the following involves a chemical change?

    A. snow melting into water

    B. an apple rotting on a tree

    C. boiling water until vapor forms

    D. making sweet iced tea

20. Which combination of mole quantities correctly balances the following double displacement reaction?

$$\_CaCl_2(aq) + \_AgNO_3(aq) \rightarrow \_Ca(NO_3)_2(aq) + \_AgCl(s)$$

    A. 1,1,1,1   B. 1,2,1,2   C. 2,1,2,1   D. 1,2,2,2

21. Which combination of mole quantities correctly balances the following synthesis reaction?

$$\_CO_2 + \_H_2O \rightarrow \_H_2CO_3$$

    A. 1,1,1   B. 1,2,1   C. 2,1,2   D. 1,2,2

22. The electrolysis of water is performed by passing an electric current through water to break the chemical bonds that hold it together. What kind of reaction is this?

$$2H_2O \longrightarrow 2H_2 + O_2$$

A. synthesis

C. single displacement

B. decomposition

D. double displacement

23. Silver (Ag) is a transition metal. As a cation, Ag always carries a +1 charge. Bromine (Br) is a halogen. As an anion, Br always carries a -1 charge. Which of the following chemical formulas correctly represents 2 mols of silver bromide?

A. $2AgBr$ B. $Ag(Br)_2$ C. Ag_2Br_2 D. $2Ag_2Br_2$

24. What type of compound is $FeCl_3$?

A. binary

C. homonuclear diatomic

B. heteronuclear diatomic

D. both A and B are correct

Chapter 9
Matter and Energy

GA HSGT SCIENCE STANDARDS COVERED IN THIS CHAPTER INCLUDE:

GPS Standards	
SPS2 a	Students will explore the nature of matter, its classifications, and its system for naming types of matter.
SPS5 a – b	Students will compare and contrast the phases of matter as they relate to atomic and molecular motion.
SPS6 a – e	Students will investigate the properties of solution.
SPS7 d	Students will relate transformations and flow of energy within a system.

We have spent the past few chapters looking at the nuclear and chemical properties of matter…but we haven't discussed matter itself yet, have we? What is matter? **Matter** is anything that has mass and takes up space. On a large scale, matter is easy to define as anything that you can see or touch.

On a small scale, the definition of matter becomes a little trickier. The electron is a good example. The mass of an electron is 9.11×10^{-31} kg, so it is very small. In addition, the electron moves so fast that we usually only measure its location in terms of **probability**, (the likelihood that the electron will be found in a certain place, like an orbital) so the space that it takes up is sometimes hard to find. Nevertheless, it *does* have a mass and it *does* take up space, so theoretically it *is* matter.

In this chapter, we will look at the physical properties of matter. Matter can be divided into two main categories: **mixtures** and **pure substances**. These two categories can be further broken down into a variety of classifications, as shown in Figure 9.1.

CLASSIFICATION OF MATTER

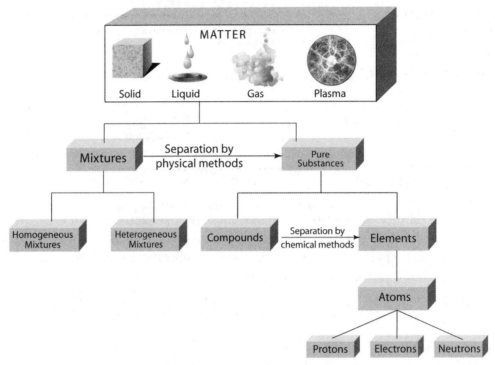

Figure 9.1 Classification of Matter

A **substance** is matter that has constant composition and distinct properties. Some examples of pure substances are oxygen, carbon, iron, sugar and water. Notice that not all pure substances are elements. The best way to determine if something is a pure substance is to ask the question: Will we get the same sample anywhere in the substance?

Elements are substances that cannot, in the absence of fission, be further broken down into simpler substances. Examples of common elements are oxygen, carbon and iron. Elements may take on different structures under different circumstances. These are called **allotropes**. For instance, diamond and graphite are two allotropes of carbon.

As we discussed in the last chapter, when two or more elements combine chemically, they form a **compound**. A compound has completely different properties than the individual elements that make up the compound. For example, water is a compound made up of hydrogen and oxygen. Hydrogen and oxygen, as stand-alone elements, are gases at room temperature. However, water is a liquid. It is not possible to separate a compound physically into its individual components, but it can be chemically separated.

When two or more substances (either elements or compounds) combine physically, they form a **mixture**. A mixture keeps the individual properties of the substances that make it up because the substances do not chemically combine. You can separate a mixture into its individual substances. For example, salt dissolved into water is a mixture. If you drink the salt water, you can taste the salt in the water. The salt is still "salty," and the water is still a liquid, so these substances have not changed chemically. Evaporation separates the salt and water. The liquid water turns into water vapor, so only the salt remains.

We can further classify mixtures as **homogeneous** or **heterogeneous** depending on the distribution of substances in the mixture.

A **homogeneous mixture** occurs when substances are evenly distributed, and one part of the mixture is indistinguishable from the other. The ratio of "ingredients" in a mixture does not have to be in definite proportions in order to be homogeneous. Mixtures of gases are homogeneous. All **solutions** are also homogeneous. A

Figure 9.2 Example of a Homogeneous Solution

solution consists of a substance (the **solute**), dissolved in another substance (the **solvent**). Solutions can be mixtures of solids, liquids or gases. For example, brass is a solid solution of copper, tin, and other elements. Soda is a solution of carbon dioxide gas dissolved in water, a liquid. Salt water is a solution of salt (a solid) dissolved in water (a liquid). Filtering a solution cannot separate its individual parts.

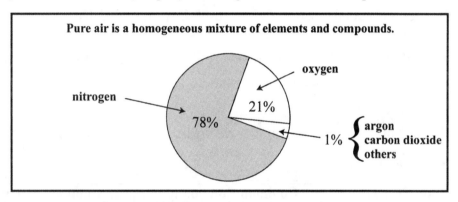

Figure 9.3 Example of a Homogeneous Mixture

A **heterogeneous mixture** occurs when one part of the mixture is distinguishable from the other. Examples of heterogeneous mixtures include granite, dirty air, oil and vinegar salad dressing, paint, blood and soil. Filtering separates many heterogeneous mixtures.

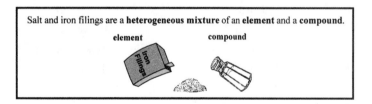

Figure 9.4 Example of a Heterogeneous Mixture

Section Review 1: Classification of Matter

A. Define the following terms.

element	mixture	heterogeneous mixture
compound	homogeneous mixture	solution
		allotrope

B. Choose the best answer.

1. Which of the following is a heterogeneous mixture?

    A. salt water   B. carbon dioxide   C. bronze   D. vegetable soup

2. Which of the following can be separated by filtering?

    A. a solution   C. an element

    B. a compound   D. a heterogeneous mixture

3. Which of the following combinations would result in a substance that is chemically different than its components?

    A. Carbon and oxygen form carbon dioxide.

    B. Sugar and water make a sugar-water solution.

    C. Copper and tin form bronze.

    D. Oxygen and nitrogen form the air that we breathe.

Use the table to answer questions 4 – 6.

Common Elements	Common Compounds	Common Mixtures
oxygen	table salt	vinegar
carbon	water	salad dressing
helium	sugar	brass
nitrogen	baking soda	blood
aluminum	Epsom salts	gasoline
gold	carbon dioxide	soda
neon	ammonia	orange juice

4. Which of the following could be physically separated?

    A. oxygen   C. salt dissolved in water

    B. carbon dioxide   D. pure water

5. Which of the following must be chemically separated to isolate individual elements?

    A. ammonia   C. oil and vinegar salad dressing

    B. brass   D. air

6. Which of the following can be described by its atomic number?

   A. carbon dioxide   B. Epsom salts   C. brass   D. aluminum

7. What is a physical combination of two or more substances called?

   A. an element   B. a compound   C. a mixture   D. an isotope

Examine the following product label.

8. Which statement best describes Soft Hands lotion?

   A. Soft hands lotion is a compound formed from the chemical reaction of the ingredients.

   B. Soft hands lotion is a homogeneous mixture of the ingredients.

   C. Soft hands lotion is a heterogeneous mixture of the ingredients.

   D. Soft hands lotion consists of elements, rather than compounds.

C. Answer the following questions.

1. What is the difference between an element and a compound?

2. What is the difference between a compound and a mixture?

3. Identify the following substances as element (E), compound (C), or mixture (M).

A.	carbon ____	E.	calcium carbonate ____
B.	carbon dioxide ____	F.	blood ____
C.	milk ____	G.	sand and sugar ____
D.	calcium ____	H.	chicken noodle soup ____

4. Identify the following mixtures as homogeneous (HO) or heterogeneous (HE).

A.	gasoline ____	D.	oil and vinegar ____
B.	chunky peanut butter ____	E.	soda ____
C.	filtered apple juice ____	F.	glue ____

STATES OF MATTER

Matter exists in different states, called **phases**. The four states of matter are **solid**, **liquid**, **gas** and **plasma**.

- **Solid**- The atoms or molecules that comprise a solid are packed closely together, in fixed positions relative to each other. Therefore, the solid phase of matter is characterized by its rigidity and resistance to changes in volume. A solid does not conform to the container that it is placed in.

- **Liquid**- The molecules that comprise a liquid can move relative to one another, but are fixed within the volume of the liquid by temperature and pressure. A liquid does conform to the container that it is placed in but may not fill that container.

- **Gas**- The atoms and molecules that comprise a gas move independently of one another. The space between them is determined by the temperature and pressure of the gas, as well as the volume of the container in which it is placed. A gas placed in a container will spread out to uniformly fill that container.

- **Plasma**- A plasma is an ionized gas. This means that atoms and molecules that make up a plasma are charged. As a result of this charge, the atoms and molecules of a plasma "communicate" with each other; they move together because each particle interacts simultaneously with many others. A plasma is characterized by its temperature, density and electrical conductivity.

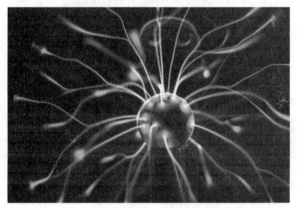

You are familiar with all four phases, though you may not realize it. Figure 9.5 shows a plasma lamp, which many stores sell as a decorative item. If you have ever touched one of these lamps, you know that the filaments of ionic gas reach out toward the conducting surface- that is, your hand. This is a good visual example of how plasma ions move together; if the lamp was just filled with unionized gas, there would be no collective movement of the state in reaction to a stimulus (your hand).

Figure 9.5 Plasma

Table 9.1 Common Substances for Each State of Matter

Solids	Liquids	Gases	Plasma
silver	water	oxygen	fire
diamond	milk	helium	lightening
copper	alcohol	carbon dioxide	the sun and stars
rocks	syrup	hydrogen	the ionosphere
wood	oil	nitrogen	neon signs

The particles making up matter are in constant motion. The phase of the matter depends on the amount and type of motion of those particles. In general, the particles of the gas and plasma states have the highest kinetic energy, while solids have the least. According to kinetic theory, particle motion increases as temperature increases. Adding or subtracting energy in the form of heat changes matter from one state to another. These are called **phase changes**.

PHASE CHANGES

The phase of matter is determined by the physical condition of that matter. When the physical conditions change, a phase change may occur. Two physical conditions of primary importance are **temperature** and **pressure**. To determine how temperature and pressure changes affect phase, we must define **phase barriers** — that is, the point at which matter changes phase.

The **freezing point** of a substance is the temperature at which a liquid becomes a solid, or freezes. The **melting point** of a substance is the temperature at which a solid becomes a liquid or melts. The freezing point and the melting point for a given substance are the same temperature. For example, liquid water begins to freeze at 0°C. Likewise, a cube of ice begins to melt at 0°C.

The **boiling point** of a substance is the temperature at which a liquid becomes a gas. The **condensation point** is the temperature at which a gas becomes a liquid. The boiling point and the condensation point for a given substance are the same temperature. For example, water boils at 100°C, and water vapor (steam) cooled to 100°C begins to condense.

Sublimation is the evaporation of a substance directly from a solid to a gas without melting (or going through the liquid phase). For example, mothballs and air fresheners sublime from a solid to a gas. Dry ice, which is frozen carbon dioxide, is also a common example of sublimation because the solid dry ice immediately sublimes into carbon dioxide gas (looking like fog).

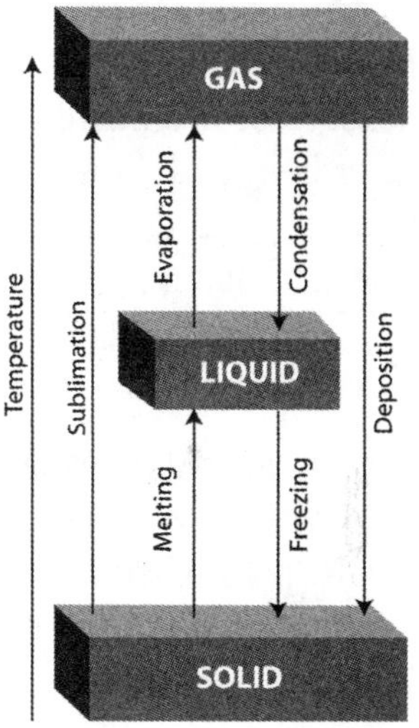

Deposition is the condensation of a substance directly from a vapor to a solid without going through the liquid phase. This term is mostly used in **meteorology** (the study of weather) when discussing the formation of ice from water vapor. The phase changes between solid, liquid, and gas are summarized in Figure 9.6.

Figure 9.6 Possible Phase Changes

Depending on the temperature and pressure, water can exist in all four states of matter. Figure 9.7 shows a common way to illustrate phase transitions, called a **phase diagram**.

Note the dot in the center of the diagram, called the **triple point**. The triple point is the exact temperature and pressure at which the solid, liquid and gas phases can exist simultaneously. When there is more than one solid phase form (an **allotrope**). There will be more than one triple point. The **critical point** is the point at which the liquid phase ceases to be distinguishable from the gas phase.

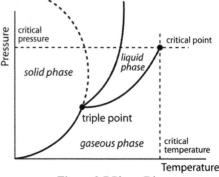

Figure 9.7 Phase Diagram

Phase changes can also be illustrated in terms of the amount of heat added. Figure 9.8 shows this perspective. Ice remains solid at temperatures below 0°C, but once ice reaches 0°C, it starts to melt.

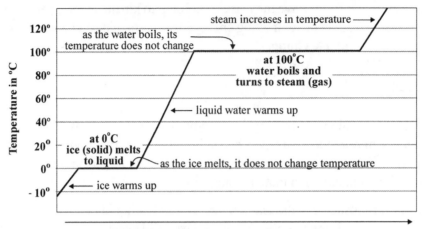

Figure 9.8 The Changing States of Water

As ice melts, it continues to absorb energy, but the temperature of the ice-water mixture does not change. As we apply heat to the ice cube, the heat energy breaks up the molecular bonds of the ice, rather than raising the temperature of the surrounding water. The temperature does not change again until all of the ice melts. Once in a liquid state, the temperature of the water increases until it reaches 100°C. At 100°C, the water boils and turns to steam. While the liquid changes to vapor, the liquid absorbs energy, but the temperature does not increase. Once all of the liquid turns to steam, the temperature of the steam increases. In summary, the temperature remains constant through any phase change whether it be melting, freezing, or boiling. The temperature does not increase during a phase change because the energy is being used to break and/or form molecular bonds rather than to heat the substance.

So, where is the plasma phase in these diagrams? A plasma is very like a gas in some ways. For instance, it has no defined volume. It is also greatly influenced by temperature. If you were to place the plasma state in the phase diagram shown in Figure 9.7, it would be at the extreme right if the diagram, beyond the gas phase. Remember that a plasma is an ionized gas; enough energy must be added to the plasma in order to keep the electrons separate from the ions in the plasma. This can be done by adding heat.

The top temperature shown in Figure 9.8 is 130°C (which is about 400 Kelvin). Around 650 K and 218 atm, water reaches its critical point. Above that temperature and pressure, it is a supercritical fluid.

Steam will begin to **dissociate** (split) into hydrogen and oxygen atoms at around 1500 K. Above 4000 K, hydrogen ions will begin to ionize, generating a "water plasma." Lowering the pressure and adding an electric field will produce plasma at lower temperatures and at different percentages, but this example allows you to see the amount of heat that must be added to reach the fourth state of matter without those measures.

Section Review 2:   States of Matter

A. Define the following terms.

solid	gas	boiling point
melting point	freezing point	condensation point
liquid	plasma	sublimation
allotrope	triple point	deposition

B. Choose the best answer.

1.   When might a substance absorb heat but not change temperature?

    A.   when it is in its solid state

    B.   when it is changing from one physical state to another

    C.   when it is in its gaseous state

    D.   Under no circumstances will a substance absorb heat but not change temperature.

2.   What state of matter has a definite volume but no definite shape?

    A.   solid   B.   liquid   C.   gas   D.   plasma

Use the diagram to answer questions 3 and 4.

3.   What element does this phase diagram describe?

    A.   diamond

    B.   graphite

    C.   carbon

    D.   carbon dioxide

4.   There appear to be two triple points in the diagram. What is the explanation for this?

    A.   There are two forms of the solid phase.

    B.   There are two forms of the liquid phase.

    C.   There are two forms of the gas phase.

    D.   The plasma phase is included in the diagram.

C. Answer the following question.

1.   List the states of matter in order of most kinetic energy to least kinetic energy.

2.   Describe the movement of molecules in each of the four states of matter.

    A.   solid   B.   liquid   C.   gas   D.   plasma

3.   Can you think of a way that liquids are more similar to plasmas than they are to gases?

PHYSICAL PROPERTIES OF MATTER

Physical properties help to describe matter. As you know, the state (or phase) of matter is of primary interest when observing and recording the physical properties of a sample. However, there are many other physical properties that can be observed and measured. These are divided into two categories: extensive properties and intensive properties.

Extensive properties depend on the amount of matter present. Mass, volume and energy are all extensive properties of matter. **Intensive properties** of a substance do not depend on the amount of matter present in the sample. Color, melting point, boiling point, hardness and electrical conductivity are all intensive properties. Another important intensive property is **density**.

DENSITY

Each pure substance has particular properties unique to that substance. Density is one of these properties. **Density** (D) is the mass (m) per unit volume (V) of a substance. We express density in units of kg/m^3 or g/cm^3. At the atomic level, the atomic mass of the element and the amount of space between particles determines the density of a substance. Use the following formula to calculate density:

$$D = \frac{m}{V}$$

When comparing objects of the same volume, the denser something is the more mass it has and, therefore, the greater its weight. This explains why even a small amount of pure gold is very heavy.

The following are general rules regarding density:

Rule 1.   **The amount of a substance does not affect its density. The density of iron at 0°C will always be 7.8 g/cm^3. It does not matter if we have 100 g or 2 g of iron.**

Rule 2.   **Temperature affects density. In general, density decreases as temperature increases. Water is an exception to this rule. The density of ice is less than the density of liquid water; therefore, ice floats.**

Rule 3.   **Pressure affects the density of gases and plasmas, but it does not substantially affect solids or liquids, since those two states are not very compressible. As the pressure on a gas or plasma increases, density also increases.**

Mixing substances of different densities changes the density of the mixture. For example, the density of fresh water is less than the density of salt water. We will explore density in more detail as we look at other physical properties of different phases of matter.

PROPERTIES OF FLUIDS

Fluids are plasmas, liquids and gases. The physical properties of a fluid are determined by the interactions among its particles. Fluids are generally **compressible**, which means their volume can be reduced by applying pressure to the sample. There is a range of compressibility: plasmas and gases are the most compressible and liquids are the least. In fact, the volume of a liquid will change very little unless huge pressures are applied.

INTERACTIONS IN PLASMAS

Plasma is an electrically conductive collection of charged ions. Plasmas are generated by varying degrees of heat which produce varying degrees of ionization. The primary feature of the plasma is that enough energy must be added to keep the ions ionized. Lowering the added energy results in a plasma that reverts to a neutral gas. Increasing the pressure on a plasma forces ions and electrons into closer proximity and will also force them to recombine into a neutral gas. Decreasing the pressure on a plasma generally allows for a greater separation of ions and electrons and allows less energy to be required to maintain the plasma state.

On a separate note, the charged nature of the plasma means that it is strongly affected by both electric and magnetic fields. Plasmas can be shaped into sheets and filaments by the application of an electromagnetic field or any electrical stimulus.

INTERACTIONS IN LIQUIDS

The interactions of molecules in the liquid state affect its physical properties. Substances that are liquids at room temperature are most often molecular compounds. Molecular compounds can be polar or nonpolar.

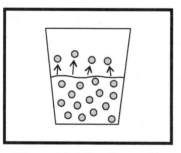

Figure 9.9 A Volatile Liquid

Volatility of Liquids. Volatility is the tendency of a liquid to vaporize (or evaporate) at a low temperature. Volatility of a liquid depends on molecular interactions. The weaker the interactions between molecules, the more volatile the liquid. In general, smaller molecules have a higher volatility than larger molecules. For example, nonpolar liquids with small molecules tend to be very volatile. The interactions between small nonpolar molecules are very weak, so it takes very little energy for the molecules to escape from their liquid state. Polar molecules have more of an attraction between particles because of the partial positive and negative charges, so they tend to be a little less volatile.

Boiling Points and Freezing Points of Liquids. Molecular interactions also affect boiling points and freezing points of liquids.

- A molecule that has little attraction for other molecules of its kind, such as nonpolar molecules, will have a low boiling point and a low freezing point.

- A molecule that has a strong attraction for other molecules of its kind, such as polar molecules, will have a high boiling point and a high freezing point.

For example, water is a molecule that exhibits polar covalent bonding. The polarity of the O-H bond induces a second type of bonding, called **hydrogen bonding**. As shown in Figure 9.10, hydrogen bonding occurs between hydrogen and oxygen molecules of neighboring molecules. Hydrogen bonds are weaker than covalent bonds, but they do give water a long-range stability. This increased stability results in a higher boiling point and a higher freezing point than might be expected for this relatively small molecule.

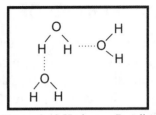

Figure 9.10 Hydrogen Bonding

PROPERTIES OF SOLIDS

Ionic solids. Ionic compounds have strong bonds because of the electrostatic attractions between positive and negative ions. These compounds are usually hard and have high melting points. For example, table salt is an ionic compound, and its melting point is around 800 °C (over 1400 °F). Ionic solids form geometric crystals (or **crystal lattices**) based on the arrangement of positive and negative ions. These solids are usually soluble in water, which means they will dissolve. When in a dissolved state, the ionic compound separates into ions. In a solid state, ionic compounds are not good conductors of electricity, but they will conduct electricity in their **molten** (melted) state or when dissolved in water.

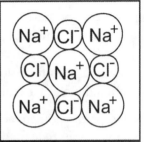

Figure 9.11 Ionic Compound Salt (NaCl)

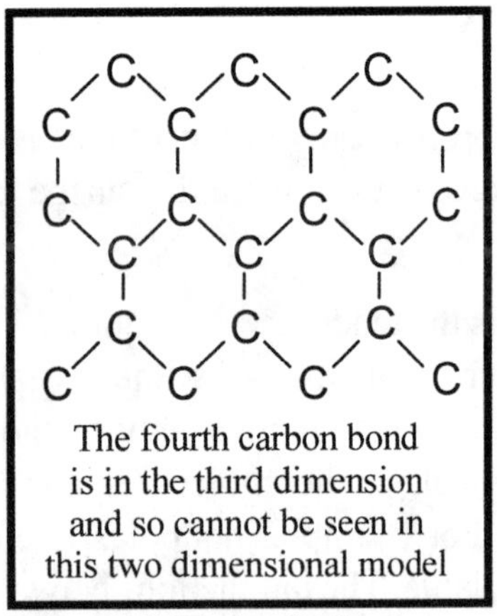

The fourth carbon bond is in the third dimension and so cannot be seen in this two dimensional model

Figure 9.12 Molecular Structure of a Diamond

Covalent solids. When nonmetal atoms share electrons to form a geometric crystalline structure, they form a **covalent solid**. This kind of solid does not form individual molecules. Instead, the atoms form a network of covalent bonds. Covalent solids are not generally good conductors of electricity (although some, like graphite can conduct). The bonds formed by the sharing of electrons are stronger than their attraction to any other substance that could act as a solvent. Therefore, these solids are not soluble. Some other examples are waxes and diamonds.

The allotropes of carbon, for example, are formed of carbon atoms arranged in a variety of covalently-bonded lattice structures. Diamond has a cubic crystal structure while graphite forms hexagonal sheets.

Molecular solids. These solids are also solids formed by covalent bonding between atoms, but the atoms form individual molecules instead of a network of bonds. For example, a sugar molecule, which has the chemical formula of $C_6H_{12}O_6$, forms a molecule with 6 atoms of carbon, 12 atoms of hydrogen and 6 atoms of oxygen. Molecular solids may still form some type of crystalline structure, but there is no sharing of electrons between molecules. Molecular solids are not good conductors of electricity. Molecular solids fall into two categories: polar molecular solids and nonpolar molecular solids. **Polar molecular solids** are usually soluble and have moderate melting points. Sugar is an example of a polar molecular solid. **Nonpolar molecular solids** are usually insoluble, and their melting points are moderate or low. Benzene is an example of a nonpolar molecular solid.

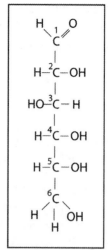

Figure 9.13 Molecular Structure of Sugar

Metallic solids. These solids have a special type of bonding in which the electrons are free to move. This specific interaction of electrons in relation to the metallic nuclei gives metals some special characteristics. They have **luster** which means they reflect light. They are **ductile** which means they can be drawn out into a thin wire. They are **malleable**, which means they can be pounded into sheets. Because of the arrangement of electrons, they are also good conductors of electricity. Some metals exhibit **magnetism**. Melting points vary, but most metals are solids at room temperature.

PROPERTIES OF GASES

Size and polarity of molecules also affect the interaction of gases. Substances that are gases at room temperature are most often stand-alone atoms, diatomic molecules or small, nonpolar molecular compounds. A small, stable atom such as helium has little attraction for other helium atoms; therefore, it exists as a gas at room temperature. The condensation point for helium or other atmospheric gases is very low. Hydrogen, oxygen, and nitrogen exist as diatomic molecules. Carbon dioxide is a small, relatively nonpolar molecular compound. *In general, the smaller the gas molecule, the lower the condensation and freezing points it has.*

GAS LAWS

The collisions of the gas particles against the surface of the container cause the gas to exert pressure upon the container. **Pressure** is a force (push or pull) applied uniformly over an area. The SI unit of pressure is called a **pascal (Pa)**. It is a derived unit equal to 1 newton per square meter (N/m_2). The velocity of the gas particles relates to the temperature of the gas. The **gas laws** describe the relationship between the temperature, pressure and volume of gases. The gas laws are summarized below.

Boyle's law can be thought of as pressure-volume (P-V) relationship. Increasing the pressure at a constant temperature decreases the volume of the gas. Conversely, decreasing the pressure at a constant temperature will increase the volume of the gas. Boyle's law is expressed in equation form as:

$$P_1V_1 = P_2V_2 \qquad \textbf{Equation 9.1}$$

V_1 and V_2 are the volumes of a gaseous sample at pressures P_1 and P_2, respectively. The temperature must remain constant for *Boyle's* law to hold.

Charles' law can be rewritten as temperature-volume (T-V) relationship. Heating a fixed amount of gas at constant pressure causes the volume of the gas to increase, and vice versa: Cooling a fixed amount of gas at constant pressure causes the volume of the gas to decrease.

$$\frac{V_1}{T_1} = \frac{V_2}{T_2} \qquad \textbf{Equation 9.2}$$

V_1 and V_2 are the volumes of a gaseous sample at temperatures T_1 and T_2, respectively. Both temperatures are in Kelvin. The pressure must remain constant for Charles' law to hold.

The Ideal Gas Equation is a pressure-temperature-volume relationship. Heating a gas in a fixed volume container causes the pressure to increase. Conversely, cooling a gas in a fixed volume container causes the pressure to decrease. The ideal gas equation combines the three gas laws into one master equation to describe the behavior of gases.

$$PV = nRT \qquad \textbf{Equation 9.3}$$

The value R is the gas constant. You can remember Equation 9.3 by using the ridiculous mnemonic Piv Nert.

Results from these properties can be observed around us. Pressurized gases pose hazards during handling and storage. Pressurized gases should not be stored in hot locations or be handled near flames.

Balloons, whose volumes are not fixed, can also illustrate the behavior of gases. For example, if you put a balloon in a freezer, it will shrink because of the decreased pressure inside the balloon resulting from the lower temperature. If you take it to the top of a very high mountain, it will expand because of the decreased atmospheric pressure.

Section Review 3: Physical Properties of Matter

A. Define the following terms.

physical properties	volatility	directly proportional
extensive properties	Ideal Gas equation	inversely proportional
intensive properties	pressure	Boyle's law
density	pascal	Charles' law
fluids	hydrogen bonding	

B. Choose the best answer.

1. If a physical property depends on the amount of matter present, it is a(n) _____ property.
   - A.   intensive
   - B.   extensive
   - C.   chemical
   - D.   dense

2. Density generally _____ as temperature increases.
   - A.   increases
   - B.   decreases
   - C.   stays the same
   - D.   disappears

3. Pressure can substantially affect the density of
   - A.   solids.
   - B.   liquids.
   - C.   gases.
   - D.   none of these

4. Based on particle interactions, which of the following types of substances is most volatile?
   - A.   small, nonpolar molecules
   - B.   ionic compounds dissolved in a polar liquid
   - C.   large, polar molecules
   - D.   small, polar molecules which also exhibit hydrogen bonding

5. Cartridges used to fire paint balls are filled with carbon dioxide gas. Each time a paint ball is fired, some carbon dioxide gas escapes. The volume of the cartridge is rigid and does not change. Hampton buys a new carbon dioxide cartridge. Lisa has an equivalent cartridge, but hers has been used to fire several paint balls. Which of the following is true of the cartridges, assuming both cartridges are at the same temperature?
   - A.   The pressure in Hampton's cartridge is greater than the pressure in Lisa's cartridge.
   - B.   The pressure in Hampton's cartridge is less than the pressure in Lisa's cartridge.
   - C.   The pressure in Hampton's cartridge is equal to the pressure in Lisa's cartridge.
   - D.   No relationship can be determined from the given information.

6. A sample of neon gas is at a constant pressure of 3 atm and an initial temperature of 350K. Its volume is reduced by half. What it the final temperature T_2?
   - A. 1050 K
   - B. 175 K
   - C. 700 K
   - D. 950 K

7. What would be the best way to convert a sample from a plasma to a gaseous state?
    A. increase the pressure   C. increase the temperature
    B. decrease the pressure   D. apply an electric field

8. Which type of solid is the best conductor of electricity?
    A. ionic solid   C. metallic solid
    B. covalent solid   D. molecular solid

9. Which of the following states of matter would be least likely to respond to a change in pressure?
    A. liquid
    B. gas
    C. plasma
    D. All of these will respond to a change in pressure.

10. Which of the following types of solid is the most soluble in water?
    A. ionic solid   C. polar molecular solid
    B. nonpolar molecular solid   D. A or C are both water soluble

11. Which Gas Law gives a proportional relationship between temperature and volume?
    A. Boyle's Law   C. The Ideal Gas Law
    B. Charles' Law   D. B and C

C. Answer the following questions.

1. One molecule of carbon dioxide, CO_2, and one molecule of water, H_2O, are each made up of 3 atoms. Use your knowledge of particle interactions to explain why carbon dioxide is a gas at room temperature, but water is a liquid at room temperature.

2. Look at the two containers below. Assuming they have identical contents, which container is most likely to have the highest pressure? Why?

A.    B.

3. Look at the two pictures right. Which position of the piston creates the least pressure in the container? Why?

SOLUTION PROPERTIES

A **solution** is a homogenous mixture of one or more substances, called **solutes,** dissolved in another substance, called a **solvent**. A good example of a common solution is salt water. In that case, salt is the substance that dissolves, and water is the substance that does the dissolving. Together, they make a uniform solution in which one part is the same as any another part: the solution is homogenous.

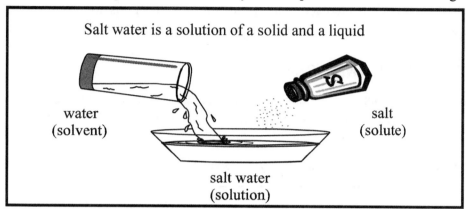

Salt water is a solution of a solid and a liquid

water
(solvent)

salt
(solute)

salt water
(solution)

Figure 9.14 Salt Water as an Example of a Solution

You are probably very familiar with this kind of solution, where a solid solute dissolves in a liquid solvent. Keep in mind, though: *the solute and the solvent can be any phase of matter.* Let's look at a few examples.

Table 9.3 Examining Common Solutions

Solution	Solute(s)	Solute phase	Solvent	Solvent phase
air	oxygen	gas	nitrogen	gas
brass	copper	solid	zinc	solid
steel	carbon	solid	iron	solid
soda water	carbon dioxide	gas	water	liquid
humid air	oxygen, water	gas, liquid	nitrogen	gas

But wait — aren't all these just mixtures? Well, yes! Solutions are a particular kind of mixture, called a homogeneous mixture. **Homogeneity** is a property of all solutions. Another solution property is that they cannot be separated by filtering. Recall in our discussion of the matter, that a compound and a mixture were defined as follows:

- A compound is a chemical union that cannot be separated by physical means.

- A mixture is a physical union that can be separated by physical means.

Well, a solution is somewhere in between:

- A solution is a physical union that can be separated by *some* physical means.

In particular, a solution is a mixture that cannot be separated by filtering. It may, however, be separated by drying. As an example, allowing the water to evaporate from a salt water solution will leave behind the salt. Removing the water affected the **solubility** of the salt. There are several other factors that affect solubility, which are covered in the following sections.

SOLUBILITY OF MATTER

A solution can contain dissolved molecules or ions or a combination of the two. Some ionic solutions, such as salt water where NaCl dissociates into Na^+ ions and Cl^- ions, can conduct electricity (this explains why swimming during a thunderstorm is dangerous). The solubility of a substance is one property that is used to distinguish one substance from another. The solubility is measured by the **concentration** of the solute in the solvent. The concentration is the grams dissolved per volume of H_2O. Many factors affect the solubility of solutes in solvent, which we will look at next.

IDENTITY OF SOLUTE AND SOLVENT

There is a saying among scientists that explains why a solute will dissolve in some solvents but not in others. The saying is: **Like Dissolves Like**. It means that solutes and solvents that have similar molecular polarity will interact. Let's use a few examples.

Polar/Polar: Water is a polar solvent and easily dissolves the polar NaCl molecule, as in Figure 9.15

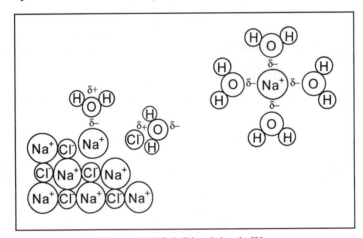

Figure 9.15 Salt Dissolving in Water

Polar/Nonpolar: Water will not dissolve the non-polar solute wax.
Nonpolar/Polar: The nonpolar solvent gasoline will not dissolve polar sugar molecules.
Nonpolar/Nonpolar: Gasoline will dissolve the nonpolar solute oil, like the oil stains on a driveway.

Keep in mind the following general rules:
- Most organic (carbon-based) compounds are nonpolar and will not dissolve in water.
- Most ionic solids are polar and will dissolve in water.
- Most importantly: LIKE DISSOLVES LIKE!

PRESSURE

Air pressure has no effect on solid or liquid solutes. However, an increase in pressure of a gaseous solute above the solvent pressure increases the solubility of the gas. For example, when a carbonated drink is placed in a can, pressure is added to keep the carbon dioxide in the liquid solution. However, when the tab is popped and the pressure is released, the carbon dioxide begins to escape the liquid solution.

The effect of pressure on gas solubility has important implications for scuba divers. Underwater, pressure increases rapidly with depth. The high pressure allows more nitrogen than usual to dissolve in body tissues. If divers ascend too rapidly, the lower pressure causes the nitrogen gas to come out of solution, forming gas bubbles in the blood and tissues. The gas bubbles result in a condition called "the bends," which can cause severe pain, dizziness, convulsions, blindness and paralysis. Divers must ascend to the surface slowly in order to keep air bubbles from forming.

SURFACE AREA

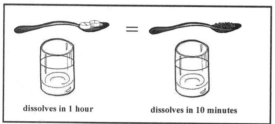

Figure 9.16 Effect of Surface Area on Solubility

The surface area of a solid solute also affects the rate of its solubility. *The more surface area that is exposed to the solvent, the more readily the solute can interact with the solvent.* This increased rate of reaction occurs because there is an increased chance of collisions between reactant particles. Since there are more collisions in any given time, the rate of reaction increases. For example, suppose you had a medicine which you can take in the form of a pill or a powder.

Which substance would enter the body more quickly, the pill form or the powder? The answer is the powder because there is more surface area available for interaction with the solvent — in this case, stomach acid.

AGITATION

To agitate something means to shake it up. In many cases, people agitate a solution in order to mix it. For instance, you may shake a salad dressing bottle before pouring it to make sure that the dressing you pour is mixed and not separated.

In most cases, agitation will help to mix a solution. By increasing the motion of the solution particles, you increase their interaction with each other and also the degree to which they will mix. There is one type of solution in which agitation decreases solubility. Can you guess it? Yes, any time a gas is the solute, agitation decreases solubility.

TEMPERATURE

Have you ever noticed that you can dissolve more sugar in hot tea than you can in cold? As you increase the temperature of a solvent, you can increase the solubility of liquids and solids. Viewing the graph in Figure 9.17, you see how the solubility of the salt potassium nitrate increases with higher temperatures.

The solubility of gases, however, has the opposite relationship with temperature. As the temperature increases, the solubility of gases in solution decreases. For

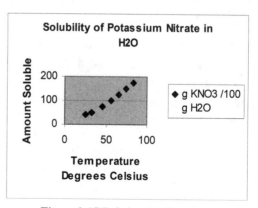

Figure 9.17 Relationship Between Solubility and Temperature

example, an open carbonated beverage will lose its fizz quickly in a hot environment, while the fizz escapes slowly in a cool environment. A decrease in temperature gives gas a greater solubility.

DEGREE OF SOLUBILITY

NaCl dissolves very well in water because they are both polar. Granulated NaCl will dissolve more quickly than a big block of the same mass. Also, the salt will always dissolve more quickly when the water is heated. But how much salt can be dissolved? At some point, the solution becomes **saturated** — that is, it cannot dissolve any more solute. The solubility of sodium chloride in water is 36.0 g/100 mL at 20°C. That means if you add 37.2 grams of NaCl to 100 mL of water in your beaker, 1.2 grams will not dissolve. The excess salt will settle to the bottom of the beaker.

However, we know that if we heat a solution, that we can dissolve more solute in it, more quickly. If we heat the NaCl solution, we should be able to dissolve more salt, creating a **supersaturated** solution. Is this true for every solute? Look at the **solubility curves** in Figure 9.18.

It is quite clear that all salts do not respond in the same way to heating. KNO_3 (potassium nitrate) becomes dramatically more soluble as temperature increases. Copper sulfate shows a more modest rise

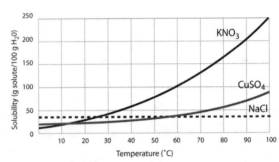

Figure 9.18 Solubility Curves of Three Salts

and NaCl barely increases at all. You might be surprised to learn that increasing the temperature actually decreases the solubility of some ionic compounds, like $CaSO_4$ (calcium sulfate).

ACIDS AND BASES

One particular area of solution chemistry deserves special attention. Acid-base reactions are very important to almost every chemical process on Earth. Let's first examine what acids and base are.

According to the Arrhenius theory, an **acid** is a compound that contains hydrogen and dissociates in water to produce **hydronium ions** (H^+ or H_3O^+). To **dissociate,** means to break down into smaller parts. **Strong acids** are acids that almost completely dissociate in water. Hydrochloric acid (HCl) is a strong acid because the hydrogen ion separates to a great extent from the chloride ion in water. The list of strong acids is short. See Table 9.4 to the right. **Weak acids** are acids that partially dissociate in water. Most acids are weak. Examples of common acids are citric acid in a lemon, tannic acid in tea, lactic acid in sour milk and acetic acid in vinegar.

Table 9.4 Strong Acids

hydrochloric acid	HCl
nitric acid	HNO_3
sulfuric acid	H_2SO_4
hydrobromic acid	HBr
hydroiodic acid	HI
perchloric acid	$HClO_3$

Table 9.5 Examples of Bases

hydroxide ion	OH^-
silicate ion	SiO_3^{2-}
phosphate ion	PO_4^{3-}
carbonate ion	CO_3^{2-}
ammonia	NH_3

The **Arrhenius theory** states that a **base** is a compound that produces **hydroxide ions** (OH^-) in a water solution. Solutions containing a base are **alkaline**. Examples of common bases are sodium hydroxide in lye, ammonium hydroxide in ammonia, magnesium hydroxide in milk of magnesia, aluminum hydroxide in antiperspirant and calcium hydroxide in limewater. Many bases do not dissolve in water. but a few (like NaOH) do.

A more inclusive theory of acids and bases is the Brønsted-Lowry theory. According to the **Brønsted-Lowry theory**, an acid is a proton donor, and a base is a proton acceptor. Remember that a proton is a hydrogen ion (H^+). This theory explains why substances like ammonia, NH_3, are bases even though they don't have a hydroxide (OH^-) group. The NH_3 compound becomes a proton acceptor.

A list of different Brønsted-Lowry bases is shown in Table 9.5.

pH SCALE

We measure acidity and alkalinity using the **pH scale**, pH being short for "potential of hydrogen." The pH scale ranges from 0 to 14. It is logarithmic, so that a difference of one pH unit represents a tenfold change in hydrogen (or rather, hydronium) ion concentration. While we are not concerned with how to calculate pH, it is important to know how pH changes with hydronium ion concentration: it is a reciprocal scale. This means that as the pH values decrease, the concentration of hydronium ions (H_3O^+) increases. For instance, a substance with a pH of 2 has 10 times the hydronium ion concentration as a substance with a pH of 3. As the pH values increase, concentration of hydroxide ions (OH^-) increases.

A substance with a pH of 11 has 100 times (10×10) the hydroxide ion concentration as a substance with a pH of 9. Although it may be confusing, remember that if you hear about a solution having a low pH, it actually means that it is quite acidic.

Water is a neutral compound, except for that very small amount — one in half a billion molecules — that is dissociated. When this is translated to the pH scale, water has a pH of 7. This is considered the neutral point. Acids have pHs lower than 7, and bases have pHs higher than 7. One way to think of this is that for every pH point lower than 7, the solution has 10 times more H^+ floating around than is present in regular water. Likewise, every pH point above 7 means that 10 times more OH^- is present than is in water.

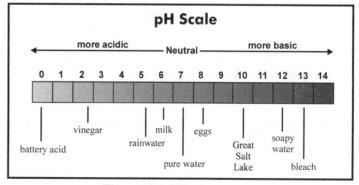

Figure 14.6 pH Scale

Section Review 4: Solutions

A. Define the following terms.

solution	saturated	supersaturated
solute	Like Dissolves Like	solubility curve
solvent	polar	homogeneity
pH	hydronium ion	Arrhenius theory
acid	hydroxide ion	Brønsted-Lowry theory
base	dissociate	alkaline

B. Choose the best answer.

1. In which of the following will sugar be hardest to dissolve?

   A. hot tea   B. warm milk   C. hot coffee   D. iced tea

2. The substance that dissolves the solute is called the

   A. solution.   B. solvent.   C. solid.   D. salt water.

3. What would be the best way to increase the solubility of carbon dioxide gas in water?

   A. heating the solution

   B. agitating the solution

   C. cooling the solution

   D. decreasing the pressure above the solution

4. Which form of matter increases its solubility as pressure is increased?

   A. solid   B. gas   C. liquid   D. powder

5. A given compound dissociates almost completely in water. What could it be?

   A. acetic acid   B. H_2O C. sulfuric acid   D. lactic acid

6. Which solid would be the MOST likely to dissolve in gasoline?

   A. motor oil   B. ice   C. salt   D. wood

7. Which of the following has the highest concentration of OH^- ions?

   A. nitric acid   B. bleach   C. soapy water   D. rainwater

CHAPTER 9 REVIEW

A. Choose the best answer.

1. An object with a mass of 30 g and a volume of 6 cm³ has a density of

    A. 5 g/cm³.　　　　B.　15 g/m³.　　　　C.　180 g/cm³.　　　D.　180 g·cm³.

2. In which of the following situations would water molecules have the most energy?
    A. when water is frozen as ice
    B. in a mixture of ice and water
    C. when water is boiling
    D. when water is superheated steam

3. The term "fluid" applies to
    A. liquids only.
    B. gases and liquids.
    C. gases, liquids and plasmas.
    D. gases only.

4. Volatility is the tendency of a liquid to
    A. disappear.　　　B.　vaporize.　　　C.　burn.　　　　D.　explode.

5. When a substance condenses, it changes from
    A. a liquid to a solid.
    B. a liquid to a gas.
    C. a gas to a liquid.
    D. a gas to a solid.

6. Mixtures can be separated by physical means. Which is *not* a way to separate mixtures?
    A. evaporation
    B. filtering
    C. magnetic separation
    D. stirring

7. A substance that can be separated into its simplest parts by physical means is
    A. water.　　　B.　salt.　　　C.　salt water.　　　D.　hydrogen dioxide.

8. Two equivalent samples of argon gas are placed in two containers of equal and constant volume. The temperature of Sample A is increased by 10°C. The temperature of Sample B is kept constant. Which statement is true?
    A. The pressure of Sample A increases.
    B. The pressure of Sample A decreases.
    C. The pressure of Sample A is constant.
    D. The pressure of Sample B and Sample A are equal.

9. Which of the following does *not* create a mixture?
    A. melting ice
    B. stirring flour in water
    C. salting rice
    D. making a salad

10. Which state of matter consists of ions, rather that atoms or molecules?
    A. solid
    B. liquid
    C. gas
    D. plasma

11. A student made an unsaturated solution by dissolving sugar in tap water. She wanted to increase the concentration of her sugar solution. Select the best way for her to do that.
    A. add more sugar to the existing solution
    B. add more water to the existing solution
    C. warm the solution
    D. agitate the solution

12. Identify the liquid that is the best conductor of electricity.
    A. concentrated sugar solution
    B. molten candle wax
    C. pure water
    D. saltwater

13. Identify the property of water that makes water an excellent solvent.
    A. low freezing point
    B. high specific heat
    C. polar molecules
    D. translucent

14. A given solid and a given gas both dissolve in a given liquid. Identify the result that vigorously shaking the liquid will have on the amount of the solid and the amount of gas that can dissolve in the liquid.
    A. More solid and more gas can dissolve after agitation.
    B. More solid but less gas can dissolve after agitation.
    C. Less solid but more gas can dissolve after agitation.
    D. Less solid and less gas can dissolve after agitation.

15. A given solid and a given gas both dissolve in a given liquid. Identify the result that cooling the liquid will have on the amount of the solid and the amount of gas that can dissolve in the liquid.
    A. More solid and more gas can dissolve after cooling.
    B. More solid but less gas can dissolve after cooling.
    C. Less solid but more gas can dissolve after cooling.
    D. Less solid and less gas can dissolve after cooling.

16. Rita is melting old wax to make a new candle. In what form should she add the wax to the hot pan if she wants the wax to melt quickly?
    A. candle sticks and stubs of various lengths and widths
    B. candle stubs 5 cm long and 4 cm wide
    C. candle stubs 10 cm long and 1 cm wide
    D. shavings of candle sticks and stubs

Chapter 10
Energy Transfer and Transformation

GA HSGT SCIENCE STANDARDS COVERED IN THIS CHAPTER INCLUDE:

GPS Standards	
SPS7 a – c	Students will relate transformations and flow of energy within a system.

TYPES OF ENERGY

Let's turn our attention to different kinds of energy. Energy is sometimes described by its source or form. Some of these are listed below.

Nuclear   Mechanical
Chemical   Electrical
Thermal   Electromagnetic

You can distinguish these intuitively, even if you think that you cannot. Look at Table 10.1, which gives sources for each of these types of energy.

Table 10.1 Energy Sources

Type of Energy	Example of Energy
Thermal	fire, friction
Sound	thunder, doorbell
Electromagnetic	sunlight, microwave, ultraviolet light, X-rays
Chemical	battery, wood, match, coal, gasoline
Electrical	lightning, generator
Mechanical	gasoline engine, windmill, simple machines
Nuclear	radioactive elements, Sun and stars

So there are many different kinds of energy that we can categorize by the form (or forms) in which the energy is found. All of these types of energy can actually be divided into the two broad categories that we have already mentioned: potential energy and kinetic energy.

Potential energy is stored energy due to the object's position or state of matter. Examples of potential energy are water behind a dam, the chemical energy stored in a lump of coal or a match, the electrical potential of a battery and the elastic potential energy of a set mouse trap.

Kinetic energy is energy of motion as an object moves from one position to another. Examples of kinetic energy are falling water, electrons moving through a circuit, a rolling ball. The increased movement of particles as a result of increased temperature is another example of kinetic energy.

There are many other examples of energy transfer between different forms of energy. A match, for example, has potential energy in the form of chemical energy. Once the match is struck, the chemical energy is converted to radiant and thermal energy as light and heat. Notice the picture to the right, Figure 10.1. Water behind a dam has potential energy due to the position of the water it blocks. Once the water is released from the dam, its potential energy is converted to kinetic energy. More specifically, gravitational energy is transferred to motion energy, just like a bike going downhill.

Figure 10.1 A Dam

If the dam is part of a hydroelectric plant, the falling water will turn the turbines of an electric generator. The motion energy of the turning turbine is converted to electrical energy by the generator. As the generator turns, thermal energy is created and dispersed into the environment. The main product of the generator is electrical energy.

Electrical energy may then be converted to radiant energy and thermal energy in a light bulb. Or into motion energy in a desktop fan. Or into chemical energy in a charging battery.

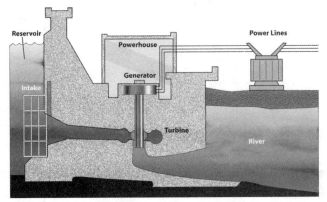

Figure 10.2 Hydroelectric Plant

Are you starting to see how this works? Energy is a commodity, a product that gets traded between every single thing in the universe, every single moment of the day. The **Law of Conservation of Energy** states this clearly, by saying that energy cannot be created or destroyed. It can, however, be transferred from one form to another.

THERMAL ENERGY LOSS

Table 10.2 gives common energy changes from one form to another.

Table 10.2 Common Energy Changes

Use of Energy	Resultant Change in Energy	Energy Lost As
turning on a battery-powered flashlight	chemical to electrical to light	heat from flashlight bulb
turning the turbine in an electric generator	mechanical to electrical	heat from friction within the generator
turning on a light bulb	electrical to light	heat from bulb
using a nuclear reaction to produce heat	nuclear to thermal	heat from reaction
rock rolling down a hill	potential to kinetic	heat from friction of rock against earth

Notice that the third column is titled "Energy Lost As." The Law of Conservation of Energy says that energy cannot be destroyed, so where does this lost energy go? Well it's not really lost, it is transformed into thermal energy. Thermal energy is the common by-product of almost every energy transformation. Sometimes that is good. For instance, nuclear power plants are designed to use the heat from nuclear reactions to turn the turbines of a generator. Sometimes it is not as good. For instance, a car engine loses much of the chemical energy as its fuel (gas) due to friction between the engine parts.

The amount of thermal energy lost tells us how **efficient** the energy conversion is — that is the ratio of how much energy came out of the transition as compared to how much went into the conversion. In an equation, the efficiency of energy conversion from one form to another can be stated as

$$\text{Efficiency} = \frac{\text{Energy out}}{\text{Energy in}}$$

The value of this ratio is always less than 1, because of thermal energy loss during the process of conversion.

Activity 1

Write the appropriate energy transition in the space provided.

_____

_____

_____

_____

Section Review 1: The Law of Conservation of Energy

A: Define the following terms.:

Law of Conservation of Energy   potential energy

efficient   kinetic energy

B: Choose the best answer.

1. The energy in a battery is

    A. chemical potential energy.   C. electromagnetic kinetic energy.

    B. mechanical potential energy.   D. thermal kinetic energy.

2. An engine converts 95% of energy input into useful work output. What happens to the remaining 5% of the energy?

    A. It is converted to heat or to some other form of unusable energy.

    B. It is destroyed in the process of converting from one type of energy to another.

    C. It is stored in the engine for later use.

    D. It is lost along with the mass of the fuel.

3. Which of the following is an example of the conversion of electromagnetic energy to electrical energy?

    A. chemical battery   C. light bulb

    B. nuclear fission   D. solar cell

4. Which of the following is an example of the conversion of thermal energy to nuclear energy?

    A. a generator turbine   C. nuclear fusion

    B. a light bulb   D. nuclear fission

5. Which of the following is an example of the conversion of electrical energy to electromagnetic energy?

    A. a generator turbine   C. nuclear fusion

    B. a light bulb   D. a solar cell

C. Answer the following questions.

1. Give an example of an object that has potential energy and an example of an object that has kinetic energy. Be sure to identify which is which.

2. A power generation plant burns coal to heat water and produce steam. The steam turns a turbine. The turning turbine produces electricity. Identify the types of energy mentioned in this example and record how each energy source is converted to another.

THERMAL ENERGY AND HEAT

All matter is made up of atoms and molecules. Within these atoms and molecules, there is a lot of action going on. Electrons are constantly in motion within the atoms and molecules due to electrical charges. Additionally, the atoms and molecules that make up the matter are in motion with respect to each other, transferring energy as they move. Fortunately, there are also strong forces inside each atom holding it together. There are also forces holding atoms together with other atoms to form molecules. These electrically charged particles possess energy together known as **internal energy**. When internal energy transfers between materials, we call the transferred energy **heat**, or **thermal energy**. The measure of heat is **temperature**. Energy transfer always occurs from an area of high energy to an area of low energy.

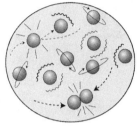

Figure 10.3 Thermal Energy

Let's say you have one container of gas in which the atoms are moving slowly and another container of gas with faster moving atoms. If you mix the two, the atoms will bump into each other. As they do, the faster moving atoms will transfer energy to the slower moving gas atoms. When the gas atoms are all colliding at the same speed, they will have the same internal energy. The energy of the combined gases can then be measured as temperature.

Every substance has a different ability to absorb heat. The **specific heat** of a substance is the number of joules (unit of work and energy) required to raise 1 gram of the substance 1°C or 1K. Table 10.3 shows the specific heat capacity of a few common substances.

Table 10.3 Specific Heat Capacity

Specific Heat Capacity (Cp)	
Substance	(J/kg °C)
Air	995
Aluminum	920
Copper	390
Glass	840
Iron	450
Lead	130
Water	4,200
Ice (0°C)	2,100
Steam (100° K)	2,100

The equation to calculate how much heat energy (Q) is needed to raise one gram of a substance 1°C is:

Heat gained or lost = (mass in kilograms)(specific heat capacity)(change in temperature)

$$Q = mCp\Delta T$$

Equation 10.1

HEAT TRANSFER

There are three common ways to refer to heat transfer: conduction, convection and radiation. Figure 10.4 shows examples of these three means of heating. In **conduction**, kinetic energy is transferred as particles hit each other directly. During this type of heat transfer, the two objects at different temperatures are in direct contact with one another. **Convection** occurs when circulation of heat through gases or liquids raises the temperature of the whole fluid. Finally, **radiation** is the transfer of thermal energy as waves. Various kinds of matter transfer thermal energy to different degrees. **Thermal insulators** such as cork, fiberglass, wool or wood inhibit the transfer of thermal energy. Thermal insulators can improve efficiency by slowing heat loss. **Thermal conductors** are substances that promote thermal energy transfer. Many types of metal, such as copper and aluminum, are good thermal conductors.

Conduction   Convection   Radiation

Figure 10.4 Conduction, Convection and Radiation

EXOTHERMIC AND ENDOTHERMIC REACTIONS

Chemical changes in matter occur because of chemical reactions. Chemical reactions are either exothermic, which means they give off energy, or endothermic, which means they absorb energy. (Physical changes in matter can also be exothermic or endothermic.) The energy is usually given off or absorbed is in the form of heat. This is not always the case, however. Some chemical reactions generate or absorb energy in the form of light or electricity. For example, a burning candle gives off heat, but it also gives off light energy. The burning of fossil fuels also releases heat and light energy. A car battery produces electrical energy, and a recharged battery stores electrical energy. In all cases, energy is conserved, which means it is neither created nor destroyed. The energy is just transferred from one form to another.

EXOTHERMIC REACTIONS

Exothermic reactions release thermal energy. Exothermic reactions or processes are often spontaneous. This release or production of heat warms the surrounding area. One example of an exothermic reaction is combustion. The combustion of fossil fuels is the source of most of the world's energy. Condensing steam is an example of an exothermic process. The steam gives up energy to condense into a liquid form. The liquid state of a substance has less atomic/molecular motion than its gaseous state, and so it has less internal energy. Therefore, going from a gas to a liquid is an exothermic transition. An example of an exothermic chemical reaction is the decomposition of food in a compost pile. Compost made up of grass clippings and leftover vegetable peels gives off heat because bacteria and other organisms break down the matter into simpler substances. Another example is rusting. Iron exposed to oxygen will react to form rust and give off heat. Rust, the product, has less energy than iron and oxygen, the reactants. Other examples of exothermic reactions are personal hand warmers and portable heating pads.

Often, a chemical change or reaction must be started by adding energy or heat. Once the chemical reaction begins, it gives off more energy than was added to start the reaction. The energy needed to start the reaction is called the **activation energy**. If the energy at the end of the reaction is less than the energy at the beginning of the reaction, it is still exothermic. Burning wood gives off energy in the form of light and heat, but wood does not burn spontaneously under ordinary conditions. For example, a match does not burn until friction is added to form a spark. Once the spark ignites the match, it burns and gives off more energy in the form of heat and light than the initial spark. Once the match has burned, it cannot be used again to give off energy. The total energy of the match after it has burned is less than the energy before it burned; therefore, it is an exothermic reaction.

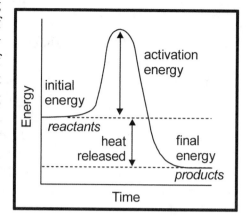

Figure 10.5 Exothermic Reaction

ENDOTHERMIC REACTIONS

Some reactions absorb energy causing the products to have more energy than the original reactants. These endothermic reactions are not as common. In an **endothermic** reaction, heat energy is absorbed. This absorption of energy results in the cooling of the surrounding area. Heat transfers from the surrounding area to the point of the chemical reaction. An example of an endothermic process is melting ice. Ice must absorb energy to melt. The liquid water has more energy than the ice; therefore, it is an endothermic process. Another example of an endothermic chemical reaction is the medical cold pack included in some emergency first aid kits. A membrane separating two chemicals must be broken by bending or kneading the pack. Once the chemicals mix, they react and absorb heat causing it to feel cold.

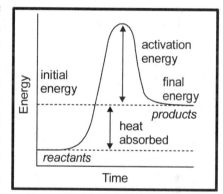

Figure 10.6 Endothermic Reaction

CATALYSTS

Catalysts can increase the rate of reaction. They do this by decreasing the activation energy needed for a reaction. Figure 10.7 shows what an energy graph of a reaction might look like with and without a catalyst. Notice that the beginning energy and the final energy are the same for both reactions, but the energy needed for the reaction to occur is less with a catalyst.

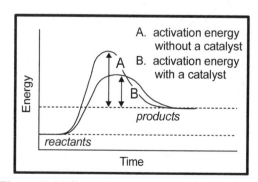

Figure 10.7 Effect of Catalysts on Activation Energy

Section Review 2:   Heat

A. Define the following terms.

thermal energy	temperature	thermal insulator
specific heat capacity	conduction	thermal conductor
heat	convection	exothermic reaction
	radiation	endothermic reaction

B. Choose the best answer.

Use Table 10.3 to answer questions 1-5.

1. Paul removed 2 kg cubes of ice, copper, lead and glass from a freezer and placed them in four separate ovens. They were then heated from 0°C to 50°C. Which oven used the LEAST amount of energy to heat its sample?

    A.   the oven containing the ice cube   C.   the oven containing the lead cube

    B.   the oven containing the copper cube   D.   the oven containing the glass cube

2. How much heat is needed to raise the temperature of 2 kg of copper from 20°C to 30°C?

    A.   15,600 J   B.   23,400 J   C.   7,800 J   D.   3,900 J

3. The temperature of a 1 kg water sample drops by 1°C, resulting in a release of energy from the sample. In which phase will the greatest amount of energy be released?

    A.   liquid water at 25°C

    B.   ice at 0°C

    C.   steam at 100°C

    D.   This question cannot be answered unless the volume of the sample is given.

4. Aluminum has a lower specific heat capacity than liquid water. What is the result of this?

    A.   It takes less energy to increase the temperature of a 1 kg water sample by 1°C than a 1 kg aluminum sample.

    B.   It takes more energy to increase the temperature of a 1 kg water sample by 1°C than a 1 kg aluminum sample.

    C.   It takes more energy to increase the temperature of a 1 kg aluminum sample by 1°C than a 1 kg water sample.

    D.   This question cannot be answered unless the volume of the sample is given.

5. 450 J of heat are added to a 100 kg block of iron. What is the resulting temperature change?

    A.   10°C   B.   1°C   C.   0.1°C   D.   0.01°C

CHAPTER 10 REVIEW

A. Choose the best answer.

1. When the temperature of a particle of matter rises, there is an increase in the
    A.   size.
    B.   potential energy.
    C.   mass.
    D.   kinetic energy.

2. Mixing salt and sugar is a(n)
    A.   physical change.
    B.   chemical change.
    C.   endothermic change.
    D.   exothermic change.

3. A package of frozen gravy is heated in a microwave. This is an example of heat transfer by
    A.   conduction.   B.   convection.   C.   radiation.   D.   insulation.

4. Water heating in a water heater is an example of heat transfer by
    A.   conduction.   B.   convection.   C.   radiation.   D.   insulation.

5. Water is heated in an Erlenmeyer flask. After the water boils, the flask is removed from the burner and placed on a wooden cooling trivet. The wood _____ the transfer of _____ from the glass to the laboratory bench top.
    A.   speeds up, thermal energy
    B.   slows, radiant energy
    C.   slows, thermal energy
    D.   speeds up, radiant energy

6. Beating a drum represents what kind of energy conversion?
    A.   electrical to mechanical
    B.   mechanical to sound
    C.   chemical to electrical
    D.   sound to heat

7. A car uses gasoline for fuel. Which of the following describes the energy conversion from gasoline to the movement of the car?
    A.   mechanical to electrical
    B.   heat to light
    C.   electrical to nuclear
    D.   chemical to mechanical

8. Which of the following is an example of electrical energy being converted to light energy?
    A.   ringing a doorbell
    B.   striking a match
    C.   turning on a computer monitor
    D.   water falling over a dam

9. Which of the following is an example of potential energy?
    A.   a rock rolling down a hill
    B.   a rock at the bottom of a hill
    C.   a rock at the top of a hill
    D.   a rock bouncing down a hill

10. Which of the following is an example of kinetic energy?
    A. a baseball flying through the air   C.   a baseball in a locker
    B. a baseball in a catcher's mitt   D.   a baseball stuck in a house gutter

11. Which of the following is a mechanical example of potential energy?
    A. an unlit match   C.   a mousetrap
    B. a battery   D.   a screw

12. A 2 kg sample of lead has a specific heat of 130 J/kg°C. What change in temperature is required to generate an energy gain of 500 J?

    A. temperature increase of 1°C

    B. temperature increase of more than 1°C but less than 2°C

    C. temperature decrease of 1.5°C

    D. temperature decrease of more than 1°C but less than 2°C

13. A 3 kg iron sample requires a 1°C change in temperature to gain 390 J of heat. What is its specific heat capacity?
    A. 1170 J   B. 1170 J/kg °C   C. 130 J   D. 130 J/kg °C

14. The reactants in an exothermic chemical reaction have an initial energy of 800 kJ. After the chemical reaction, what could be energy of the products?

    A. 600 kJ

    B. 800 kJ

    C. 810 kJ

    D. 1600 kJ

15. Which of the following processes gives off energy?

    A. melting ice

    B. burning propane in a gas heater

    C. sublimation of carbon dioxide ice to carbon dioxide gas

    D. recharging a car battery

16. What is the primary function of a catalyst?
    A. to decrease energy of the product
    B. to increase energy of the reactants
    C. to decrease activation energy
    D. to increase activation energy

Chapter 11
Forces and Motion

GA HSGT SCIENCE STANDARDS COVERED IN THIS CHAPTER INCLUDE:

GPS Standards	
SPS8 a – e	Students will determine relationships among force, mass and motion.

MOTION

MOVING IN SPACE

Everything in the universe moves. This may be hard to believe when you look out your window on a calm day and see no movement, but this apparent lack of movement is an illusion. We only need to watch the Sun for a little while to see that it changes its location in the sky throughout the day. This is a simple observation that gives us qualitative data. However, if we want to accurately describe the movement of the Sun or any other object, we need to learn how to measure the movement and collect quantitative data. This requires a whole new vocabulary that will ensure accurate descriptions of movement.

An object's location in space is called its **position**. The **motion** of an object is defined as the change in its position during a specific amount of time. Motion is a **rate**. Before we concern ourselves with how much time it requires for an object to move, we will just focus on changing positions. We know that objects can change positions in a variety of ways. To make it very straightforward, let's consider **linear motion** where objects move along lines.

An object that moves from one position to another has traveled a **distance**, that is, a certain measure of length through space. **Displacement** is a term that describes the distance an object moves *in a specific direction*. The terms distance and displacement are similar, but displacement always includes a direction. For instance, "5 miles due north" is an example of a displacement value. The distance is 5 miles, but the direction of due north makes it a displacement value. Now, say a person walks 2 miles north and 3 miles east. The distance traveled is still 5 miles but there are two displacements. We can describe this person's movement as a path. A path is the overall course or track that an object travels along. So, to accurately describe the motion of any object, we need to consider its specific path, which consists of one or more displacements.

For example, imagine that you could have a satellite record your motion throughout a typical day. You would see a series of displacements that would follow a course beginning and ending at your home. Your motion would define a path that might look something like Figure 11.1.

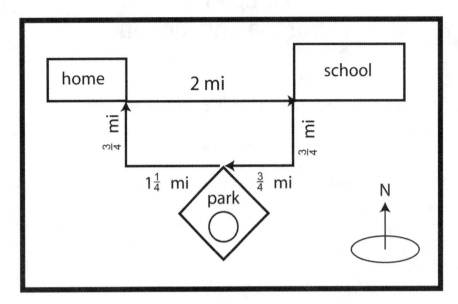

Figure 11.1 A Satellite View of Your Typical Day

Your motion defines a path from home to school to the park and back home again. This path involves a series of displacements that returns to the same position. Your overall displacement then at the end of the day is zero because you are back where you started. However, no one can say that you didn't go anywhere because the distance you traveled is 2 + ¾ + ¾ + 1 ¼ + ¾ = 5 ½ miles! And that only includes walking between places, not the moving around you did when you were actually there. Altogether, there are five displacements, each with a specific distance and direction. Notice that if we removed the arrowheads, you would lose information about the direction of motion. The fact that the arrowheads are shown means that you traveled exactly 2 miles east, then ¾ miles south, and so on. So, it is the distances and the directions that define the path of motion.

These quantities have specific mathematical names. The distance alone is called a **scalar quantity**. It can be completely described using only the magnitude (a number). Displacement is called a **vector quantity**. A vector quantity must be described by both a magnitude and a direction.

VELOCITY VS. SPEED

THE TIME OF MOTION

Remember that the motion of an object is defined as the change in position during a specific amount of time. So far, we talked about changing positions. Now we are ready to bring in the element of time. Imagine you are standing in line at a fast food restaurant. After a while, your might think, "It's taken ten minutes to move two feet! I'm never going to eat!" You notice that the other line is moving much faster because your friend, who chose the other equally long line, is already being served. He gets his food and comes up to you and says, "Man, that only took five minutes!"

While you have time to wait, you naturally begin to think about the difference in your motion versus your friend's. If the distance from the back of the line where you started and the register is ten feet, then you have only traveled 20% of the distance while your friend traveled 100%. But what about the time it has taken? If it took ten minutes to move two feet, how long will it take for you to get to the register if the line keeps moving in the same way? You calculate that it will take 50 minutes! Hardly the definition of *fast* food. Now, what if we wanted to describe how fast you were moving per minute? If it took ten minutes to move two feet, then you are traveling at 0.2 feet per minute. Your friend, on the other hand, moved ten feet in five minutes, or 2 feet per minute. No wonder he already has his food!

When motion is described as distance (feet) per unit time (min), it is called **speed**. We are most familiar with speed when driving in a car. A speedometer in a car that reads 55 mph or "miles per hour" means that if the car continues moving at the same rate for one hour, it will travel 55 miles. In general, any measurement that involves a change in something per unit time is referred to as a rate. Notice that the speed says nothing about the direction or the actual amount of time that the car is traveling for. It could be that the car is being driven for 15 minutes or 15 hours; either way, the speed is the same. Now, when someone typically drives a car, she starts at 0 mph and increase her speed as she travels. At a stop sign or traffic light, she returns to 0 mph. The pattern is continued until the final destination is reached. But at any given moment, the speedometer only gives the present speed. This is referred to as an **instantaneous rate** because it only gives information about exact points in time (that is, at a particular instance) and not how the rate may have changed over the path of motion. The car may have traveled 30 miles in an hour, in which case the **average rate** of the car is 30 mph. However, the instantaneous rate of travel changed constantly throughout the trip, and rarely had a value of 30 mph.

As you can see, we have used familiar units, like feet and minutes, to describe speed. That is okay, as a thought exercise, but it is important to use SI units when making measurements. The box for Equation 11.1 shows the unit derivation or speed.

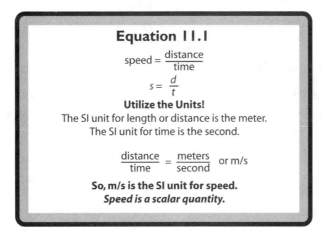

Equation 11.1

$$\text{speed} = \frac{\text{distance}}{\text{time}}$$

$$s = \frac{d}{t}$$

Utilize the Units!
The SI unit for length or distance is the meter.
The SI unit for time is the second.

$$\frac{\text{distance}}{\text{time}} = \frac{\text{meters}}{\text{second}} \text{ or m/s}$$

So, m/s is the SI unit for speed.
Speed is a scalar quantity.

Velocity differs from speed in much the same way as displacement differs from distance. The **velocity** is the speed plus the direction along the path. Another way to say this is that it is the displacement of an object over a period of time. The SI unit for velocity is meter per second (m/s). The numerical value of velocity and speed will be the same, but velocity implies that there is also information about the direction of motion. For example, what is the velocity of a car traveling 550 miles due south for 12 hours? Simply dividing 550 miles by 12 hours gives a rate of about 46 mph. This answer alone does not tell us direction nor does it reveal what the instantaneous rates were. It simply gives the average rate. If we wanted to know more information about the different rates the car traveled along the path, we would need more information. In order to avoid the confusion between instantaneous and average rates, many problems you will encounter deal with **uniform motion**, that is, motion that has a constant rate. Equation 11.2 is the equation used to calculate velocity between two positions.

Equation 11.2

$$\text{velocity} = \frac{\text{final position} - \text{initial position}}{\text{final time} - \text{initial time}}$$

$$v = \frac{\Delta x}{\Delta t}$$

Utilize the Units!

The Δ symbol means "change in." Change in position is a distance. The SI unit for length or distance is the meter. The SI unit for time is the second.

$$\frac{\text{distance}}{\text{time}} = \frac{\text{meters}}{\text{second}} \quad \text{or m/s}$$

So, m/s is the SI unit for velocity.

Velocity is a vector quantity.

Practice Exercise 1: Calculating Displacements and Rates

Find the displacement for the following problems. Use graph paper and a protractor when needed, and use a convenient scale.

1. Shawn runs 4 times around a 400-meter oval track and stops at the same point he started.

2. A truck driver travels 50 miles north, then turns west and drives another 50 miles.

3. Dupree Park has a perfectly circular walking track that has a circumference of 200 feet and a diameter of about 64 feet. Dale starts at the westernmost point and walks to the easternmost point.

4. A father runs errands with his children. He leaves his home, drives five miles south to the gas station, 10 miles southeast to the dry cleaners, 5 miles east to the grocery store, 10 miles northeast to the eye doctor, 5 miles north to the park, and 19 miles west to return home.

Calculate the rate of speed for the following problems.

1. James drives 400 km in 5 hours.

2. A man hang glides down a 3,048 m mountain in 20 minutes.

3. A turtle crawls 120 cm in 4 minutes.

4. Michelle swims 100 m in 50 seconds.

Velocity or speed can also be shown graphically with distance on the *y*-axis and time on the *x*-axis. Figure 11.2 shows the distance that two cars travel versus time. You can use a graph like this to determine speed. Remember, speed is distance divided by time.

Since the line for car 1 is straight, the speed is constant. From the graph, you can see that car 1 travels 15 meters every second. Between any two points, the distance divided by the time is 15 meters per second. Therefore, the speed of the car is 15 m/s. The slope of the line (the change in distance divided by the change in time) represents the speed. Recall from math class that the slope of a line equals rise over run, or the difference in the *y*-value divided by the difference in the *x*-value. The graph for the second car is not a straight line. Therefore, the speed is not constant. Car 2 travels 30 meters in the first second, and then 15 m in the next second. Finally, the car only travels 15 meters in the last 2 seconds. The speed of the car is decreasing from 30 m/s initially, to 15 m/s, and finally to 7.5 m/s.

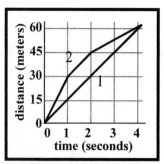

Figure 11.2 Graphical Representation of Car Speed

RATE CHANGES

How do you describe motion that does not have a uniform rate? **Acceleration** is the change in velocity over time. You are probably familiar with this term in the sense of a car "accelerating." For instance, car enthusiasts often compare the time it takes for different cars to go from 0 to 60 mph. Notice that this is describing the change in a rate over a period of time. So, one car may take 4.2 seconds to go from 0 to 60 mph, while another car may take 5.0 seconds. When acceleration is a positive number, the object is increasing its speed. Likewise, when acceleration is a negative number, the object is decreasing in speed. Negative acceleration is also called **deceleration**.

Equation 11.3

$$\text{acceleration} = \frac{\text{final velocity} - \text{initial velocity}}{\text{final time} - \text{initial time}}$$

$$a = \frac{\Delta v}{\Delta t}$$

Utilize the Units!

The Δ symbol means "change in." Change in velocity is a rate. The SI unit for rate is the meter per second. The SI unit for time is the second.

$$\frac{\text{velocity}}{\text{time}} = \frac{\text{m/s}}{\text{s}} = \frac{\text{m}}{\text{s}} \times \frac{1}{\text{s}} = \text{m/s}^2$$

So, m/s² is the SI unit for speed.
Acceleration is a vector quantity.

Example: A car accelerates from 10 m/s to 22 m/s in 6 seconds. What is the car's acceleration?

$$a = \frac{22 \text{ m/s} - 10 \text{ m/s}}{6 \text{ s}} = 2 \text{ m/s}^2$$

Notice that the units for acceleration are distance per time squared. In this example, the car accelerates 2 meters per second each second, or 2 m/s^2.

Practice Exercise 2: Calculating Acceleration

Calculate the acceleration in the following problems. Use a negative quantity to indicate deceleration.

1. A sky diver falls from an airplane and achieves a speed of 98 m/s after 10 seconds. (The starting speed is 0 m/s.)

2. A fifty-car train going 25 meters per second takes 150 seconds to stop.

3. A runner speeds up from 4 m/s to 6 m/s in the last 10 seconds of a race.

4. A car traveling 24 m/s comes to a stop in 8 seconds.

Acceleration can also be shown graphically, with speed on the *y*-axis and time on the *x*-axis. Figure 11.3 shows the acceleration of a car by graphing speed versus time. The line in this graph is straight; therefore, the acceleration is constant. Since acceleration is the change in speed over time, the slope of this graph represents the acceleration of the car.

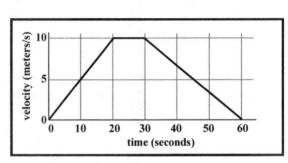

Figure 11.3 Acceleration of a Car

Example: Use the graph to determine the car's acceleration. Pick any two points to calculate the change in speed and the change in time. Using the two points marked on the graph;

$$a = \frac{30 \text{ m/s} - 10 \text{ m/s}}{3 \text{ s} - 1 \text{ s}} = \frac{20 \text{ m/s}}{2 \text{ s}} = 10 \text{ m/s}^2$$

The acceleration of the car is 10 m/s^2.

Now, look at Figure 11.4. Let's interpret the meaning of this graph. First, notice the plot is time versus velocity. The plot will show changes in velocity over the course of 60 seconds. At a time equal to zero (t=0), the car had no speed, meaning that it was at rest. Between 0 and 20 seconds, the speed changes from 0 m/s to 10 m/s. During this time interval, the car's speed is changing, which means that the car is accelerating. Between 20 and 30 seconds, the speed remains at 10 m/s and does not increase or decrease

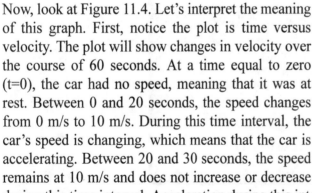

Figure 11.4 Acceleration of a Car

during this time interval. Acceleration during this interval is zero, and the car travels at a constant speed of 10 m/s. From 30 seconds to 60 seconds, the car's speed changes again, but this time the speed decreases. Therefore, between 30 and 60 seconds, the car decelerates. At 60 seconds, the speed is zero, meaning the car has completely stopped.

Challenge Question

What information is missing from the graph shown in Figure 11.4?

Section Review 1: Motion

A. Define the following terms.

position	speed	acceleration
motion	instantaneous rate	deceleration
linear motion	scalar	rate
distance	average rate	
displacement	velocity	
vector	uniform motion	

B. Choose the best answer.

1. Calculate the average speed of a bicyclist who travels 20 miles in 60 minutes.
   A. 0.33 miles per hour
   C. 40 miles per hour
   B. 3 miles per hour
   D. 20 miles per hour

2. Calculate the acceleration of a race car driver if he speeds up from 50 meters per second to 60 meters per second over a period of 5 seconds.
   A. 2 m/s^2
   B. 5 m/s^2
   C. 60 m/s^2
   D. 50 m/s^2

3. Which of the following is a vector quantity?
   A. 0 mph
   B. 55 mph
   C. distance
   D. acceleration

C. Use the graph to the right to answer the following questions.

1. What is the acceleration of the train between 0 and 20 seconds?

2. What is the acceleration of the train between 20 and 40 seconds?

3. What is the acceleration between 100 and 120 seconds?

4. At 80 seconds, what is the train's speed?

5. Calculate how far the train traveled during the period of time when its speed was 10 m/s.
   (Hint: speed = distance/time, so distance = speed × time.)

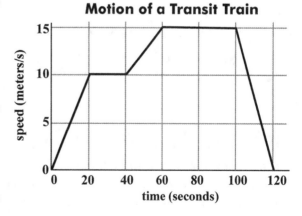

FORCES AND MOTION

How do objects move? Well, if you think about it, there are really only two possibilities that could explain the mechanism of movement: either there is something inside the object that makes it move or there is something outside the object that influences its motion.

So, let's perform a test in our mind. Imagine that you have gathered a bunch of different kinds of rocks. You decide to drop them from a few feet off the ground. You know what will happen: they would all fall back to the ground, each demonstrating very similar motion. You could cut them open or smash them, but you would never isolate anything inside the rocks that made them behave this way. On the other hand, they all behaved similarly, right? There is no string or spring or anything dragging the rocks back to the ground, yet they all appear to be pulled in a similar way. Just from watching rocks fall, we can determine that something pulls objects down toward the Earth. Whatever that "something" is, it is undetectable to the human eye. If we examine more objects, we soon find that this phenomenon is not limited to rocks. All things seem to experience this phenomenon.

So, what is this invisible something that makes things move? It is a force. A **force** is a push or pull on matter. Forces act on objects and sometimes cause them to move. For example, you use force to pull a door open or to push a shopping cart. Force can cause matter to speed up, slow down, to stop or to change direction. For example, applying force to the brakes of a bicycle causes the bicycle to slow down. When a rock falls and hits the ground, the force of the ground against the rock stops the rock's motion. The force of a swinging bat connecting with a baseball changes the direction of the baseball. Recall that a change in speed or direction of motion with time results in some change in acceleration of the object. Therefore, force can change the acceleration of an object.

Forces are pushing or pulling on matter in the world around us all the time, even when the matter appears to be at rest! For instance, the force of gravity pulled those dropped rocks toward the Earth. When they landed, they stopped moving – but NOT because the force of gravity stopped pushing. The motion of the rock ceased because the force of the Earth pushing UP on the rock was balanced by the force of gravity pushing DOWN on the rock. Overall, the rock doesn't move up or down, because the forces acting upon it are in balance. We can generalize this by saying that when the forces that act on an object at rest are in balance, the object remains at rest. When the forces that act on an object are unbalanced, the object moves in the direction determined by the sum of all forces acting on it.

Sir Isaac Newton (1642 – 1727) formulated three laws of motion that describe how forces affect the motion of objects. Newton's laws and their consequences are often referred to as **Newtonian**, or **classical mechanics**.

NEWTON'S FIRST LAW OF MOTION

Newton's first law of motion states that an object at rest will remain at rest, and an object in motion will remain in motion, unless acted on by an unbalanced force. The state of "rest" can occur in either of two ways. First, an object will be at rest if no forces are acting on it. Second, an object will be at rest if two or more forces are acting on the object in such a way that they all balance each other, so that the sum total of their push or pull on the object is zero.

Balance of forces can be illustrated by a classic tug-o-war competition. If the teams pulling on either end of the rope are not well-matched, the rope will move in the direction of the stronger team. The stronger team has the greater force. If the teams are well-matched, then they will be pulling with equal strength. In this case, the forces on the rope are balanced. The result: the rope will not move.

Newton's first law is also referred to as the **law of inertia**. The tendency of an object to remain at rest or in motion is called **inertia**. Another way to think about inertia is that it is an object's resistance to a change in its motion. It is not a measurable property of an object but more of a qualitative description. You feel inertia when you are in a car that starts suddenly, stops suddenly, or goes around a sharp curve. When a car starts suddenly, the inertia of your body keeps you at rest even though the car moves forward. The result is that you feel pushed back into the seat, even though, the seat is actually being pushed into you! The opposite occurs when you are in a car that stops suddenly. The inertia of your body is going forward, but the car is stopping. The result is that you feel like your body is being thrown forward. When you are riding in a car that goes around a sharp curve, the inertia of your body keeps you moving in a straight line, but the car's motion is in the opposite direction. You feel pushed in the opposite direction. These are the forces that seatbelts are designed to counteract. The seatbelt stops at the same rate as the vehicle, and because it surrounds your body, it exerts a stopping force on your body.

Figure 11.5 Newton's 1st Law: Examples of Inertia

FRICTION

So, if Newton's first law is true, why does a ball slow down — and eventually stop — when you roll it down a long hallway? It slows down and stops because **frictional forces** are acting on the object in the opposite direction of motion. The forces of friction occur because of the interaction of an object with matter it is in contact with. If the object is moving along a surface that is rough, frictional forces will be stronger and slow the object down more quickly than if the surface was smooth. You only need to think about roller skating to understand this. Roller skating on carpet or grass is much harder than skating on linoleum or tile. The frictional force exerted by a smooth surface inhibits motion less than that exerted by a rough surface.

Friction occurs between any two surfaces in contact, because the irregularities on the surfaces interact with one another. These surfaces can be solids, liquids or gases. If you've ever skipped rocks on a lake, you know that the rock will slow down after a few skips and eventually, fall in. This occurs because the rock is slowed down by the frictional forces from the surface of the water. Frictional forces also apply when you bounce a ball across cement or if you throw a paper airplane through the air. In each case, frictional forces slow objects down — that is, they impede motion.

Let's take a closer look at types of friction.

1. **Static friction** is the force required to overcome inertia of a stationary object. In other words, it is the force required to start a stationary object in motion. This kind of friction is the hardest to overcome.

2. **Kinetic friction** is the force required to keep an object moving at a constant speed. Kinetic friction is less than static friction because the object is already in motion.

3. **Rolling friction** is the force required to keep an object rolling at a constant speed. Rolling friction is the easiest to overcome.

4. In all cases, friction is greater between rough surfaces than smooth surfaces. To further decrease friction, surfaces can be lubricated with a liquid such as oil or even water. Friction between a liquid and a solid is less than friction between two solids. Friction between a gas and a solid is even less.

NEWTON'S SECOND LAW OF MOTION

Newton's second law of motion states the mathematical relationship between force, mass and acceleration. Equation 11.4 relates force, mass and acceleration. The mass of an object multiplied by the acceleration of an object determines the force exerted by the object.

Equation 11.4

Force = mass × acceleration

$$F = ma$$

Utilize the Units!
The SI unit for mass is the kilogram (kg).
The SI unit for acceleration is the m/s^2.

$$kg \times \frac{m}{s^2} = \frac{kg \cdot m}{s^2} = a \text{ newton (N)}$$

So, the newton (N) is the SI unit for force.
Force is a vector quantity.

An important point about force is that it goes both ways. A force is the push or pull exerted *on* matter (it is a vector!), but it is also the push or pull exerted *by* matter. Newton's second law not only allows you to determine the amount of force that object can exert by its motion, but also the amount of force required to change the motion of the object.

A second point about the calculation of force is that mass and acceleration play equal roles. Look at Figure 11.6. A set of bowling pins at rest is experiencing balanced forces. In order to knock the pins down, a force must be applied to them that is unbalanced by another force. Obviously, the object applying this force will be a bowling ball. Is the mass of the bowling ball or the acceleration with which you throw it more important? They both are!

If you throw a bowling ball with a high acceleration, the bowling ball hits the pins with a large force, and you may get a strike. But, if a small child throws the same bowling ball with a low acceleration, then the ball will not hit the pins with as much force and only a few pins will be knocked down. Similarly, if you bowl with a basketball, which has a much lower mass than a bowling ball, the force it generates may not be enough to knock down many of the pins, even if you throw it quite hard.

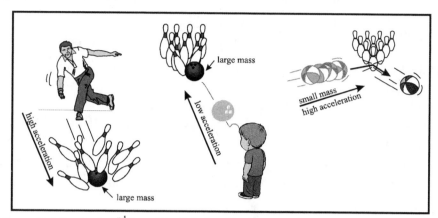

Figure 11.6 Newton's 2nd Law: The Relationship Between Force, Mass and Acceleration

Rearrange the terms of Equation 11.4 to see how mass and force affect acceleration. Writing F=ma as a=F/m shows that acceleration can be determined by dividing the force of an object by its mass.

Now, let's look briefly back to the point that force goes both ways. The bowling ball applied a force to the pins. But what applied force to the bowling ball? Well, the bowler did! The amount of force applied to the pins is directly related to (but not equal to) the amount of force applied by the bowler. Why aren't the forces equal? Because the motion of the bowling ball rolling down the alley was opposed by both the frictional force of the alley and the frictional force of air resistance. These frictional forces lowered the acceleration of the bowling ball, so that the force applied by the ball when it reached the pins was less than the initial force applied to the ball by the bowler.

NEWTON'S THIRD LAW OF MOTION

Newton's third law of motion is the law of action and reaction. It states that for every force or action, there is an equal and opposite force or reaction. Your book lying on your desk exerts a force on the desk. The desk exerts an equal and opposite force on the book. The force of the desk on the book is called the **normal force**. The word "normal" is a mathematical term that means at a 90° angle, or perpendicular, to the object.

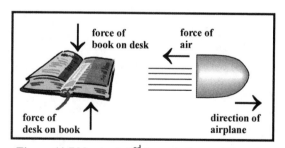

Figure 11.7 Newton's 3rd Law: Action and Reaction

You might recall from math class that when objects are perpendicular to each other, they are said to be normal to each other. The normal force is basically a resistance force of matter interacting with matter. It is actually an observable force because you don't ever see your book suddenly sink into the desk. The normal force of the desk onto the book has enough force to prevent this but not enough force to push the book into the air. Instead, they remain in contact.

In a jet engine, air is forced out in one direction, which then drives an airplane forward in the opposite direction. Although they are not shown in Figure 11.7, the plane also has forces exerted on it in the vertical direction. The weight of the plane acts as a downward force and air resistance acts as an upward, frictional force. When describing the motion of an object, it is helpful to visualize the motion by drawing a diagram of all the forces acting on the object. This type of diagram is called a **free body diagram**. Figure 11.7 shows some examples of free body diagrams for the motion of different objects.

Notice the arrows in Figure 11.7. They show the direction of the forces. Because force is a vector quantity, it can be described with vector diagrams, in which arrows show both direction and magnitude.

Take a look at the vector diagram in Figure 11.8 and see if you can figure out what it shows:

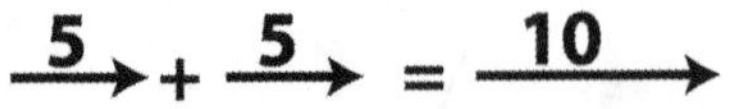

$$\underrightarrow{5} + \underrightarrow{5} = \underrightarrow{10}$$

Figure 11.8 Additive Vector Diagram

You have probably guessed that the diagram shows one force of 5 newtons (N) moving to the right, adding to another force of 5 N moving to the right. This equals a total force of 10 N moving to the right.

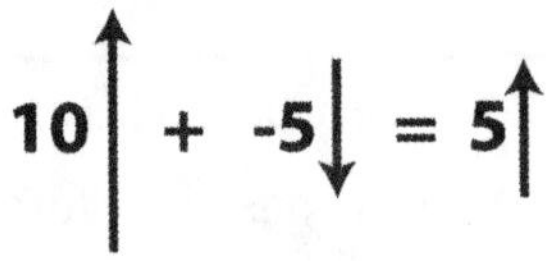

$$10\uparrow + -5\downarrow = 5\uparrow$$

Figure 11.9 Subtractive Vector Diagram

In Figure 11.9, we have something very different going on. There is a force of 10 N pushing up, and a force of 5 N pushing down, creating a net force of 5 N pushing up. A **net force** is the sum of all the forces acting on an object. Remember that forces have magnitude and direction (a vector) and if two forces are equally acting in opposite directions, they will cancel each other out! Give this a try on your own by working through the challenge activity on the next page.

Challenge Activity

This vector diagram corresponds to the discussion in the chapter. Use the diagram to answer the following questions.

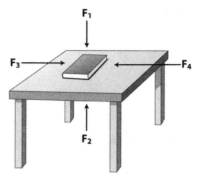

1. Define the four forces in the diagram, according to the discussion in the text.

    _____

2. If F_1 equals 9.81 N, what does F_2 equal?

    _____

3. Describe what must happen to the forces in order for the book to move to the left.

    _____

4. Describe what must happen to the forces in order for the book to move up.

    _____

5. Tom applies a force $F_3=12N$ to the book. Laura applies a force F_4 of 9N to the book. Draw a vector diagram that shows this in the space below. Indicate which direction the book will move.

Section Review 2:   Forces and Motion

A. Define the following terms.

force	frictional forces	newton
Newtonian mechanics	static friction	Newton's third law
Newton's first law	kinetic friction	normal force
law of inertia	rolling friction	free body diagram
inertia	Newton's second law	net force

B. Choose the best answer.

1. Which of the following is a force that can oppose or change motion?

   A.   gravity   B.   air resistance   C.   friction   D.   all of the above

2. A passenger in a car that suddenly stops will

   A.   lean forward.   C.   lean to the right.

   B.   lean backward.   D.   feel no motion.

3. A book lying on your desk will only move if

   A.   an unbalanced force acts on it.   C.   a normal force acts on it.

   B.   a downward force acts on it.   D.   the frictional force on it is reduced.

4. Mariah and Charley each pull at opposite ends of a rope. Charley is stronger. Who will move backwards?

   A.   The rope will move but Mariah and Charley won't.

   B.   Both Mariah and Charley will move backwards.

   C.   Mariah will move backwards.

   D.   Charley will move backwards.

5. A car engine works harder to accelerate from zero to 10 km/hr than it does to maintain a 10 km/hr velocity. Why is this?

   A.   Because static friction is harder to overcome than kinetic or rolling friction.

   B.   Because static friction is easier to overcome than kinetic or rolling friction.

   C.   Because static friction is harder to overcome than potential friction.

   D.   Because static friction is easier to overcome than potential friction.

THE FUNDAMENTAL FORCES

Most of the observations that we make every day can be described with Newtonian mechanics…but not all of them. Scientists became increasingly aware of situations where Newtonian mechanics did not adequately explain a phenomenon. Physicists, chemists and theorists began to discuss, hypothesize, theorize and debate, heatedly looking for the solutions to these apparent mathematical anomalies. Among those involved were Albert Einstein, Niels Bohr, Max Plank, Erwin Schrödinger and Werner Heisenberg. The result was a 20th century revolution in physical science. Thanks to the contributions of many great minds, observations that could not be easily explained by **classical mechanics** could now be explained by quantum and relativistic mechanics.

Quantum mechanics is the physics of the smallest pieces of matter. Without the powerful mathematical tools of quantum mechanics, the nature of matter in its most basic form cannot be explained. For instance, the behavior of the nucleus of an atom and the orbit of electrons around that nucleus are both completely contrary to Newtonian mechanics, but are easily explained in quantum mechanical terms.

Relativistic mechanics explains the physics of motion at speeds near the speed of light. It defines the speed of light ($c = 3.0 \times 10^8$ m/s) as a fundamental constant that plays a role in the way that space and time are tied together. Einstein's theory of special relativity also explains with the famous equation $E = mc^2$ that energy (E) and matter (m) are linked states.

Equation 11.5

Energy = mass × speed of light

$$E = mc^2$$

Utilize the Units!

The SI unit for mass is the kilogram.
The SI unit for speed is m/s.

$$kg \times \frac{m}{s} \times \frac{m}{s} = \frac{kg \cdot m^2}{s^2} = \text{a joule (J)}$$

The joule was named in honor of James Prescott Joule, as he discovered this quantity that related work to thermal energy. Note that a joule can also be described as a newton·meter (N·m)

So, the SI unit for energy is the joule (J).
Energy is a scalar quantity.

All forces can be divided into four **fundamental forces**. These are the gravitational force, the electromagnetic force, the weak nuclear force and the strong nuclear force. We will discuss each in turn and connect them to forces that are more familiar and directly observable. Of the four fundamental forces, you are probably most familiar with gravity.

Activity

Use an Internet search engine or wikipedia.com to search for information on one of the 20th century scientists mentioned above. Write an essay describing their contributions to modern physics.

GRAVITATIONAL FORCE

Sir Isaac Newton also formulated the **universal law of gravity**. This law states the following:

- Every object in the universe pulls on every other object;
- The more mass an object has, the greater its gravitational force (pull);
- The greater the distance between two objects, the less attraction they have for each other.

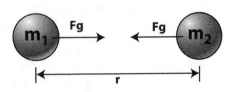

Figure 11.10 Attractive Gravitational Force Between Two Masses

Newton's law of gravitation is expressed in Equation 11.6.

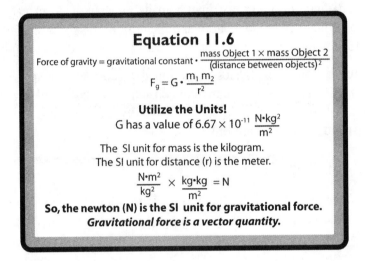

Equation 11.6

$$\text{Force of gravity} = \text{gravitational constant} \cdot \frac{\text{mass Object 1} \times \text{mass Object 2}}{(\text{distance between objects})^2}$$

$$F_g = G \cdot \frac{m_1 m_2}{r^2}$$

Utilize the Units!

G has a value of $6.67 \times 10^{-11} \frac{N \cdot kg^2}{m^2}$

The SI unit for mass is the kilogram.
The SI unit for distance (r) is the meter.

$$\frac{N \cdot m^2}{kg^2} \times \frac{kg \cdot kg}{m^2} = N$$

So, the newton (N) is the SI unit for gravitational force.
Gravitational force is a vector quantity.

The universal gravitational constant is necessary to correct the result of the equation (kg^2/m^2) to the correct unit for force (N). Even though the units of G look complicated, they are really just a way to translate the value obtained from the mass-distance infraction into units we are familiar with. This relationship is an example of the **inverse square law** in physical science: the gravitational force is proportional to the inverse square of the distance between the objects. So, gravitational force increases with increased mass and decreased distance.

Gravity gives the mass of an object its weight. Many people confuse the terms "mass" and "weight." Mass is *not* the same as weight. As we know, mass measures the amount of matter an object consists of. **Weight** is a measure of the force of gravity exerted on an object by the Earth. Weight depends on the mass of the object and its distance from the earth. In the SI measurement system, weight is measured in newtons, the same unit as force. Weight is calculated by using the same equation as given in Equation 11.4, Newton's second law.

Gravity is a force that attracts objects to one another. In other words, it is a force that pulls. Objects are pulled or accelerate toward the Earth at a rate of about 9.81 m/s². This is referred to as the **free-fall acceleration,** or the acceleration due to gravity. If you drop a ball, the Earth's gravity will cause that ball to accelerate towards the Earth's surface at 9.81 meters per second, each second. This value is not actually the same everywhere on Earth. However, for our calculations, we will assume that it is a constant. This value for acceleration can be substituted into Equation 11.4 and multiplied by mass to calculate weight. Since acceleration due to gravity on the Earth is different than the gravity on the Moon, you do not weigh the same on the Earth as you would on the Moon. Your mass, however, is constant. Equation 11.7 is the formula to calculate weight. It replaces "force" with "weight," and "acceleration" with "acceleration due to gravity." Using Newton's second law, we can express weight with the following equation where w is the weight and g is the acceleration due to gravity.

Equation 11.7

Weight = mass × acceleration due to gravity

$$W = mg$$

Utilize the Units!
g is the free fall acceleration, with units of m/s²
The SI unit for mass is the kilogram.

$$kg \times \frac{m}{s^2} = \frac{kg \cdot m}{s^2} = N$$

So, weight is a force, and its SI unit is the newton (N).
The force of weight is a vector quantity.

ELECTROMAGNETIC FORCE

The electromagnetic force should also be quite familiar to you, although you might think of it more naturally in terms of its component forces, the electrical force and the magnetic force. The **electrical force** causes static electricity and drives the flow of electric charge (electric current) in electrical conductors. The **magnetic force** is associated with magnets. These two forces are caused by their respective fields- in effect, the field produces the force.

The electric and magnetic fields are interconnected. For example, the presence of an electric field will actually produce a magnetic field. Similarly, a change in the magnetic field produces an electric field. Because the fields are so intimately linked, they are referred simply as the electromagnetic field. The **electromagnetic force** is the force exerted by the electromagnetic field on any charged particle.

We will discuss the everyday phenomena of electricity and magnetism in Chapter 12. For now, we will simply note how the electromagnetic force is different from the gravitational force. The gravitational force describes the push and pull of the components of the universe based on *mass and distance*. The electromagnetic force describes the push and pull of the components of the universe based on *charge and distance*. (Incidentally, the law describing electromagnetism is Coulomb's Law and it is another example of the inverse square law.)

The electromagnetic force is powerful down to a very tiny scale — it is the primary cause for the bonding between molecules and atoms. Inside the nucleus, however, even more powerful forces actually reside.

NUCLEAR FORCES

The nucleus of an atom contains protons and neutrons. If you think about this arrangement for a moment, you will realize that it means that the nucleus of the atom is packed with positively charged material (protons). There are no negative charges to balance the positive charge, because neutrons are neutral. That should seem unusual to you — opposites attract, right? Well, most of the time they do. In our everyday experience, opposite charges attract (and like charges repel) because of the electromagnetic force. However, the inside of a nucleus is not like any environment that we have ever seen.

In the nucleus, protons and neutrons are both referred to as **nucleons,** and they are held together in the nucleus by a force called the **nuclear force**. The nuclear force is *totally different* than the electromagnetic force — it has nothing at all to do with the charge of the nucleon. It is actually the result of the exchange of much smaller and more fundamental particles than the proton and neutron, particles called **mesons**. A full discussion of this subject is not merited at this stage — here, it is enough to understand that the nuclear force only operates between nucleons inside the nucleus, and only at very specific distances.

The typical separation of each nucleon from its nearest neighboring nucleon is about 1.3 femtometers (that is, 1.3×10^{-15} meters). That inter-nucleon distance is nearly constant because of the nuclear force. At 1.3 fm, the nuclear force is an *attractive* force of about 104 N, much stronger than the electrostatic force. At distances shorter than 1.3 fm, the nuclear force is very *repulsive,* forcing the protons and neutrons to keep that respectful 1.3 fm distance from one another. At distances farther than 1.3 fm, the nuclear force drops off quickly to zero. From that point outward, the electromagnetic force is dominant. For instance, two protons separated by 3 fm would exert powerful repulsive electromagnetic forces on one another, but be totally unaffected by the nuclear force.

To be clear, the nuclear force is actually two different forces: the strong nuclear force and the weak nuclear force. Both are short range interactions that operate within the atomic nucleus. The **strong nuclear force** holds the atomic nuclei together, as described above. The much weaker but very distinct **weak nuclear force**, causes changes in the nucleus that result in radioactive decay, particularly beta decay (see Chapter 7 for a review of nuclear process).

Section Review 3: The Fundamental Forces

A. Define the following terms.

quantum mechanics	universal law of gravity	electromagnetic force	mesons
relativistic mechanics	inverse square law	electrical force	magnetic force
fundamental forces	free-fall acceleration	weight	strong nuclear force
classical mechanics		nucleon	weak nuclear force

B. Choose the best answer.

1. Which force is responsible for chemical bonding?

   A. gravitational force

   B. electromagnetic force

   C. strong nuclear force

   D. weak nuclear force

2. Which force is responsible for radioactive decay by beta emission?

   A. gravitational force

   B. electromagnetic force

   C. strong nuclear force

   D. weak nuclear force

3. Which force is responsible for static electricity?

   A. gravitational force

   B. electromagnetic force

   C. strong nuclear force

   D. weak nuclear force

4. Steve drops a marble from the top of the bleachers in the gym. What is the marble's acceleration just after he releases the marble (a_{drop}) and the moment before it hits the floor (a_{floor})?

   A. $a_{drop} = 9.81$ m/s^2, $a_{floor} = 9.81$ m/s^2

   B. $a_{drop} = 9.81$ m/s^2, $a_{floor} = 0$ m/s^2

   C. $a_{drop} = 0$ m/s^2, $a_{floor} = 9.81$ m/s^2

   D. $a_{drop} = 0$ m/s^2, $a_{floor} = 0$ m/s^2

5. If the mass of the marble is 20 grams, what is the force (F) with which the marble hits the floor?

   A. 196.2 kg m/s^2

   B. 19.62 kg m/s^2

   C. 1.962 kg m/s^2

   D. 0.196 kg m/s^2

C. Answer the following questions.

1. The gravitational pull of Mars is less than the gravitational pull of Earth. Would you weigh more or less on Mars than you do on Earth? Explain why you think so.

2. If an object weighs 49 N on Earth, how much does it weigh on the moon if the gravitational acceleration of the moon is approximately 1.63 m/s^2? HINT: Solve for mass first. Then calculate the weight on the moon.

WORK

We described how forces can change the motion of an object. A change in the motion of an object is a change in its kinetic energy. When a force is applied over a distance, it is called **work**. To calculate work, multiply the force applied to an object by the distance that the object moves, as shown in Equation 11.8. An object can have multiple forces applied to it at any given time, but unless it moves, no work is being done.

Equation 11.8

Work = force × distance

$$W = Fd$$

Utilize the Units!
The SI unit for force is the Newton (N).
The SI unit for distance is the meter (m).

N × m = N•m = a joule (J)

So, the SI unit for work is the joule (J).

Example: Jason moved a chair 2 meters using 10 newtons of force. How much work did he do?

Step 1. Set up the equation: $W = Fd$

Step 2. Insert the known information. In this problem, the force is 10 N and the distance is 2 m.

Therefore, the equation becomes $W = (10\ N) \cdot (2\ m)$

Step 3. Solve: $W = 20\ J$

Practice Exercise 3: Work

Use the equation for work to answer the following problems.

1. How much work does Bill do if he uses 15 N of force to move a ladder 30 m?

2. How far was a box of books moved if Mike used a force of 50 N by expending 300 joules?

3. What force was applied by Cedrick if he moved a table 11 m by expending 990 joules?

4. How much work was done by Amy if she lifted her 12 N book bag 1.2 meters?
   (Remember, weight is a force.)

Machines make work easier by changing the speed, the direction or the amount of effort needed to move an object. **Effort force** is the force exerted by a person or a machine to move the object. The **resistance force** is the force exerted by the object that opposes movement (equals the weight of the object in newtons). A machine can change the amount of effort force needed to overcome the resistance force of an object. Figure 11.11 shows the six types of simple machines: pulley, wheel and axle, screw, inclined plane, wedge and lever.

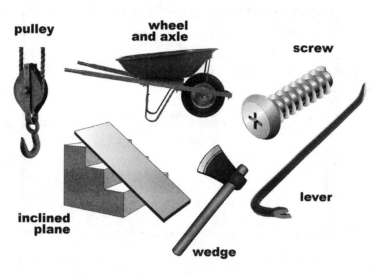

Figure 11.11 Examples of Machines

The number of times a machine increases the effort force is called the **mechanical advantage**. Mechanical advantage, MA, equals resistance force, F_r, divided by effort force, F_e, as given in Equation 11.9. Friction decreases the mechanical advantage of a machine. Recall from earlier in this chapter that **friction** is resistance to motion. Lubricating two surfaces decreases the friction between them, making movement easier.

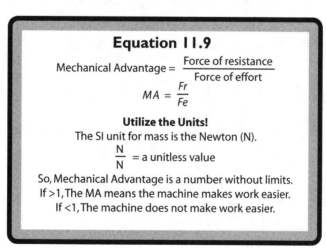

Equation 11.9

$$\text{Mechanical Advantage} = \frac{\text{Force of resistance}}{\text{Force of effort}}$$

$$MA = \frac{Fr}{Fe}$$

Utilize the Units!
The SI unit for mass is the Newton (N).

$$\frac{N}{N} = \text{a unitless value}$$

So, Mechanical Advantage is a number without limits.
If >1, The MA means the machine makes work easier.
If <1, The machine does not make work easier.

Example 1: The Inclined Plane

The inclined plane, or ramp, allows you to overcome a large resistance force by applying a smaller effort force over a longer distance. The mechanical advantage comes from the ratio of the length of the ramp (L) to the height of the ramp (h), as in:

$$\frac{L}{h} = \frac{F_r}{F_e} \qquad \textbf{Equation 11.10}$$

To illustrate, let's look at two scenarios that confront Pete, who wants to lift a 100N box a vertical distance of 1 meter into the back of a moving van.

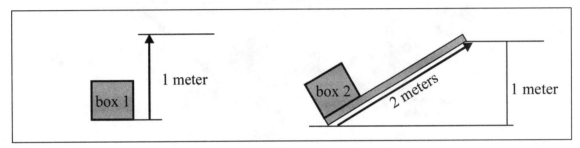

Figure 11.12 The Advantage of Using an Inclined Plane

In scenario A, Pete lifts the box straight up. The work that he does is:

$$W = F \times d = 100N \times 1m = 100\ J$$

In scenario B, Pete chooses to push the box up a 2 meter ramp to get it into the van. The work that he does is the same, 100J. The reason is that the weight is distributed by the angle of the ramp. Pete actually only has to push part of the weight of the box up the ramp. Let's find out how much MA he's gained.

From Equation 11.9 and 11.10, you can see that the mechanical advantage of the inclined plane equals the length of the plane divided by the height (h) of the plane's terminal end (L).

$$MA = \frac{L}{h} = \frac{2\ meters}{1\ meter} = 2$$

That means that Pete's effort force, when using the plane, is

$$F_e = \frac{F_r}{MA} = \frac{100\ N}{2} = 50\ N$$

So, the incline plane made the work *easier*. You know it was easier, because it required a lower effort force to move the box up the ramp than it did to lift it straight up.

In real life, an inclined plane will have friction that opposes motion. Remember, friction decreases mechanical advantage. What would be the mechanical advantage of the inclined plane if Pete had to apply an additional 10 N of force to overcome friction as he pushed the box up the inclined plane?

$$MA = \frac{F_r}{F_e} = \frac{100 \text{ N}}{50 \text{ N} + 10 \text{ N}} = \frac{100 \text{ N}}{60 \text{ N}} = 1\frac{2}{3}$$

The force necessary to move the box up the inclined plane is still less than lifting it vertically, but friction increases the effort force and, therefore, decreases the mechanical advantage.

*Test hint: The mechanical advantage of a frictionless inclined plane will always be the length of the plane (in our example, 2 meters) divided by the height of the plane's terminal end (in our example, 1 meter).

Example 2: The Lever

Another simple machine is the lever. The important parts of a lever are the **fulcrum**, which supports and distributes weight, the resistance arm and the effort arm. The mechanical advantage of a lever comes from manipulating the length of the arms: L_e is the length of the effort (or lifting) arm and L_r is the length of the resistance arm. The equation is:

$$\frac{L_e}{L_r} = \frac{F_r}{F_e}$$

A seesaw is a perfect example of a lever. On a seesaw, the fulcrum is placed in the center, between two equal length arms…which means that its mechanical advantage is one, right? Well, yes, because a seesaw is made for fun, not work.

Figure 11.13 Seesaw- Example of a Lever

So think about a modified seesaw, where one side (L_e) is 2 meters and the other (L_r) is 0.5 meters. The mechanical advantage of this lever is

$$MA = \frac{L_e}{L_r} = \frac{2 \text{ meters}}{0.5 \text{ meters}} = 4$$

Now, if Wanda puts her 6N bookbag at the end of the resistance arm (that is the short arm), what kind of effort force must be used to lift it 3 meters? That is:

$$F_e = \frac{F_r}{MA} = \frac{6 \text{ N}}{4} = 1.5 \text{ N}$$

So, Wanda needs to apply 6N of effort force to lift the bookbag by herself, but only 1.5N of effort force to lift it using the lever. Now *that* is a mechanical advantage!

Example 3: The Pulley

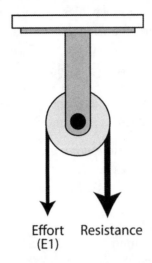

Figure 11.14 The Fixed Pulley

In the simplest arrangement, a pulley is **fixed** and **immovable** (Figure 11.14). In this arrangement, a 100 N load will require a 100 N of effort, that is, the mechanical advantage is 1 (100 N/100N).

$$ MA = \frac{F_r}{F_e} = \frac{100N}{100N} = 1 $$

Although this does not reduce the effort required to lift heavy loads, it does allow you to change the direction that you must lift. Instead of lifting an object up, you can pull down in order to lift up. This lets you use your body weight to help in the lifting.

A **moveable** pulley is more versatile. This type of pulley hangs from a rope attached at one end. The effort force is split, as shown in Figure 11.15.

A moveable pulley has a greater mechanical advantage than a fixed pulley because both sides of the rope exert an equal effort force on the load. That means that the man pulling on one side of the rope is only exerting half of the effort force.

$$ MA = \frac{F_r}{F_e} $$

$$ = \frac{100N}{50N} = 2 $$

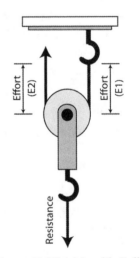

Figure 11.15 A Movable Pulley

More complex pulley systems can be designed by attaching pulley to one another. This is known as the "**block and tackle**." Figure 11.16 consists of a block and tackle that combines a fixed and moveable pulley. The MA of this set-up is the same as that of the movable pulley, that is MA=2. This is the same mechanical advantage as in a normal movable pulley, but the difference is that the addition of the fixed pulley allows the rope to be pulled downward, rather than upward, to lift the load.

Figure 11.17 shows a movable plus movable block and tackle system. Looping the rope through these pulleys gives a mechanical advantage of 4 because each length of rope carries an equal amount of force. This means that the final effort force is a quarter of what is would be without the two movable pulleys.

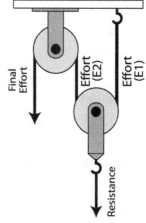

Figure 11.16 Fixed + Movable Block and Tackle System

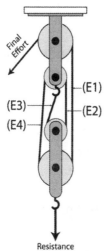

Figure 11.17 Movable + Movable Block and Tackle System

*Test Tip: If you add up the number of rope segments that go both to and from a moveable pulley, you will have the mechanical advantage of that pulley. Remember not to add in the rope segment going from the fixed pulley; all it does is change the direction that the rope is pulled.

Section Review 4: Work and Mechanical Advantage

A. Define the following terms.

work	resistance force	pulley
machines	mechanical advantage	inclined plane
effort force	lever	fulcrum
block and tackle		

B. Choose the best answer.

1. Which simple machine would be the most useful for reducing the effort force need to lift a large box into a pickup truck?

   A. lever   B. inclined plane   C. wedge   D. pulley

2. Larry uses a hammer to nail two boards together. Which simple machine can be found at the point of the nail?

   A. screw   B. lever   C. pulley   D. wedge

3. The weight of a rock is 100 newtons. Using a lever, the rock was lifted using 80 newtons of force. What was the mechanical advantage of the lever?

   A. 1.25   B. 2   C. 0.8   D. 180

4. A man used a lever to lift a boulder. The lifting arm is 2 m long. The resistance arm is 1.5 m long. What is the mechanical advantage?

   A. 3   B. 0.25   C. 3.5   D. 1.33

C. Use the picture to answer the following questions.

1. Describe this simple machine.

2. What is the mechanical advantage of this system?

3. The man is pulling at an odd angle. How could he improve his leverage?

4. In the picture, the man lifts a barrel weighing 40 newtons. What force must be exerted to lift the barrel?

CHAPTER 11 REVIEW

Choose the best answer.

The graph to the right shows the motion of a roller coaster from the beginning of the ride to the end. Use the graph to answer questions 1 and 2.

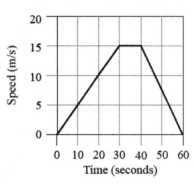

Roller Coaster Motion

1. Calculate the acceleration of the roller coaster for the first 30 seconds of the ride.

    A. 0 m/s^2

    B. 15 m/s^2

    C. 2 m/s^2

    D. 0.5 m/s^2

2. Identify the motion of the roller coaster during the first 30 seconds, the middle 10 seconds and the final 20 seconds of the ride.

    A.   acceleration, constant speed, negative acceleration

    B.   acceleration, stopped, acceleration back to starting point

    C.   constant speed up hill, stopped at top of hill, acceleration down hill

    D.   constant speed up hill, constant speed at top, constant speed down hill

3. Identify the changes in mass and distance between two objects that act together to produce an increase in the gravitational force between those two objects.

    A.   increased mass and increased distance   C.   decreased mass and increased distance

    B.   increased mass and decreased distance   D.   decreased mass and increased distance

4. An object is taken from the Earth to the Moon. Identify the statement that describes the mass and weight of the object on the Moon compared to its mass and weight on Earth.

    A.   Mass is the same and weight is the same on the Moon.

    B.   Mass is greater and weight is greater on the Moon.

    C.   Mass is the same and weight is less on the Moon.

    D.   Mass is less and weight is less on the Moon.

5. Which surface will exert the most friction on a rolling ball?

    A.   grass   B.   concrete   C.   glass   D.   gravel

6. Which of the following describes the rules of motion for objects on a very small scale?
   A. Newtonian mechanics
   B. relativistic mechanics
   C. quantum mechanics
   D. classical mechanics

7. Two pinballs, each with a mass of 1.0 kilograms, are placed 0.50 meters apart from each other. What is the attractive gravitational force between the pinballs?
   A. 4.0G   B. 0.50G   C. 0.25G   D. 5.0G

8. The two inclined planes in the diagram come together to form what other simple machine?

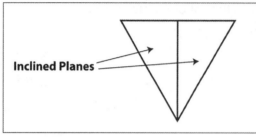

Inclined Planes

   A. lever   B. wedge   C. pulley   D. screw

Use the following scenario to answer questions 9 – 11.

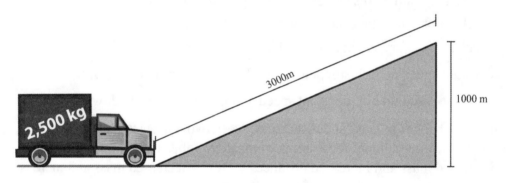

9. What is the mechanical advantage of this inclined plane?
   A. 3000   B. 300   C. 30   D. 3

10. What effort force would be required for a helicopter to lift the truck up 10 m?
    A. 245,000 N   B. 24,500 N   C. 2,500 N   D. 2,450 N

11. How much effort force would be required for a bulldozer to push the truck up the mountain?
    A. 245,000 N   B. 81,667 N   C. 300 N   D. 30 N

Chapter 12
Electricity and Magnetism

GA HSGT SCIENCE STANDARDS COVERED IN THIS CHAPTER INCLUDE:

GPS Standards	
SPS10 a – c	Students will investigate the properties of electricity and magnetism.

ELECTROMAGNETIC FORCE

In the last chapter, electromagnetic force was introduced as one of the four fundamental forces. The electromagnetic force can be divided into two distinct but inseparable elements: the electric field and the magnetic field. Each of these fields generates a force. In this chapter, we will explore both components of the electromagnetic force.

ELECTRIC FORCE AND FIELD

There are four major forces of nature. The electric force, which involves charged particles, both positive and negative, is one of these forces. The **electric force** between two charged particles is described by **Coulomb's Law**, which is expressed mathematically in Equation 12.1. Although this equation looks confusing, the important points to remember are:

- Charged particles exert forces on each other.

- Like charges repel; opposite charges attract.

- The greater the distance between charges, the less force they will exert on each other.

Coulomb's law is shown in Equation 12.1.

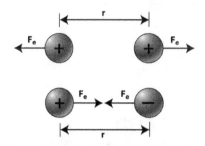

Figure 12.1 Electric Force Between Two Charged Particles

Equation 12.1

Electrostatic force $= k_e \times \dfrac{\text{(charge particle 1} \cdot \text{charge particle 2)}}{\text{(distance between particles)}^2}$

$$F_e = k_e \frac{q_1 \cdot q_2}{r^2}$$

Utilize the Units!

k_e is the Coulomb constant, equal to 8.998×10^9 Nm²/C².
The SI unit for charge is the Coulomb (C).
The SI unit for distance is the meter (m).

$$\frac{\text{N} \cdot \text{m}^2}{\text{C}^2} \times \frac{\text{C} \cdot \text{C}}{\text{m}^2} = \text{the newton (N)}$$

So, the SI unit for electrostatic force is the Newton (N).

When the two charges have the same sign, they repel one another. When they have opposite signs, they attract each other. Notice that the equation for electric force has the same form as the equation for gravitational force but charge replaces mass, and the constants are different. While the electric force can be attractive or repulsive, the gravitational force can only be attractive.

Recall that atoms are made of a positively charged nucleus surrounded by negatively charged electrons. The attractive electrical force between these charges is what holds the atom together.

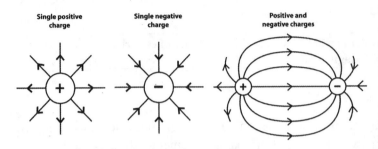

Figure 12.2 Electric Field Lines

The concept of an **electric field** helps to visualize the effects electric charges have on one another. An electric field surrounds every electric charge. If a test charge (a small, charged particle) were placed in the electric field of a charged particle, a force would be exerted upon it. The **electric field lines** or **lines of force** point in the direction that a positive charge would move when in the presence of an electric field. A positively charged particle would be repelled by a positive charge and attracted by a negative charge. Thus, electric field lines always point away from positive source charges and towards negative source charges. Electric field lines do not actually exist in the physical world; they are simply used to illustrate the direction of the electric force exerted on charged particles. The strength of the field surrounding a charged particle is dependent on how charged the particle generating the field is and separation distance between the charged objects.

ELECTRICITY

Electricity describes the movement of electrons in response to a field. Electrons may be channeled through a material, or they may arc out on their own. For electrons to flow through a material, it must have a structure that allows for the free movement of electrons. This type of material is called a **conductor**. Metals are usually good conductors. For instance, copper is a metal commonly used to safely conduct electrons from one place to another; this is called **current electricity.**

Materials that do not allow electrons to move freely through them are called **insulators**. Ionic and covalent solids are usually insulators. Since charge cannot move efficiently through an insulator, it will often build up on its surface. Insulators often accumulate and transmit **static electricity** in this way.

STATIC ELECTRICITY

We experience static electricity in everyday life in the form of a shock when we touch a metallic object after dragging our feet along the carpet, or the standing up of our hair when we take off a winter hat. **Static electricity** occurs as a result of excess positive or negative charges on an object's surface. Static electricity is built up in three ways: friction, induction and conduction.

Figure 12.3 Static Electricity

Rubbing two objects together will often generate static electricity through **friction**. Some electrons are held more loosely than others in an atom. The loosely held electrons can be rubbed off and transferred to the other object. Static electricity occurs when an object gains electrons (giving the object a negative charge) or an object loses electrons (giving it a positive charge). Rubbing a balloon on carpet or combing your hair with a hard plastic comb on a dry day causes static electricity to build up. Like charges repel, and unlike charges attract. Rub two balloons on the carpet and then slowly move the balloons together. Both balloons will have the same negative charge, and you should be able to feel the mild repulsive force. The charged balloon or comb, however, will attract small pieces of paper or other small, light objects having an opposite positive charge. These attractive or repulsive forces are weak forces, but they can overcome the force of gravity for very light objects.

Quick Challenge

Which electrons would be most easily rubbed off and transferred to another object?

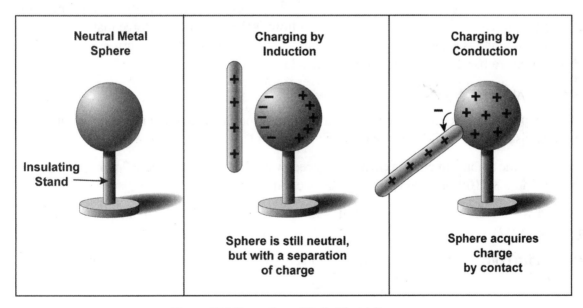

Figure 12.4 Generation of Static Electricity

Electrical charge generated by **induction** occurs when a charged object is brought near — but not touching — an insulator. Molecules within the uncharged object begin to shift, with the negative side of the molecule moving closer to the positively charged object.

Electrical charge can also be generated by **conduction**. Conduction occurs when two objects, one charged and one neutral, are brought into contact with one another. The excess charge from the charged object will flow into the neutral object, until the charge of both objects is balanced.

Lightning is another example of static electricity. The actual lightning bolt that we see is a result of electric discharge from clouds that have built up too much excess charge.

CURRENT ELECTRICITY

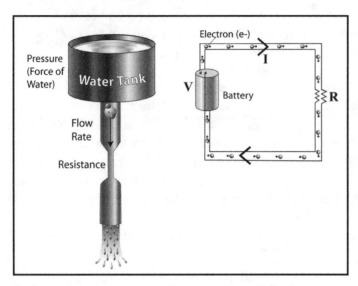

Figure 12.5 Analogy Between Flowing Water and Electric Current

To understand **current electricity**, let's compare electricity to the water flowing through a pipe. The flow rate of water in a pipe might be given in units of gallons per minute. In an electrical circuit, electrons flow through the circuit like water flows through a pipe. **Current (I)** is the flow rate of electrons through the circuit and is measured in **amperes**. As water flowing through a pipe rubs against the walls of the pipe, the water slows down. In the same way, electrons slow down as they move through a circuit. This slowing down of the electrons is called resistance. **Resistance (R)** is the measure of how difficult it is to move electrons through a circuit. Why does water flow through a pipe? A force like gravity or the force of a pump causes water to flow. **Voltage (V)** is the force that moves electrons through a circuit and is measured in **volts**. In other words, voltage drives the current in a circuit. In an electrical circuit, a battery commonly produces this force.

ELECTRICAL UNITS

The unit **ampere** expresses the rate of flow of the electrons past a given point in a given amount of time. One ampere is equal to the flow of one coulomb per second.

A **coulomb** is the amount of electric charge produced by a current of one ampere flowing for one second, and is equal to 6.3×10^{18} times the charge of an electron.

Resistance is the measure of how difficult it is to move electrons through a conductor. Resistance has units of **ohms (Ω)**.

Potential difference (voltage) is measured in **volts**, or joules of work done per coulomb of charge.

OHM'S LAW

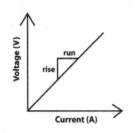

$$\frac{rise}{run} = \frac{voltage}{current} = resistance$$

Figure 12.6 Current - Voltage Relationship

Ohm's Law states that the resistance is equal to the voltage divided by the current as shown in Equation 12.2.where resistance has units of **ohms** (Ω).You may notice that Ohm's law reveals a linear relationship between voltage and current. Given a linear graph of voltage versus current, the slope of the line (i.e. rise over run) is equal to the resistance. Thus, the resistance of a device can be determined experimentally by taking several voltage and current measurements, then plotting the data on a graph. Not all electronic devices have this linear relationship between voltage and current. Those that do have a linear relationship are called ohmic devices.

Ohm's law is more frequently written in the form shown in Equation 12.2. Ohm's law can be used to calculate either resistance, voltage, or current when two of the three quantities are known.

Example: A flashlight bulb with an operating resistance of 50 ohms is connected to a 9.0 V battery. What is the current through the light bulb?

Step 1. Set up the equation: $V = I \cdot R$

Step 2. Insert the known information: $9.0 \text{ V} = I \cdot 50 \text{ Ω}$

Step 3. Solve: $I = \dfrac{9.0 \text{ V}}{50 \text{ Ω}} = 0.18 \text{ A}$

Equation 12.2
Ohm's Law

Voltage = Current × Resistance

$$V = IR$$

Utilize the Units!

The SI unit for voltage is the volt (V).

$$1 \text{ volt} = \frac{1 \text{ joule}}{1 \text{ coulomb}}$$

The SI unit for current is the ampere (A).

$$1 \text{ ampere} = \frac{1 \text{ coulomb}}{\text{second}}$$

The SI unit for resistance is the ohm (Ω).

$$1 \text{ ohm } Ω = \frac{1 \text{ volt}}{\text{amp}}$$

The volt was named for Italian physicist Alessandro Volta, who invented the voltaic pile (the first chemical battery). The ampere is named in honor of the French physicist André-Marie Ampère for his contributions to the discovery of electromagnetism. The ohm is named in honor of German physicist George Ohm, who established the fundamental relationship between voltage, current and resistance that today we call Ohm's Law.

ELECTRICAL CIRCUITS

Electricity is a form of energy caused by moving electrons called electric current. The path through which the electricity is conducted is called a **circuit**. When we draw electrical circuits, we use the symbols shown in Figure 12.7 to represent voltage sources, resistors and wires. **Batteries** are commonly used as voltage sources. Devices such as radios and televisions draw current from the circuit, and so provide resistance to the flow of electricity. These devices, or **loads**, are usually

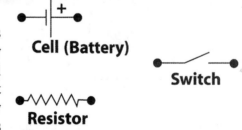

Figure 12.7 Symbols for Circuit Elements

represented as a simple resistor in circuit diagrams. There are two types of circuits: series and parallel circuits.

Ohm's law (Equation 12.2) can be used to determine the voltage, current or resistance in simple circuits, provided enough information is given.

SERIES CIRCUITS

In a **series circuit**, all current is the same through each part or load. If a resistor is broken or damaged, current will no longer be able to flow through a series circuit.

Figure 12.8 Series Circuit

We can use the symbols from Figure 12.7 to represent the series circuit as a **circuit diagram**. The three resistors represent the resistance provided by each light bulb. In a series circuit, you can determine the total equivalent resistance of the circuit by adding the individual resistance values. Equation 12.3 illustrates this relationship.

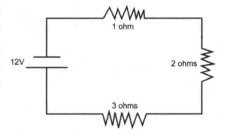

Figure 12.9 Series Circuit

$$R_{eq} = R_1 + R_2 + R_3 \qquad \textbf{Equation 12.3}$$

Thus, adding a resistor in series increases the overall resistance of the circuit. All resistors in a series have the same amount of current, or amperage.

A **switch** may be used to open and close the circuit. When the switch is open, electricity will not flow through a series circuit.

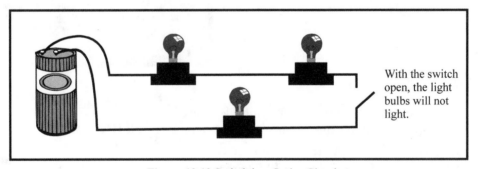

With the switch open, the light bulbs will not light.

Figure 12.10 Switch in a Series Circuit

Figure 12.10 is shown as a circuit diagram in Figure 12.11.

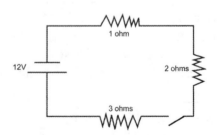

Figure 12.11 Series Circuit with Switch

Challenge Question 1

Determine the equivalent resistance of the circuits shown in Figures 12.9 and 12.11.

PARALLEL CIRCUITS

A **parallel circuit** has more than one path for the electricity to flow. The voltage is the same through all of the resistors in the circuit. If one path is removed or broken, current will still be able to flow in a parallel circuit. Most households are wired with parallel circuits, so that when you turn off a light, the television doesn't turn off as well.

A parallel circuit

Figure 12.12 Parallel Circuit

We can also represent a parallel circuit with a circuit diagram using the symbols shown in Figure 12.13. The overall resistance of a parallel circuit is reduced as more resistors are added. Thus, more current flows through the circuit. The equivalent resistance of a parallel circuit is expressed by Equation 12.5 below.

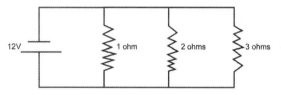

Figure 12.13 Parallel Circuit

$$\frac{1}{R_{eq}} = \frac{1}{R_1} + \frac{1}{R_2} + \frac{1}{R_3} \qquad \textbf{Equation 12.5}$$

Challenge Question 2

Determine the equivalent resistance of the circuits shown in Figure 12.13.

Practice Exercise 1: Series and Parallel Circuits

Draw the appropriate circuit diagram based on the descriptions given. Determine the equivalent resistance (R_{eq}) in each circuit. For #1 and #2, determine the current (I) running through the circuit also.

1. Two light bulbs, one with a resistance of 100 ohms and one with a resistance of 150 ohms, are connected in series to a 25-V battery.

2. Three resistors, all with a resistance of 50 ohms, are connected in parallel to a 9-V battery.

3. A strand of lights with five bulbs are connected to a 120-V voltage source. When one bulb goes out, the other four bulbs go out as well.

4. A strand of lights with four bulbs are connected to a 210-V voltage source. When one bulb goes out, the remaining bulbs stay lit.

Activity

Identify the following circuits as either parallel or series.

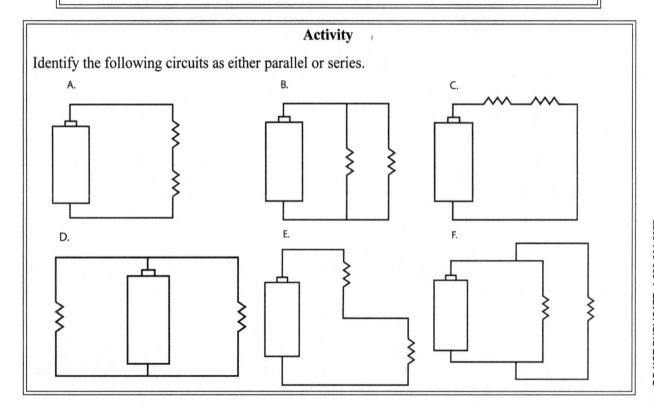

A.

B.

C.

D.

E.

F.

Section Review 1: Electric Force and Electricity

A. Define the following terms.

electric force	electrical conductor	conduction	coulomb
Coulomb's law	superconductor	current electricity	potential difference
electric field	static electricity	current	volt
electric field lines	friction	resistance	Ohm's Law
electricity	induction	voltage	ohms
		ampere	

B. Choose the best answer.

1. A switch is inserted into a series circuit of Christmas lights. During the night, the switch is left open. The lights will

    A. continue to burn.   C. become a parallel circuit.

    B. be turned off.   D. burn brighter.

2. A series and a parallel circuit each have two resistors of 2Ω each. A third 2Ω resistor is then added. The overall resistance of the _____ circuit _____.

    A. parallel, increases   C. parallel, decreases

    B. series, increases   D. B and C only

3. A series circuit has three resistors. R1 = 2 ohms, R2 = 2 ohms and R3 = 3 ohms. What is the total resistance of the circuit, and what will happen if R3 fails?

    A. The total resistance of 0.75 ohms will increase to 2 ohms when R3 fails.

    B. The total resistance of 7 ohms will decrease to 4 ohms if R3 fails.

    C. The total resistance of 0.75 ohms will decrease to 0 ohms of R3 fails.

    D. The total resistance of 7 ohms will increase infinitely; current will not flow if R3 fails.

Use the following figure to answer questions 4 and 5.

4. Batteries can also be connected in series or parallel. The batteries in this flashlight

    A. are connected in series.   C. are connected in parallel.

    B. are resisters.   D. are loads.

5. Turning one battery around

    A. makes it a parallel circuit.

    B. allows the flashlight to burn brighter.

    C. opens a switch, so electricity will not flow.

    D. closes a switch, so electricity will not flow.

MAGNETISM AND MAGNETIC FORCE

A **magnet** is a metallic substance capable of attracting iron and certain other metals. It has a north and south pole which creates a **magnetic field** consisting of invisible lines of force around the magnet between the two poles. These invisible lines, called **magnetic field lines**, always point from the north pole to the south pole of a magnet. The earth acts as a giant magnet having a North Pole and a South Pole, and the magnetic field circles the earth longitudinally.

A **compass** contains a small, thin magnet mounted on a pivot point. The end of the magnet that points toward the earth's geographic North Pole is labeled as the north pole of the magnet; correspondingly, the end that points south is the south pole of the magnet.

The Earth's current *geographic north* is thus actually its *magnetic south.*

To avoid confusion between geographic and magnetic north and south poles, the terms *positive* and *negative* are sometimes used for the poles of a magnet. The positive pole is that which seeks geographical north.

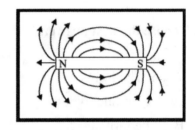

Figure 12.15 Field Lines in a Magnet

The like poles on two magnets exhibit a repulsive (magnetic) force, but two unlike poles exhibit an attractive force. For example, the north pole of one magnet will repel the north pole of another magnet, but the north pole of one magnet will attract the south pole of another magnet.

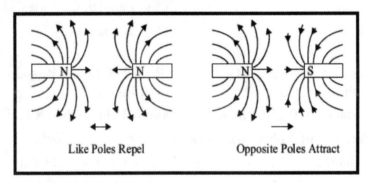

Figure 12.16 Interaction of North and South Poles

Natural occurring magnets are found as the mineral **magnetite**, Fe_3O_4 (s). Discovery of this mineral led to the ancient use of the **lodestone,** a primitive compass. In modern times, most magnets are man-made from a mixture of iron and other metals. A **bar magnet** is a man-made magnet, commonly used to illustrate the properties of magnetism.

Let's look inside a bar magnet to find out what makes it magnetic. Using a powerful microscope to look into a magnetic material, you would see that its atoms are aligned in a regular pattern, a series of tiny poles arranged end on end, as in Figure 12.17.

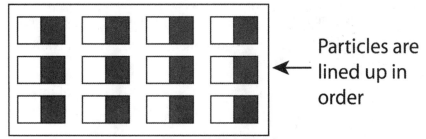

Particles are lined up in order

Figure 12.17 A Bar Magnet

So there is no *one* north or south pole in a magnet, but many. The accumulation of these poles creates the magnetic field, resulting in a magnet with an overall north and south pole.

Think of a line of people, each facing the back of the person in front of them. There is no one place where all the faces or the backs are, but the line as a whole has a beginning (the face of the first person) and an end (the back of the last person). What happens if you ask the two people in the middle of the line to separate? Now you have two lines, each with a beginning and an end. The same thing happens if you break a magnet in half. You create two new magnets, each with its own north and south pole.

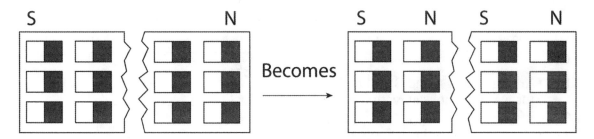

Becomes

Figure 12.18 Breaking a Bar Magnet

The magnet can be subdivided again and again, but at some point (depending on its original size) the divisions become too small to maintain a magnetic field. The magnet has no long-term internal order and is now just a piece of de-magnetized metal. To see this, think of the line of people again. You can keep dividing the line of people, creating more and smaller lines, until you just have a bunch of individual people standing around.

This is one way to **de-magnetize** a magnet or remove its magnetic quality. Other ways include heating it to a high temperature or dropping it. Both physical actions will upset the internal order of the magnet, and destroy its field.

Section Review 2: Magnetism and Magnetic Force

A. Define the following terms.

bar magnet   magnetic field   magnetic field lines   compass

de-magnetize   magnetite   lodestone

B. Chose the best answer.

1. The magnetic field lines of a magnet always point from the magnet's

     A. north pole to its south pole.

     B. south pole to its north pole.

     C. south pole to the north pole of another magnet.

     D. south pole to the south pole of another magnet.

Use the following Figure to answer questions 2 and 3.

2. Correctly arrange the poles of the magnets in the following diagram so that each magnet is attracted to the next, forming one continuous bar magnet.

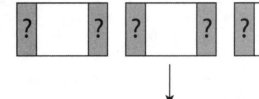

     A. N-S-N-S-N-S

     B. S-N-S-N-S-N

     C. N-S-S-N-N-S

     D. Arrangements A and B will both form a continuous attraction.

3. Once formed, what is the net polarity of the continuous magnet?

     A. N-S

     B. S-N

     C. Either N-S or S-N, depending on the original arrangement.

     D. The continuous magnet will be demagnetized, with no net polarity.

C. Answer the following questions.

1. In a magnetic compass, explain why the needle points north. What characteristics of Earth cause a magnetic compass to work? What material(s) must the needle be made of?

2. Why do like poles on magnets repel? Draw a diagram to show the magnetic forces around two magnets and use the diagram to explain your answer.

3. Name two ways to de-magnetize a material, and describe why the material loses its magnetic character.

ELECTROMAGNETIC FORCE AND FIELDS

An electric current, as described in a previous section, can produce a magnetic field and, thus, a magnetic force. We know from Newton's third law that for every action there is an equal and opposite reaction. Therefore, it stands to reason that a magnet must exert a force on a wire carrying an electric current. As you can tell from this phenomenon, the electric and magnetic forces are intimately related. They are actually considered to be one force, called the **electromagnetic force**, which is one of the four fundamental forces of nature.

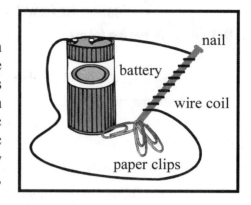

Figure 12.19 Electromagnet

Electrical and magnetic fields are related. For example, a magnetic field can be created by winding a wire around a conducting core and passing electricity through the wire. This type of man-made magnet is called an **electromagnet**. The magnetic field of an electromagnet can be strengthened by the number of turns in the wire coil or by the amount of electric current going through the wire. More coils, more current or greater voltage equates to larger magnetic force. Note that the current used to create an electromagnet is **direct current** or **DC**, which is the kind of current produced by a battery. Direct current flows in only one direction.

When an electromagnet is placed between the poles of a permanent magnet, the poles attract and repel each other as the electromagnet spins. Electrical energy is converted to mechanical energy. Electromagnets become more powerful as the amount of applied current to them is increased. They are often used to lift heavy metal objects, carry them and set them down again by turning off the current.

Not only can an electrical current create a magnetic field, but a magnet can produce an electric current by moving the magnet through a coil. Creating an electric current using a magnet is called **electromagnetic induction**. **Electric generators** are devices that use electromagnetic induction to create electricity. Figure 12.20 is a simple diagram of electromagnetic induction. Note that the magnet or the coils must be in motion in order for an electric current to be generated. The direction that the electrons travel depends on the direction that the magnet travels.

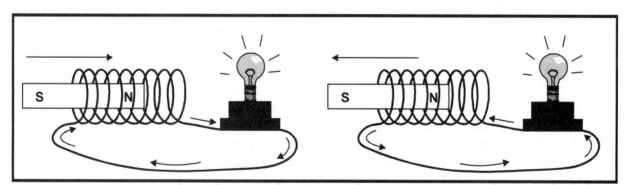

Figure 12.20 Electromagnet Induction

In the United States, electric power generators produce electricity by turning a coil between north and south poles of a magnet. Each time the coil switches from north pole to south pole, the direction of the current changes direction. This type of current is called **alternating current** or **AC**.

Section Review 3:   Electromagnetic Force and Fields

A. Define the following terms.

electromagnetic force

electromagnet

electromagnetic induction

electric generator

alternating current

direct current

B. Choose the best answer.

1.   Which of the following would strengthen an electromagnet?

A.   increasing the electric current

B.   increasing the number of coils

C.   increasing the voltage of the circuit

D.   all of the above

2.   How can a magnet be used to produce an electric current?

A.   by wrapping a wire around the magnet

B.   by moving a magnet through a wire coil

C.   by placing a magnet next to a battery

D.   all of the above

Look at the diagram below, and then answer the following question.

3.   What would happen if the poles of the magnet were reversed?

A.   The direction of the current would be reversed.

B.   The light bulb would not light.

C.   No current would be produced.

D.   The current would increase.

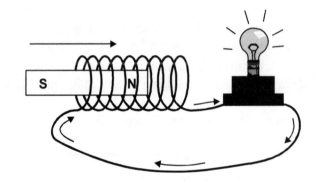

C. Answer the following questions.

1.   In physics class, two groups of students experimented with making an electromagnet using a 9-volt battery, an iron nail, and copper wire. The first group made an electromagnet that would pick up 5 paper clips. The second group of students was able to make an electromagnet that picked up 7 paper clips. If the paper clips were all the same size, what other factor could have accounted for the difference? How would you suggest making an electromagnet that would pick up even more paper clips?

2.   What is the difference between direct current and alternating current? How is alternating current produced?

CHAPTER 12 REVIEW

CHAPTER REVIEW

A. Choose the best answer.

1. A current of 0.5 amps flows in a circuit that is powered by a cell that produces 9.0 volts. Identify the resistance of the circuit.

   A.   18.0 ohms   B.   9.5 ohms   C.   8.5 ohms   D.   4.5 ohms

2. A voltage (V) is applied to a circuit with a resistance (R), producing a current (I). Identify the current when a voltage (5V) is applied to a circuit of resistance (R).

   A.   0.2 I   B.   I   C.   5 I   D.   10 I

3. A 125 volt battery delivers a current of 2.0 amperes to a portable radio. What is the resistance of the radio?

   A.   0.02 ohms   B.   2.0 ohms   C.   63 ohms   D.   250 ohms

4. A 120 volt line supplies the electricity to a light bulb with an operating resistance of 60 ohms. How many amperes of current will it take to light the bulb?

   A.   720 amperes   C.   20 amperes

   B.   0.5 amperes   D.   2 amperes

5. Which of the following statements is NOT true?

   A.   A magnet can produce an electric field.

   B.   The flow of electricity can produce a magnetic field.

   C.   An electromagnet can be strengthened by increasing the number of wire coils.

   D.   An electromagnet can be strengthened by decreasing the number of wire coils.

6. The diagram below shows two bodies, X and Y, that are distance, d, apart. Each body carries a charge of +q. The electrical force exerted on Y by X is equal to F.

   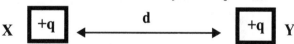
   X   +q ⟵————— d —————⟶ +q   Y

   Identify the change that would result in the biggest increase in the force exerted on Y by X.

   A.   Change the charge on Y from +q to –q.

   B.   Increase the charge on Y from +q to +2q.

   C.   Increase the distance between X and Y from d to 2d.

   D.   Decrease the distance between X and Y from d to 0.5d.

7. Identify the best description of an electric current.

   A.   a flow of protons   C.   a build up of positive charge

   B.   a flow of electrons   D.   a build up of negative charge

8. Identify the type of current used in battery-powered flashlights.

    A.   static current   C.   potential current

    B.   direct current   D.   alternating current

9. Identify the graph that shows the relationship between the voltage (V) applied across a given resister and the current (I) flowing through that resistor in an ohmic device.

  A.   **B.** 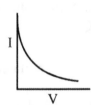   **C.** 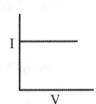   **D.**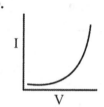

10. Identify the diagram that best represents the electrical field between two positively charged bodies.

  A. 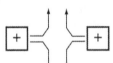   **B.** 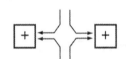   **C.**    **D.**

11. Juan places a bar magnet on a flat surface and covers it with a sheet of paper. Then he evenly sprinkles a layer of iron filings on top of the paper. Which of the following diagrams indicates the most likely arrangement of the filings on the paper?

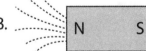

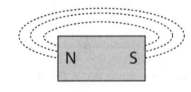

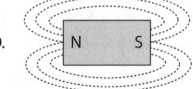

Chapter 13
Waves

GA HSGT Science Standards covered in this chapter include:

SPS9 a – f	Students will investigate the properties of waves.

OBSERVING WAVES

Imagine you and your family go fishing in the mountains. You take a motorboat out onto a large lake nestled in a valley. As you cross the lake, you watch as the boat's wake spreads out in a V-shaped pattern behind the boat, moving across the water until it laps up on the shore. Finally, the fish finder beeps, indicating that the underwater radar has detected a school of fish is moving nearby. Your mom stops the boat, and you all cast out your lines. Ripples flow out from where

Figure 13.1 Find the Waves

your bob hits the water. You squint from the sunlight reflecting off the water. Suddenly, your bob dips underwater. You yell, "I got one!" and your voice echoes in the valley. You turn the reel as fast as you can. At the last minute, a huge fish jumps violently out of the water, and the fishing line ripples and goes slack. Then, flipping his large body around, he snaps the line and splashes back in. Your dinner has escaped.

This story describes the victory of a fish, certainly. But it also describes a few different kinds of waves. See if you can pick them out. Of course, it is easy to recognize waves in water, but many other types of waves exist in natural surroundings. You may simply not notice them because of their…well, "everyday-ness."

In fact, waves are literally everywhere. To identify them, we need to know what makes a wave a wave. Simply put, a **wave** is a disturbance caused by the mechanical motion of some particle of matter. The resulting wave may travel through either space or matter. It may be visible or invisible. How it travels and whether you can see it depends on the type of wave it is. In order to differentiate between the different kinds of waves, we need to ask two questions:

1. Does the wave require a medium in order to move?

A **medium** is any form of matter whose particles transport the wave's energy. Energy is transported as each particle moves and causes the adjacent particles to move. The matter that the wave travels through can be solid like earth (earthquakes), liquid like water (ocean waves) or gas like air (sound). These kinds of waves are known as **mechanical waves** because they are waves that **propagate** (travel) by the physical motion of particles. This means that mechanical waves require a medium.

A **sound wave** is a kind of mechanical wave.

There are other waves that do not require a medium. These **electromagnetic waves** can travel through a **vacuum**, that is, empty space. They involve both an electrical and magnetic component. These components are actually perpendicular (at right angles) to one another as they travel through space, as shown in Figure 13.2.

Electromagnetic Wave

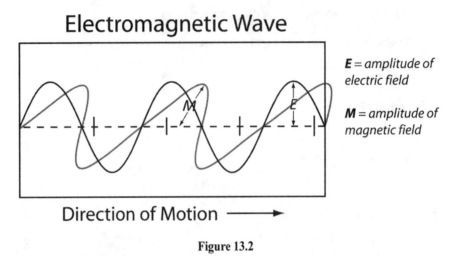

E = amplitude of electric field

M = amplitude of magnetic field

Direction of Motion ⟶

Figure 13.2

Notice that the electric field oscillates up and down, while the magnetic component appears to move into and out of the page. The two components of the waves are moving in different planes, at a 90° angle to each other. Though you cannot directly see them like waves on the ocean, electromagnetic waves are responsible for life on Earth. How? Because they are the means by which energy is transported from the Sun to the Earth.

Mechanical waves can also demonstrate this perpendicular motion, through the particles of matter that it disrupts as it passes. That brings us to our next question.

2. How do the particles of the medium move in response to the wave?

It is important to remember that waves do not transmit matter, they transmit energy. They may, however, move through matter to transmit energy. The direction that the wave travels, in relation to movement of the particles through which it moves, is another way to categorize the wave. A **transverse wave** oscillates in a direction that is perpendicular (at a right angle to) the direction in which the wave is traveling. A **longitudinal wave** oscillates parallel to (in the same direction as) the direction in which the wave is moving. That sounds hard, doesn't it? Let's look at it another way.

Lab Activity 1: Wave Motion in a Slinky

Get a long slinky. Get a friend to hold one end of the slinky on the floor about 5 –10 feet away from you. While holding the other end of the slinky, repeatedly move your hand to the right and left along the floor to introduce a wave into the slinky. Notice that the slinky is moving left and right with the movement of your hand. However, the slinky wave is traveling toward your friend. What type of wave is this?

Now, repeatedly move your hand holding the slinky toward and away from your friend. Notice that both the slinky and the slinky wave are moving toward your friend. What type of wave is this?

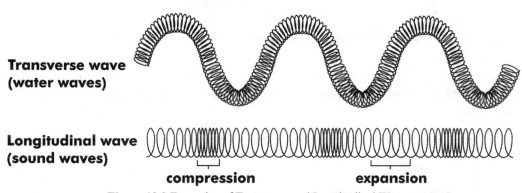

Transverse wave (water waves)

Longitudinal wave (sound waves)

compression   expansion

Figure 13.3 Examples of Transverse and Longitudinal Waves

PROPERTIES OF WAVES

The distance between any two identical points on a wave is called the **wavelength**. For example, the distance between two crests is the wavelength λ (pronounced lambda). Since wavelength is a measure of distance, its SI unit is the meter. However, wavelength is often given in nanometers (1 nm = 1×10^{-9}m) because visible light waves have wavelengths on that scale. The **amplitude (A)** is the maximum displacement of a wave particle from the midpoint between the crest and the trough. In other words, the amplitude is the height of the wave. The **period (T)** is the amount of time required for a wave particle to complete one full cycle of its motion, that is, from crest to crest. Period is measured in seconds.

Now, what if you were at the beach and you wanted to know how many waves were produced per hour? You could just count the number of wave crests over the course of an hour, right? The number of wave crests that occur in a unit of time is called the **frequency (f)**. Frequency is measured in hertz. One **hertz (Hz)** is equal to one peak (or cycle) per second, 1/sec. Now, with both the period and the frequency, you're concerned with wave crests and time. It turns out that they are related through an inverse relationship. Mathematically, this is known as a reciprocal relationship: in other words, f=1/T.

The velocity of a wave is the rate at which a wave moves through a medium, in meters/second (m/s). It is given by Equation 13.1. As wavelength increases, the wave frequency decreases (in the same medium). The frequency or wavelength of a wave can be determined by rearranging the terms of the equation.

Equation 13.1

velocity = frequency × wavelength

$$v = f\lambda$$

(λ is lambda)

Utilize the Units!

The SI unit for wavelength, which is a distance, is meters. The unit for frequency is the inverse second (Frequency is a measure of the number of times an event occurs *per length of time*.)

$$m \times \frac{1}{s} = m/s$$

So, m/s is the SI unit for velocity.

(But you already knew that, right?)

Move around the variables in Equation 13.1. If you shift the equation so that $f = v/\lambda$, you can see that a long wave (large λ) has a lower frequency than a short wave (small λ). You can see this graphically in Figure 13.4.

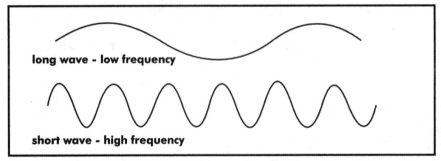

long wave - low frequency

short wave - high frequency

Figure 13.4 Relationship Between Wavelength and Frequency

As mentioned earlier, waves transport energy through a medium without transporting matter. The energy transported by a wave (wave energy) is proportional to the amplitude squared.

Section Review 1:   Types and Properties of Waves

A. Define the following terms.

wave	mechanical wave	transverse wave	period
medium	vacuum	longitudinal wave	frequency
propagate	electromagnetic wave	wavelength	hertz
	sound waves	amplitude	

B. Choose the best answer.

1. Which of the following is true regarding mechanical waves?

    A.   Mechanical waves must travel through matter.

    B.   Mechanical waves can travel through matter and space.

    C.   Mechanical waves can only travel through a vacuum.

    D.   Mechanical waves can change matter.

2. The height of a wave is its
    A.   amplitude.   B.   wavelength.   C.   period.   D.   crest.

3. Which of the following is NOT an example of a mechanical wave?
    A.   sunlight   C.   ocean waves

    B.   vibrations of a guitar string   D.   sound waves

4. The period (T) of an oscillating wave is 1/5s. What happens to the frequency (f) of the wave if T increases to 1/2s?
    A.   It stays the same.   C.   f decreases to 2 Hz.

    B.   f increases to 2Hz.   D.   f increases to 5 Hz.

5. The velocity of an electromagnetic wave in a vacuum is 3.0×10^8 m/s. If a visible light wave has a higher frequency than a radio wave, which will have the longer wavelength?

    A.   the radio wave

    B.   the visible light wave

    C.   in a vacuum, both will be equal

    D.   We need to know the amplitude in order to answer the question.

6. Name the type of wave that carries no energy.
    A.   gamma rays   C.   radio waves

    B.   visible light   D.   All waves carry energy.

BEHAVIOR OF WAVES

Whether you are aware of it or not, you have quite a bit of experience with waves. Let's see if we can clarify those experiences a little. In the story at the beginning of this chapter, your voice echoed off the hills as you yelled "I got one!" In terms of waves, what is an echo anyway? An echo is the sound waves bouncing off a surface. This same phenomenon is occurring when you look into a mirror: electromagnetic waves are bouncing off the mirror and hitting your eyes. This bouncing of waves off of a surface is called **reflection**.

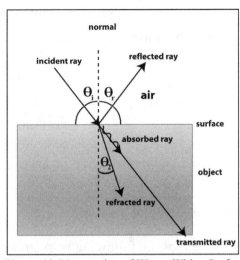

Figure 13.5 Interaction of Waves With a Surface

If the wave is only partially reflected, the leftover wave energy is **absorbed.** Think about being inside a quiet car when another car pulls up next playing loud music. If you roll up the windows of the car, the sound waves are partially absorbed, and the sound becomes muffled. But let's say that you can still hear the bass beats, even with your windows rolled up. You can still hear the music because some sound waves were **transmitted** through the solid matter of the car. So, when a wave hits a surface, it can be reflected or transmitted.

The diagram in Figure 13.5 shows the waves as straight lines called **rays** for the sake of simplicity. The type of behavior the wave shows depends on the medium it is traveling in, the material it is entering and the energy of the wave itself. Table 13.1 describes the possible responses of a wave when it hits a surface. This table should serve as a helpful guide as you read over the next few pages.

Table 13.1 Possible Interactions of a Wave with an Object

Behavior	Description of Wave Motion
Reflection	bounces off the surface at the same angle it hit with
Transmission	travels through the material at the same angle it entered with
Refraction	travels through the material, but at an altered angle
Diffraction	travels through the material until it encounters an obstacle, which it then bends around
Absorption	cannot travel all the way through the material

REFLECTION

When you turn on a light bulb, the light travels through the room until it hits an object such as the wall. The light wave then bounces off the wall and continues to travel as reflected light. The **Law of Reflection** states that the angle of reflection (θ_r) equals the angle of incidence (θ_i). In other words, the angle at which the light hits the surface equals the angle at which it bounces off the surface. Figure 13.6 illustrates these angles. Notice that the **normal line** defines the angle of reflection (90°) for incident light that is exactly perpendicular to the mirror. Let's look at a few other features of the figure.

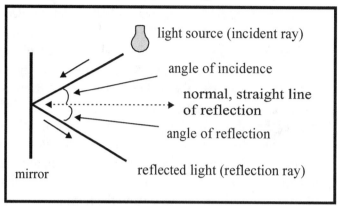

Figure 13.6 Reflection from a Mirror

- A flat mirror is a smooth, shiny surface that reflects light.
- Light travels in a straight line as it is reflected from a surface.
- The **incident ray** is the light ray that strikes the surface.
- The **reflection ray** is the light ray that reflects off the surface.

If a wave hits an object straight on, it will bounce back straight. If a wave approaches an object from the left, it will bounce off the object toward the right at the same angle.

REFRACTION

Refraction is the bending of a wave by the change in density of the medium. (Recall that density is a measure of the amount of matter in a particular volume. It has SI units of g/cm^3.) The bending of the wave is due to the reduced velocity of the wave as it enters a medium of higher density. This is often the case when light passes from the air to some liquid or solid. Figure 13.7 shows a pencil placed in a clear glass of water viewed through the glass. Since the water is more dense than the air, the light rays passing through the water will bend, causing the pencil to look broken and disconnected.

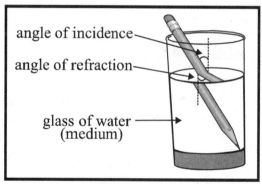

Figure 13.7 Refraction

The amount the wave bends is determined by the **index of refraction** (n) of the two materials. The amount the wave is bent, called the angle of refraction (θ_2), is determined using **Snell's law** ($n_1 \sin \theta_1 = n_2 \sin \theta_2$). A schematic representation of Snell's law is shown in Figure 13.8. Notice that, in the figure, the wave is bent toward the normal line (the dashed line perpendicular to the surface) as it moves from air into the glass. This occurs because the refractive index of glass is greater than the refractive index of air. The refractive index of a material is related to the density and atomic structure of the material. The higher the index of refraction, the more the material will bend the incoming wave. A wave moving from glass into air will bend away from the normal.

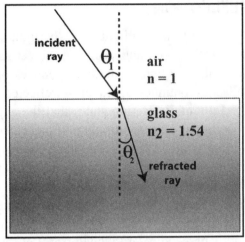

Figure 13.8 Refraction of a Wave

So far, we have only discussed the refraction of electromagnetic light waves. Refraction of sound waves also occurs. Sound travels in all directions from its source. The listener can usually only hear the sound that is directed toward him. However, refraction of the sound waves bends some of the waves downward, toward the listener, in effect amplifying the sound. Refraction of sound waves can occur if the air above the earth is warmer than the air at the surface. This effect can be observed over cool lakes early in the morning. The cold water of the lake keeps the air at the surface cool, but the rising sun starts to heat the air that is higher up. This effect is called **thermal inversion** and results in the refraction of sound. How would thermal inversion affect you if you were out fishing in the early morning? If another family was out on the lake but much further away than you would ordinarily be able to hear them, you could actually speak to one another. A pretty freaky phenomenon if you aren't expecting it!

ABSORPTION

Materials selectively absorb and transmit waves depending on the frequency of the wave and the atoms in the material. When a material absorbs a wave, the wave is no longer able to travel. The wave energy is completely transferred to the particles in the material themselves. When a material transmits a wave, the wave travels all the way through the material and eventually exits the material.

The absorption and transmission of electromagnetic waves has consequences in the color of visible light. **Visible light**, the light that humans can see with the naked eye, has wavelengths between 400 and 750 nm. Blue light has a wavelength of approximately 440 nm. (nm is the abbreviation for nanometer. 1 nm is one billionth of a meter.) What we see as the **color** of an object is actually a result of the light frequencies reflected, absorbed and transmitted by the object. Objects do not have color within themselves. For example, if a material strongly absorbs all wavelengths except those around 440 nm, the object appears to be blue, because it absorbs all wavelengths of visible light except the blue wavelengths. This means that the blue light will be reflected off of the material. Objects that reflect all wavelengths of visible light appear white, whereas objects that absorb all wavelengths of visible light are black. Chlorophyll is a pigment responsible for the green color of plants. The chlorophyll absorbs the wavelengths corresponding to red and blue, while it reflects the wavelengths corresponding to the color green.

DIFFRACTION

Another property of waves, called **diffraction**, relates to the ability of a wave to bend around obstacles or through small openings. Waves tend to spread out after going through an opening, which results in a shadow region. Diffraction depends on the size of the obstacle and the wavelength of the wave. The amount a wave bends, or diffracts, increases with increasing wavelength. Therefore, the diffraction angle is greater for waves with longer wavelengths. Waves with wavelengths smaller than the size of the obstacle or opening will not diffract.

Sound waves can diffract around objects or through very small holes. This is why we can hear someone speak even when they are around a corner, in a different room. Sound waves with long wavelengths are efficient at diffraction. Therefore, longer wavelength sounds can be heard at a greater distance from the source than shorter wavelength sounds. In addition, sound waves that have longer wavelengths become less distorted when they bend around objects. If a marching band were approaching, the first sounds that would be heard would be the long wavelength, low pitch, bass sounds. Elephants use this property of sound waves to communicate across the African plains using very long wavelength, low pitch sounds. Elephants travel in large herds, and it is easy for

Figure 13.9 Diffraction of Sound Waves

them to get separated from each other. Since they are sometimes out of visible range, they communicate using subsonic sound waves that are able to diffract around any obstacles present.

Light waves diffract differently than sound waves. The type of light diffraction that you are probably familiar with is called **scattering**. In order for scattering to occur, the obstacle must be on the *same order* of size as the wavelength of the wave. Light scattering is responsible for the corona we sometimes see around the Sun or Moon on cloudy days. The water droplets in the clouds act as obstacles to the light from these objects. The light is then bent and spread out. Therefore, the light from the object appears larger than the actual source, and we see a "crown" around the object. *In light scattering, waves with a shorter wavelength are bent more than waves with a longer wavelength.* **Light diffraction** is a special case of light scattering that occurs when a light wave encounters an obstacle with a regularly repeating pattern resulting in a diffraction pattern. The amount of diffraction of a light wave depends on the size of the opening and the wavelength of the light.

INTERFERENCE

When waves coming from two different sources meet, they affect each other. This is known as **interference**. When two waves meet, and the high point (crest) of one wave meets the crest of the other wave, the resultant wave has the sum of the amplitude of the two waves. These waves are said to be **in phase** with one another. The interaction of waves that are in phase is called **constructive interference**. The two waves come together to *construct* a new wave, with a larger amplitude.

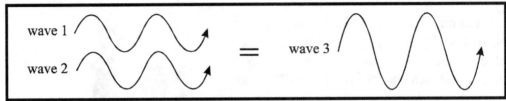

Figure 13.10 Constructive Interference

If, however, the low point (trough) of one wave meets the crest of another wave, then the waves cancel each other, and the wave becomes still. The waves are said to be **out of phase**. The interaction of out of phase waves is called **destructive interference**. The two waves meet and *destroy* each other.

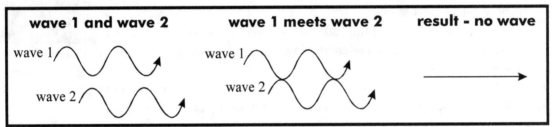

Figure 13.11 Destructive Interference

When waves interfere somewhere between these two extremes, there is some **distortion,** which results in a wave with an irregular pattern. To visualize distortion, think of what happens to the ripples made in a pond when two rocks are thrown into the water close to each other.

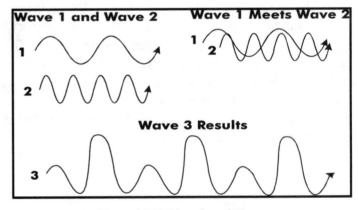

Figure 13.12 Distortion of Waves

Section Review 2: Behavior of Waves

A. Define the following terms.

reflection	incident ray	visible light	in phase
absorbed	reflection ray	color	constructive interference
transmitted	refraction	diffraction	
ray	index of refraction	scattering	destructive interference
Law of Reflection	Snell's Law	light diffraction	out of phase
normal line	thermal inversion	interference	distortion

B. Choose the best answer.

1. The indices of refraction for four materials are listed below. Which material combination will bend incoming light the most?

    A.   vacuum, (n=1.00) → air (n=1.00)   C.   ice, (n=1.31) → diamond (n=2.42)

    B.   air, (n=1.00) → ice (n=1.31)   D.   diamond, (n=2.42) → air (n=1.00)

2. A white sheet of paper appears to be white because it

    A.   absorbs all wavelengths of visible light.   C.   transmits all wavelengths of visible light.

    B.   reflects all wavelengths of visible light.

    D.   refracts all wavelengths of visible light.

Use the diagram to answer questions 3 and 4.

3. If $\theta_i = 50°$, identify the value of the angles θ_{xi}, θ_{xr}, and θ_r.

    A. $\theta_{xi} = 50°$, $\theta_{xr} = 50°$ and $\theta_r = 50°$

    B. $\theta_{xi} = 40°$, $\theta_{xr} = 40°$ and $\theta_r = 50°$

    C. $\theta_{xi} = 45°$, $\theta_{xr} = 45°$ and $\theta_r = 50°$

    D. $\theta_{xi} = 45°$, $\theta_{xr} = 45°$ and $\theta_r = 90°$

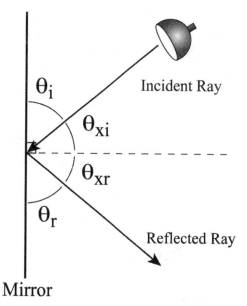

4. How would you move the light source to make the reflected ray move back toward the mirror (i.e. to increase the angle θ_{xr})?

    A.   Move the light source down.

    B.   Move the light source to the right.

    C.   Move the light source up.

    D.   Replace it with a light source that emits longer wavelengths.

SOUND WAVES

A **sound wave** is a mechanical wave produced by a vibrating object. The wave results from the compression and expansion of the molecules surrounding the vibrating object. For this reason, they are sometimes referred to as **compression waves**. Sound cannot travel through empty space or a vacuum. Sound travels faster through solids than through liquids and gases because the molecules are packed together more tightly in solids. When temperature increases, the speed of sound increases. The speed of sound also increases when the air becomes more humid (or moist).

Most people hear compression waves of the frequency 20 Hz to 20,000 Hz.

Example: A dog whistle is higher than 20,000 Hz. Elephants make a sound lower than 20 Hz. Therefore, humans cannot hear these sounds.

Sound waves of different frequencies have different wavelengths in the same medium. As frequency increases, wavelength decreases. Frequency of sound waves determines pitch. **Pitch** describes how high or low a sound is. Sounds with higher pitch have higher frequencies.

Example: A police siren has a high pitch. The growl of a large dog has a low pitch.

The intensity or volume of the sound is measured in **decibels**. The amplitude of the sound wave determines the volume. The higher the amplitude, the louder the sound and the higher the decibel value. Lower amplitudes produce softer sounds with lower decibel values.

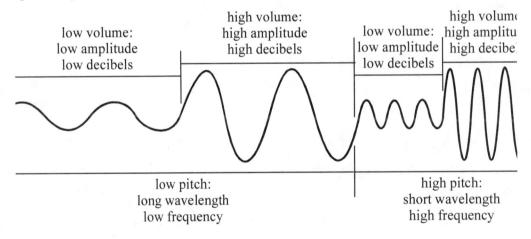

Figure 13.13 Relationship Between Volume and Pitch

THE DOPPLER EFFECT

When a sound source moves toward a listener, the pitch of the sound appears to increase. This is due to the **Doppler effect**. The reason is this: the movement of the sound emitter has the effect of increasing the frequency of the sound waves that the listener hears. It is important to realize that the frequency of the sounds that the source *emits* does not actually change. Next time you hear a siren while out walking, stop and listen to how the sound changes as it moves past you.

Section Review 3:   Sound Waves and Seismic Waves

A. Define the following terms.

sound wave   pitch   decibel   compression
Doppler effect   waves

B. Choose the best answer.

1.   Increasing the frequency of a sound wave has which of the following effects?

   A.   increases wavelength   C.   increases pitch

   B.   increases amplitude   D.   increases decibel level

2.   Through which of the following would sound travel the fastest?

   A.   a vacuum   C.   warm, dry air

   B.   warm, humid air   D.   cold, dry air

3.   The Doppler effect describes the following scenario: As a source of sound moves closer, the sound wave appears to

   A.   increase in amplitude.   C.   decrease in amplitude.

   B.   increase in pitch.   D.   decrease in pitch.

4.   What determines the volume of a sound?

   A.   the amplitude of the sound wave   C.   the Doppler effect

   B.   the frequency of the sound wave   D.   the wavelength of the sound wave

C. Answer the following question.

1.   Relate the speed of sound waves to temperature and medium. Through what type of medium does sound travel fastest? How is the speed of sound affected by temperature?

2.   Examine the following four figures. Describe the movement of the sound source (•), relative to the sound it emits. When would a stationary observer to the right of the sound source hear the sound?

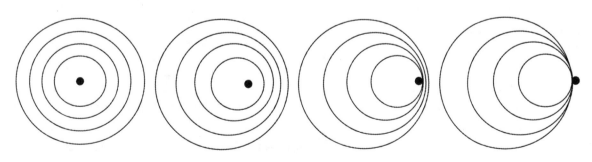

ELECTROMAGNETIC WAVES

Electromagnetic waves are transverse waves that do not need a medium through which to travel. Electromagnetic waves are produced by the acceleration or deceleration of electrons or other charged particles. The **electromagnetic spectrum** is made up of invisible and visible waves, ranging from low frequency to very high frequency, which travel at the speed of light in a vacuum.

The wave equation given in Equation 13.1 can be rewritten for electromagnetic waves by substituting c, the speed of light, for the velocity, v. The **speed of light** in a vacuum is 3×10^8 m/s.

As stated earlier, as the length of the wave increases, frequency decreases; as the length of the wave decreases, frequency increases. Notice in Figure 13.14 that radio waves have very long wavelengths, and gamma waves have very short wavelengths. Therefore, radio waves will have low frequencies, and gamma waves will have high frequencies.

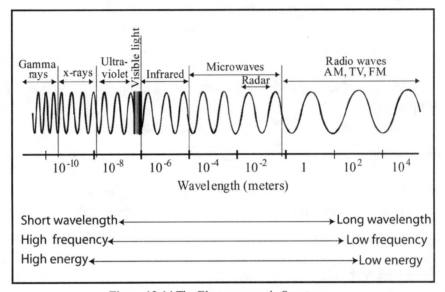

Figure 13.14 The Electromagnetic Spectrum

The energy of the wave is based on its frequency, as shown in Equation 13.2. Each type of electromagnetic wave has a different energy and is used for different purposes.

Equation 13.2

Energy = Plank's constant × frequency
$$E = hf$$
$$(h = 6.63 \times 10^{-34} \text{ J·s})$$

Utilize the Units!
The unit for Plank's constant is the joule-second.
The unit for frequency is the inverse second.

$$\text{J·s} \times \frac{1}{s} = \text{J}$$

So, the joule is the SI unit for energy.
(Look back to Eqs. 11.5 and 11.8 for other derivations of the joule.)

Figure 13.15 Radio

Radio Waves: These wavelengths of light are invisible to us, and can range from a few centimeters to more than six football fields long. Radio stations code the sound into radio waves that your radio receives, unscrambles and translates back into sound again.

Microwaves: These invisible waves have a wavelength of only a few millimeters. The microwaves generated by a microwave oven cause the water molecules in the food to vibrate and rotate. It is the thermal energy generated by the movement of the water molecules that heats the food!

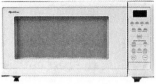

Figure 13.16 A Microwave

Figure 13.17 TV Remote

Infrared Waves: These wavelengths are up to a few micrometers in length. Your television's remote control uses a beam of infrared light to change the channel. The electronics in the TV respond to the infrared beam. Your body also radiates infrared light, but of a slightly different wavelength. That is how night vision goggles can see living things moving in the dark.

Visible Light Waves: This is the only part of the electromagnetic spectrum that our eyes can see. It's the kind of waves we are most familiar with, but in the grand scheme of the electromagnetic spectrum, it is only a very narrow band of wavelengths, from about 0.35 micrometer to 0.9 micrometer. Our eyes sense the different wavelengths in this band as color. A great way to remember in what order the colors are arranged is **Roy G Biv**. Each letter of this silly name is the first letter of a color in the visible light range, arranged from larger wavelength (red -R) to shortest (violet-V).

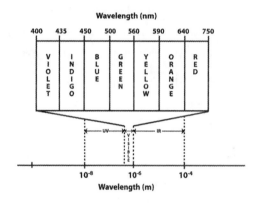

Figure 13.19 Roy G Biv

Figure 13.18 Sunscreen Blocks UV Light

Ultraviolet Waves: The ozone layer in our Earth's atmosphere helps to protect us from most of the harmful effects of these short wavelength waves. Only some of the Sun's ultraviolet light reaches the ground, and those waves can cause sunburn or even worse, skin cancer. Ultraviolet light penetrates the skin, interacts with molecules and can tear them apart. Use sunscreen!

X-rays: These waves have wavelengths in the nanometer range. They are often used to image bones in a doctor's office. X-rays can be dangerous, so it is best to minimize your exposure to them. That is why the X-ray technician or radiographer covers the parts of your body that are not being X-rayed with a lead apron. This absorbs the radiation.

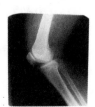

Gamma Ray Waves: These are the most energetic wavelengths in the electromagnetic spectrum, and they have the shortest wavelengths. Gamma rays are generated by the breaking apart of atomic nuclei. This happens here on Earth, but the majority of gamma rays are produced in space. Gamma radiation is increasingly used by doctors for treating cancer. The "gamma knife" uses the powerful rays to destroy cancerous cells that they are aimed at.

Section Review 4: Electromagnetic Waves

A. Define the following terms.

photon	speed of light	microwaves	X-rays
electromagnetic spectrum	Roy G. Biv	infrared waves	gamma rays
	radio waves	ultraviolet waves	visible light

B. Choose the best answer.

1. Energy from the Sun is transported by

   A. mechanical waves.   C. sound waves.

   B. electromagnetic waves.   D. compression waves.

2. How are microwaves different from gamma ray waves?

   A. Gamma rays have a higher frequency than microwaves.

   B. Gamma rays have a higher amplitude than microwaves.

   C. Gamma rays have a longer wavelength than microwaves.

   D. Gamma rays are electromagnetic, but microwaves are mechanical.

3. Which of the following color groups correctly shows increasing wavelength?

   A. green, blue, red   C. yellow, orange, red

   B. blue, yellow, violet   D. orange, yellow, green

4. What is the MOST likely reason why gamma rays are used in internal medicine?

   A. Because they can explode in the body.

   B. Because they have long wavelengths and low frequencies.

   C. Because they carry little energy and won't hurt anything.

   D. Because they have very short wavelengths, and they can be aimed to very short, specific distances.

5. What are the units of frequency?

   A. seconds (s)   C. joules (J)

   B. inverse seconds (s^{-1})   D. meters (m)

C. Answer the following questions.

1. How are electromagnetic waves different from mechanical waves? How are they similar?

2. Name the colors of the visible light spectrum, beginning with the shortest wavelength.

CHAPTER 13 REVIEW

CHAPTER
REVIEW

A. Choose the best answer.

1. What are mechanical waves?

    A. the means by which energy moves through a medium

    B. photons of energy transported through space

    C. anything that moves energy from one place to another

    D. the way that matter moves

2. Identify the property of electromagnetic waves that is NOT also a property of mechanical waves.

    A. can be reflected   C. can travel through a vacuum

    B. can cause matter to vibrate   D. can transfer energy but not matter

3. Which of the following types of electromagnetic waves has the shortest wavelength?

    A. radio wave   C. ultraviolet wave

    B. visible light wave   D. gamma ray wave

4. Identify the combination of frequency and amplitude that would maximize the energy transferred by a wave.

    A. high frequency and high amplitude   C. low frequency and high amplitude

    B. high frequency and low amplitude   D. low frequency and low amplitude

5. Identify the statement that correctly identifies the units of frequency or wavelength and the relationship between frequency and wavelength.

    A. Frequency, measured in hertz, increases as wavelength increases.

    B. Frequency, measured in hertz, decreases as wavelength increases.

    C. Wavelength, measured in hertz, increases as frequency increases.

    D. Wavelength, measured in hertz, decreases as frequency increases.

6. Identify which of the following relies on refraction.

    A. using echoes to measure distance

    B. using a mirror to see what is behind you

    C. using contact lenses to improve eyesight

    D. using soundproofing to create a quiet room

7. Which of the following is NOT a transverse wave?

    A. sound   C. vibrations of a violin string

    B. X-rays   D. rippling water

8. Which of the following lists electromagnetic radiations from lowest to highest energies?

    A.   radio waves, microwaves, ultraviolet radiation, visible light

    B.   microwaves, radio waves, visible light, X-rays

    C.   radio waves, infrared radiation, visible light, ultraviolet radiation

    D.   gamma radiation, infrared radiation, visible light, X-rays

9. The speed of sound in air at sea level and a temperature of 20 degrees Celsius is 343 meters per second. The musical note A has a frequency of 440 Hz. What is the wavelength of the note A?

    A.   0.78 meters   B.   1.3 meters   C.   1.00 meters   D.   0.5 meters

10. Which statement is true about electromagnetic radiation?

    A.   Electromagnetic waves require a medium to travel through.

    B.   Electromagnetic waves are produced by vibrating matter.

    C.   Electromagnetic waves travel through matter as compression waves.

    D.   Electromagnetic waves travel faster through a vacuum than through matter.

11. The diagram below represents the motion of two waves. Waves have equal amplitude and frequency and are moving through the same medium. Choose the statement that BEST describes the motion of the medium at point P.

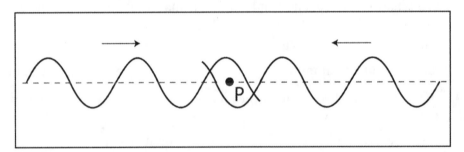

    A.   The medium at point P will vibrate up and down.

    B.   The medium at point P will vibrate left and right.

    C.   The medium at point P will vibrate into and out of the page.

    D.   The medium at point P will not move.

Practice Test 1

Directions:

Today you will be taking the Georgia High School Graduation Test in Science. Read each question carefully and then choose the *best* answer. You may refer to the formula sheet and Periodic Table on pages 1 and 2 of this text as a reference.

Be sure that the question number on the answer sheet matches the number on the test. Then mark your answer by filling in the circle on your answer sheet. Do not write your answer in the test booklet. If you do not know the answer to a question, skip it an go on. You may return to it later if time permits.

If you need to change an answer on your answer sheet, be sure to erase your first mark completely. Do not make any stray marks on the answer sheet.

Do not turn the page until instructed to do so.

1 An animal cell is placed in a solution of distilled water. If left overnight in the distilled water, what will happen to the cell?

SB1a

   A   It will swell and burst.

   B   It will shrivel and die.

   C   It will undergo chemosynthesis.

   D   It will remain the same, since it has a cell wall to protect it.

2 Electrons oscillating with a frequency of 1.5×10^8 hertz produce electromagnetic waves. Use the diagram below to classify these waves.

SPS9a

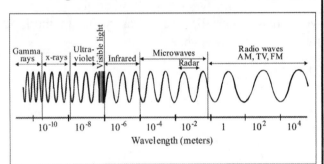

   A   ultraviolet

   B   visible

   C   microwave

   D   radio

3 On the speed vs. time graph, identify the line or curve that represents the motion of a car driven from one stop sign to a second stop sign.

SPS8a

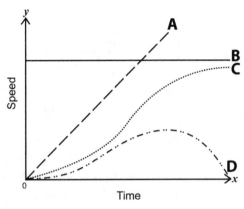

   A   line A

   B   line B

   C   curve C

   D   curve D

4 A portion of mRNA has the sequence UUCAUGGGC. What was the sequence of the original DNA segment?

SB2a, SB2b

   A   AACTACCCG

   B   AAGUACCCG

   C   TTGTAGGGC

   D   AAGTACCCG

Go On

5 Identify the type of current that powers electrical outlets in the United States. SPS7a

   A static current

   B direct current

   C potential current

   D alternating current

6 Which cell organelle is responsible for storing food and water? SB1a

   A lysosomes

   B endoplasmic reticulum

   C vacuoles

   D nucleus

7 Which pair of elements is most likely to form an ionic bond? SPS1b

   A K and H

   B N and C

   C K and Cl

   D C and H

8 It is known that the cheetah population has undergone several bottlenecks, reducing the genetic diversity in the population. Which technology below could help cheetahs regain some lost genetic variation? SB2b, SB2f

   A recombinant DNA

   B cloning

   C nuclear fusion

   D gel electrophoresis

9 This figure shows SPS1b

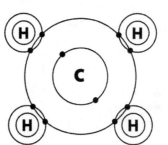

   A 5 atoms and 10 electrons.

   B 1 molecule and four ionic bonds.

   C 5 molecules and 10 electrons.

   D 1 atom and four covalent bonds.

10 Lilly wants to dissolve sugar in her iced tea to sweeten it. She performs the following four operations on her tea. Which DID NOT help the sugar dissolve? SPS6b

   A heating

   B stirring

   C adding crushed ice

   D breaking the sugar cube

11 Deuterium ($_{1}^{2}H$) and tritium ($_{1}^{3}H$) are isotopes of hydrogen. What would the fusion of these atoms produce? SPS3b

   A two hydrogen atoms ($_{1}^{1}H$)

   B two helium isotopes ($_{2}^{4}He$)

   C one helium isotope ($_{2}^{4}He$) plus one neutron ($_{0}^{1}n$)

   D two hydrogen atoms ($_{1}^{1}H$) plus three neutrons ($_{0}^{1}n$)

Go On

12 The figure below shows the pelvic bones of a sperm whale. What is the best description of this structure? SB5c, SB5d

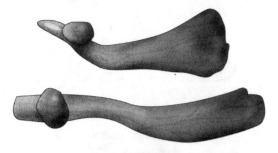

15 CM

A The structure is homologous to a human's foot.

B The structure is vestigial.

C The structure is homologous to a bird's wing.

D The structure is evidence of mutation.

13 Which of the following scenarios describes the use of mechanical waves? SPS9c

A heating a meal in a microwave

B turning on a light

C locating fish with a sonar

D laying out in the Sun

14 A tornado destroys a farm in South Georgia. The farmer decides to sell his land to the timber company and move to the city. His fields become overgrown as ecological succession begins to take place. After 50 years, what do you suppose will be the most abundant type of plant found on the former farmland? SB4c

A grasses

B herbs

C shrubs

D trees

Go On

15 A schematic diagram of the Periodic Table is shown below. Of the four shaded groups of elements, which consists of all gases? SPS4a, b

PERIODIC TABLE OF THE ELEMENTS

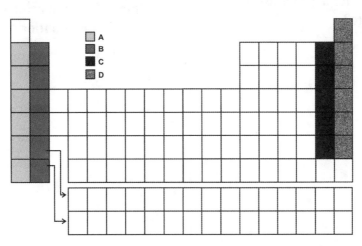

A   light gray section A   C   black section C

B   dark gray section B   D   textured section D

16 A cabbage farmer has a five acre field of cabbage. Each year, his crop is attacked by cabbage eating beetles. To combat the problem, the farmer sprays his field with a mild pesticide. The pesticide kills **85%** of the beetles on his field. In 1995, the farmer used 25 gallons to kill the beetles; however, by 2005, the farmer needed 40 gallons of pesticide to kill the same percentage of beetles. Why did the farmer need to use more pesticide to kill the same percentage of insects over the ten year period? SB4d, SB5e

A   Because he hated beetles and wanted to kill more kinds in 2005.

B   Because the beetles were weakened from previous exposure to the pesticide.

C   Because the surviving 15% of beetles were the only beetles reproducing each year, thus creating a population of beetles resistant to the pesticide.

D   Because in 2005, more beetles attacked the fields than in 1995.

17 When an element goes through radioactive decay, it may release gamma rays that can be stopped by SPS3a, c

A   thick lead or concrete.

B   living tissues.

C   a thin sheet of paper or cloth.

D   thin gold sheeting.

18 Which wave interaction is characterized by a wave bending in response to a change in speed? SPS9d

A   reflection

B   refraction

C   diffraction

D   interference

Go On

19 After fertilization, an embryo develops into a zygote through many cell divisions. If the sperm and egg each contain 8 chromosomes, how many chromosomes are contained within the zygote?   SB2e

   A   4

   B   8

   C   16

   D   32

20 The following reaction is propane burning in oxygen to produce carbon dioxide and steam.   SPS2e

$$\underline{\quad}C_3H_8 + \underline{\quad}O_2 \rightarrow \underline{\quad}CO_2 + \underline{\quad}H_2O$$

Which of the following sets of numbers will balance this equation?

   A   1, 5, 3, 4

   B   1, 3, 4, 5

   C   5, 4, 3, 1

   D   4, 5, 1, 3

Go On

21 Four beakers of water are heated to a steady temperature. Then food coloring   SPS5a
    is added. The experimental conditions are specified in the following table.

Beaker	1	2	3	4
Volume H$_2$O	50 mL	50 mL	25 mL	25 mL
Volume of food coloring added	2 mL	1mL	2mL	1mL
Temperature	100°C	50°C	100°C	75°C

In which beaker will the food coloring be completely dispersed the MOST quickly?

A   Beaker 1

B   Beaker 2

C   Beaker 3

D   Beaker 4

22 A 200 N force, F_1, and a 250 N,   SPS8b
    F_2, force are applied to the same
    point at the same time to a large trunk
    on a frictionless level surface. Which
    diagram below shows the position of the
    forces that will give the greatest
    acceleration to the trunk?

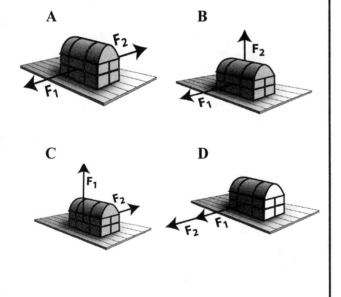

23 An organism that lives on land,   SB4a
    cannot move, and makes all of
    its food from sunlight is a

A   producer.

B   primary consumer.

C   secondary consumer.

D   decomposer.

Go On

24 Table salt (NaCl) is added to a beaker of boiling water until no more will dissolve. What will occur as the solution cools?   SPS6a

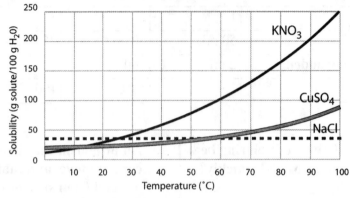

A   The concentration of salt in the water will increase.

B   The concentration of salt in the water will decrease.

C   The concentration of salt in the water will not change much.

D   The concentration will go to zero as all of the salt crystallizes.

Go On

25 **Urchins are considered a _____ to the snail and a _____ to the fish.**

SB4a, 4b

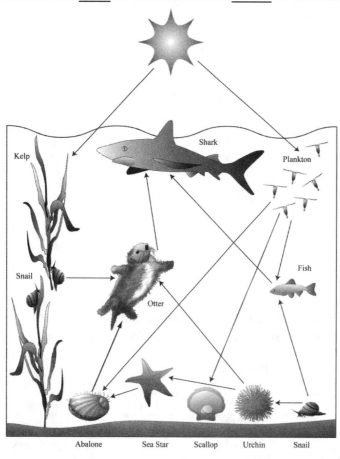

A predator, competitor	**C** predator, predator
B competitor, predator	**D** competitor, competitor

)n

26 Which of the following will have the lowest pH? <small>SPS6e</small>

   A   rainwater

   B   distilled water

   C   soapy water

   D   bleach

27 When energy is transformed from one form to another, some of the energy is lost. What is the form of the "lost" energy? <small>SPS7a, SPS7b</small>

   A   mechanical energy

   B   hydrogen gas

   C   water

   D   thermal energy

28 The following table shows the abundance and half-life of 4 of the 15 known carbon isotopes. Which is the most common stable isotope of carbon? <small>SPS3c</small>

Isotope	Natural Abundance	Half-life
^{8}C	~0%	1.99×10^{-21} seconds
^{12}C	98.89%	Infinite
^{13}C	1.11%	Infinite
^{14}C	1×10^{-10} %	5730 years

   A ^{8}C **B** ^{12}C **C** ^{13}C **D** ^{14}C

Go On

29 When lipids are immersed in a water-based system, like a cell, the long chains of carbon group together to separate themselves from the aqueous solvent. They may form one of two different lipid orientations, as shown in the diagram: a lipid bilayer (1) or a spherical arrangement called a micelle (2). Which statement explains this behavior? *SB4a*

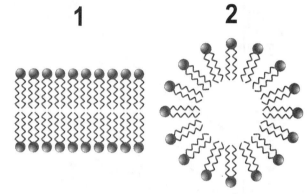

1   **2**

A   The heads of the lipid are non-polar, and the tails are polar.

B   The heads of the lipid are polar, and the tails are nonpolar.

C   Both the heads and the tails consist of non-polar carbon.

D   Both the heads and the tails consist of polar oxygen.

30 Which of the following is an isotope of hydrogen? *SPS1a*

A H_2 C ^2He

B ^1H D ^2H

31 The specific heat of lead is 130 J/kg°C. How much heat is required to raise the temperature of a 2kg lead sample by 5°C? *SPS7c*

A   2600 J

B   26 J

C   1300 J

D   13 J

32 Alan constructs a circuit that has two 1.5 V batteries arranged in series. These batteries power a single light bulb. What will happen if Alan adds another load in series? *SPS10b*

A   The resistance of the circuit has increased, so more current will flow.

B   The voltage of the circuit has increased, so more current will flow.

C   The resistance of the circuit has decreased, so less current will flow.

D   The resistance of the circuit has increased, so less current will flow.

33 The equation below summarizes what biological process? *SB4b*

Light energy + $6H_2O$ + $6CO_2 \rightarrow C_6H_{12}O_6$ + $6O_2$ +ATP

A   chemophotosynthesis

B   fermentation

C   photosynthesis

D   cellular respiration

34 What characteristic do all waves share? *SPS9a*

A   All waves move matter.

B   All waves transfer energy.

C   All waves can move through a vacuum.

D   All waves travel at 3.0×10^8 m/s.

Go On

35 A cicada is an insect with a lifespan of around 17 years. A turtle may live to be 150 years old. A honey bee lives about 1 year. A mosquito lives about 15 days. Of these organisms, which would have the highest rate of evolution?

SB5b

A   mosquito

B   honey bee

C   turtle

D   cicada

36 Sodium chlorate ($NaClO_3$) and potassium nitrate (KNO_3) are solids at room temperature. The solubility curves for sodium chlorate and potassium nitrate in water are presented in the graph below. Based on the data provided, identify the valid conclusion.

SPS6a

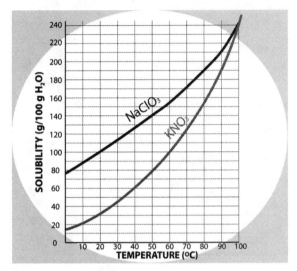

A   The solubility of these solids in water decreases as water temperature increases.

B   The solubility of these solids in water increases as water temperature increases.

C   Nitrate ions are more soluble in water than are chlorate ions.

D   Sodium is more soluble in water than is potassium.

Go On

37 Identify the force needed to
accelerate a car from 0m/s to
30m/s in 10s if the mass of the car is
2000kg. *SPS8a*

A   6.7N

B   667N

C   6,000N

D   60,000N

38 Lamar has a sample of zinc,
a metal that is capable of
sublimation. If the following
phase diagram represents the phase
transitions of zinc, what physical
conditions are necessary for Lamar's
zinc sample to sublime? *SPS7d*

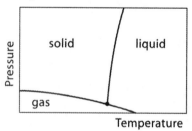

A. high pressure only

B. low temperature only

C. low temperature at low pressure

D. low pressure at high temperature

39 A solution is made by dissolving
10 g of salt in 500 g of water.
Identify the mass of the resulting
solution. *SPS2d*

A   500 g

B   more than 500 g but less than 510 g

C   510 g

D   more than 510 g

Go On

40 What is the danger of an uncontrolled chain reaction within the core of a nuclear fission reactor?　SPS3d

    A An uncontrolled chain reaction will use up all of the fuel in the reactor and force the fission of the metals that make up the core casing.

    B An uncontrolled chain reaction will produce enough heat to crack the reactor core open, releasing radioactive material.

    C An uncontrolled chain reaction will produce enough electrons to electrically charge the reactor core.

    D An uncontrolled chain reaction will produce enough heat to induce fusion in the reactor core, which will result in an explosion.

41 Rita obtains an unknown liquid sample from her teacher. It has a mass of 7 grams, and it fills a graduated cylinder to Level A. She is given the densities of the following four liquids to help her identify the sample. Which one is it?　SPS2a

	g/mL
water	1.00
vegetable oil	0.93
honey	1.42
gasoline	0.70

←A

    A water

    B vegetable oil

    C honey

    D gasoline

42 Sexual reproduction encourages genetic variation in three ways. Which of the following is NOT a feature of sexual reproduction that promotes new genetic combinations?　SB2e

    A crossing over with genetic recombination

    B independent assortment at the time of meiosis

    C increasing the cell population by mitosis

    D combination of parental genetic backgrounds at fertilization

Go On

43 In orchids, flower color and fragrance are two genetic traits. Each trait is located on a separate chromosome. In orchids, the allele for producing blue flowers (B) is dominant to the allele for producing white flowers (b). The allele for producing strong fragrance (F) is dominant to the allele for producing little fragrance (f). Two orchids that have genotypes that are heterozygous blue flowers and strong fragrance (BbFf) were crossed. Use the completed Punnett square to determine the probability of offspring that have both blue flowers and strong fragrance.

SB2c

	BF	**Bf**	**bF**	**bf**
BF	BBFF	BBFf	BbFF	BbFf
Bf	BBFf	BBff	BbFf	Bbff
bF	BbFF	BbFf	bbFF	bbFf
bf	BbFf	Bbff	bbFf	bbff

A   1/16

B   3/16

C   6/16

D   9/16

44 Which particle diagram correctly illustrates the arrangement of four molecules of hydrochloric acid (HCl)?

SPS2c

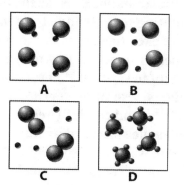

45 Cystic fibrosis is a recessive genetic disease that causes the body to produce a thick mucus. If both parents are carriers for this disease, what is the probability of a child being born WITHOUT this disease?

SB2c, SB2e

A   25%

B   50%

C   75%

D   100%

46 Which of the following is a correct statement about a periodic trend?

SPS4a, b

A   In general, the atomic radius of elements decreases going down the Periodic Table.

B   In general, an electron is more tightly bound to its atom going from left to right across the Periodic Table.

C   The reactivity of metals decreases going down the Periodic Table.

D   In general, the atomic radius of elements increases going from left to right on the Periodic Table.

Go On

47 A new graduate student in zoology SB2f decided to try to codify the characteristics of the Sumatran tigers *(Panthera tigris sumatran)* living in an Indonesian national park. He was attempting to determine the genetic lineage of each tiger, in order to see if the subspecies *sumatran* had the genetic diversity to survive. He began to track the tigers, visually observing their characteristics and carefully recording them. A colleague suggested another method. His plan was to briefly trap each tiger, take a blood sample and perform DNA sequencing. Given your knowledge of genetics, is this alternate plan a valid approach?

A No, because the sequence itself will not tell you the tiger's lineage.

B Yes, because the sequence itself will tell you the tiger's lineage.

C Yes, because you could compare the sequences of all the tigers to determine lineages.

D No, cloning should have been used to determine the lineage of each tiger.

48 In which group of the Periodic Table will you find one or more metalloids? SPS4a, b

A Group 6

B Group 10

C Group 15

D Group 17

Go On

49 A plant has a thick waxy cuticle to prevent moisture loss. The interior of the plant is SB4c
hollow and is used to store large quantities of water. The leaves of the plant have
evolved into sharp spines, which protect the flesh of the plant from water-seeking animals.
Which environment is most suited to this organism?

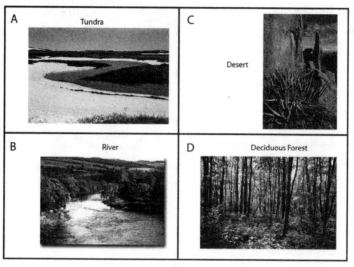

A. Tundra   **B**   Deciduous Forest   **C**   Desert   **D**   River

50 *Orcinus orca* is the scientific name SB3c
for the killer whale. These names
represent the _____ and
_____ of this organism.

   A   kingdom and phylum

   B   class and order

   C   family and genus

   D   genus and species

51 The pole bean is a plant that SB4e
climbs up trellises. Its vines
contain tendrils that reach out in search
of a surface to cling to. When the coil
reaches a surface, the cells that touch it
release a chemical that is transmitted to
untouched cells. The untouched cells
respond by lengthening, with the effect
of bending the coil around the touched
cells to grip the surface. What is this
phenomena called?

   A   chemotropism

   B   thigmotropism

   C   phototropism

   D   gravitropism

Go On

52 In aspen trees, the allele for having round leaves (R) is dominant to the allele for having oval leaves (r). Use the Punnett Square to determine the probability of heterozygous dominant parent trees having offspring with round leaves. SB2c, SB2d

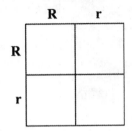

A 75%

B 25%

C 50%

D 0%

53 A jet airplane is travelling at Mach 1.6 – that is, 1.6 times the speed of sound. A stationary observer below is looking skyward. When will the observer hear the plane? SPS9f

A before the plane flies over him

B after the plane flies over him

C as the plane flies over him

D not at all

54 What is a molecule that speeds up a chemical reaction but is not changed by the reaction called? SB1b

A product

B reactant

C enzyme

D protein

Go On

Refer to the portion of the Periodic Table below to answer question 55.

```
      19
       K
   Potassium
    39.0983
    2,8,8,1
```

55 **How many neutrons are in most atoms of potassium?**   SPS1a

A   1

B   20

C   19

D   39

56 **Refer to the equation below. It gives off heat as a product. It is a/an _____ reaction.**   SPS5a

$$P_4 + 5O_2 \longrightarrow P_4O_{10}$$

A   exothermic

B   neutralization

C   endothermic

D   decomposition

57 **Which of the following statements correctly represents a negative impact of fossil fuel usage?**   SB4d

A   The burning of fossil fuels disrupts the water cycle by adding hydrogen to the atmosphere.

B   Drilling for fossil fuels disrupts the carbon cycle by adding hydrogen to the atmosphere.

C   The burning of fossil fuels releases carbon, and thus carbon-based greenhouse gases, to the atmosphere in excess volume.

D   Mining for fossil fuels has irreversibly changed the ecological biomes of the Earth.

58 **Which of the following examples represents potential energy but not kinetic energy?**   SPS7a

A   an avalanche

B   a coiled spring

C   a hot air balloon in flight

D   the pistons in a working engine

Go On

59 The diagram below shows DNA fingerprints from several people.

SB2f

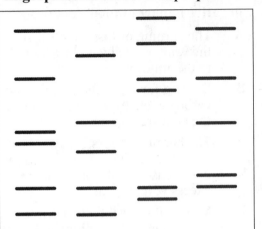

Brother's DNA   Individual 1   Individual 2   Individual 3

A mother and father die in a car accident. The three offspring, a brother and two sisters, are placed in foster homes. Many years later, the brother begins looking for his sisters. After a long and exhaustive search, three women claim that they are his sisters. Use the DNA fingerprints above to determine which two individuals are most likely his sisters?

A Individuals 1 and 2 may be his sisters.

B Individuals 1 and 3 may be his sisters.

C Individuals 2 and 3 may be his sisters.

D None of the individuals is a sibling.

60 What process does the following description refer to: "a block of dry ice sitting on a laboratory bench top has a cloud of gas around it?"

SPS7d

A melting

B sublimation

C evaporation

D fumigation

61 A recently used hot ceramic teapot is placed on a cold trivet as shown below. Which statement is correct about the sequence of thermal energy transfers?

SPS7b

Trivet

A The air transfers energy to the teapot and trivet, and they become cool.

B The teapot transfers all of its energy to the air and becomes cool.

C The teapot transfers some energy to the trivet and some energy to the air and becomes cool.

D The trivet transfers energy to the teapot and the teapot becomes cool.

Go On

62 Quin and Roseanna collected various samples of the flora in their backyard. Of the three samples shown below, which is/are non-vascular plants?

SB4e, SB3b

Sample 1
Magnolia

Sample 2
Norway Spruce

Sample 3
Moss

A   Sample 1

B   Sample 2

C   Samples 2 & 3

D   Sample 3

Go On

Use this information to answer question 49.

A species of bird lives in a canyon. This bird is reproductively isolated from other bird species in the area. The males of this type of bird species produce colorful red and blue iridescent feathers. During warmer years (greater than 78°F), more food is available and males can produce more vivid coloration. Females will only mate with males that have vivid coloration. During the warmer years, there are more successful breeding pairs of birds and more offspring. The graph below summarizes the number of offspring born each year.

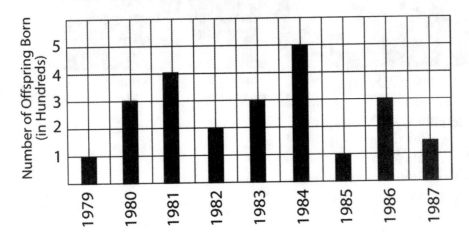

63 If the average breeding season temperature is greater than 80°F for the next five years, what trend(s) will be observed? SB4f, SB5d

   A   Bird coloration will become more dull.

   B   More offspring will be produced.

   C   Bird coloration will stay the same.

   D   Only female birds will be produced.

64 What is the molecule labeled #2 in the diagram below? SB1c

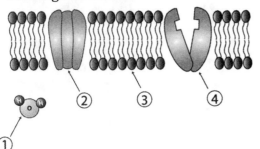

   A   a fat

   B   a protein

   C   a carbohydrate

   D   a nucleic acid

65 How is phosphorous normally released from biological systems? SB4d

   A   from the water

   B   from weathering of soil

   C   from air

   D   from the combustion of fossil fuels

Go On

66 Use the following chemical equation to predict the massing product of the reaction of carbon dioxide with tungsten trioxide.

SPS2b

$$2CO_2 (g) + 2WO_3 (S) \gg 5O_2 (g) + \underline{\qquad} (s)$$

A   WC

B   2WC

C   1/2 WC

D   4WC

67 The Atacana desert in Chile is known as the driest place on Earth, with some areas having not seen rain for over 400 years. Nighttime temperatures often drop below 0°C with daytime temperatures near 25°C. A daily deluge of fog does support some cactuses and mesquite vegetation. The Great Salt Flats found there support a healthy population of krill and flamingoes, a few species of humming-bird and viscacha (the largest member of the chinchilla family). This is a description of the ecosystem's

SB4a

A   biotic factors.

B   abiotic factors.

C   both biotic and abiotic factors.

D   succession pattern.

68 Smart glass technologies have become increasingly popular. British scientists recently developed a window glass that helps buildings stay cool. At regular temperatures, the glass allows in both infrared (IR) and ultraviolet (UV) light. But above 29°C, the coating on the glass undergoes a chemical change, causing it to block IR light. What happens to the IR light?

SPS9d

A   It is absorbed by the glass.

B   It is refracted by the glass.

C   It is reflected by the coating on the glass.

D   It is refracted by the coating on the glass.

69 One octopus unscrews a jar lid and receives a food reward. Another octopus observes this occurrence and, upon receiving a jar, proceeds to quickly unscrew the lid. This is an example of

SB4f

A   innate behavior.

B   learned behavior.

C   diurnal behavior.

D   territorial behavior.

Go On

70 ROYGBIV describes visible light SPS9b
portion of the electromagnetic
spectrum, with Red light (R) at one end
and Violet light (V) at the other. Which
of the following statements is true?

A Violet light has a higher frequency and shorter wavelength than red light.

B Violet light has a lower frequency and shorter wavelength than red light.

C Violet light has a higher frequency and longer wavelength than red light.

D Violet light has a lower frequency and longer wavelength than red light.

71 The process shown in the diagram SB2b
below

A is transcription.

B is the final process in the assembly of a protein.

C is replication.

D occurs on the surface of the ribo-some.

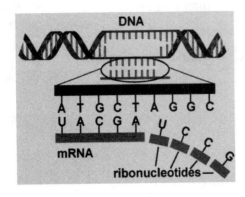

72 Rodney hammers a 3 cm nail SPS8e
into a board, using a single
blow that delivers 4 N of force. Which
statement correctly describes the
amount of work done on the nail?

A Rodney has performed 12 J of work on the nail.

B Rodney has performed 0.12 J of work on the nail.

C Rodney has performed more than 12 J of work on the nail, because of the friction between the nail and the board.

D Rodney has performed more than 0.12 J of work on the nail, because of the friction between the nail and the board.

73 The weight of an object is less SPS8d
on the Moon because

A objects on the Moon experience a greater acceleration due to gravity.

B objects on the Moon experience a lesser acceleration due to gravity.

C there are fewer frictional forces on the Moon.

D there are more frictional forces on the Moon.

74 Change is to evolution as lack of SB5b,
change is to SB5c

A polygenic traits.

B genetic equilibrium.

C genetic variation.

D gene pool.

Go On

75 Of the four main types of macromolecules active in the cell, which two primarily function to provide energy?   SB1c

A   lipids and proteins

B   lipids and carbohydrates

C   nucleic acids and proteins

D   nucleic acids and carbohydrates

76 Ross was riding his bike down a hill, and he ran straight into a mailbox. Identify the statement that most closely describes Ross's motion immediately following his collision with the mailbox.   SPS8b

A   He is thrown forward over the handlebars.

B   He is thrown backwards off the bike.

C   He is thrown sideways off the bike.

D   He is thrown upward into the air.

77 Half-life is the amount of time required for half the atoms of a radioactive substance to break down.   SPS3c

Use the graph below to determine the approximate half-life of arsenic-74.

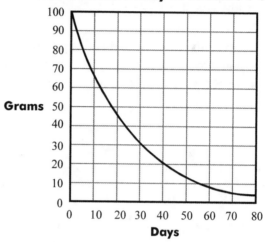

Radioactive Decay of Arsenic-74

A   10 days

B   18 days

C   36 days

D   80 days

Go On

78 The diagram to the right shows two neutral metal spheres, *X* and *Y*, that are in contact and on insulating stands.

SPS10c

Which diagram best represents the charge distribution on the spheres when a positively charged rod is brought near sphere *X*, but does not touch it?

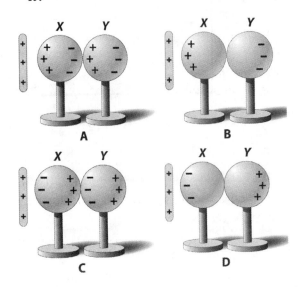

79 Plant and animal cells are similar in structure, function and development. What does the plant cell have that the animal cell does not have?

SB3a

A   nucleus

B   cell membrane

C   organelles

D   cell wall

80 Four boys were working out with free weights in gym class.

SPS8e

• Brett was holding a 150 pound barbell above his head.

• Philip was spotting for Brett.

• Bryan was walking toward the teacher carrying a box full of weights.

• Doug was holding a squat with a 30-pound barbell in each hand.

The physical science teacher came by and said only one boy was actually doing any work. Who was it?

A   Brett

B   Philip

C   Bryan

D   Doug

STOP

Practice Test 2

Refer to the formula sheet and Periodic Table on pages 1 and 2 as you take this test.

1 A cell contains a nucleus, **SB1a** mitochondria and endoplasmic reticulum. Given only this knowledge, what can you conclude about the identity of the cell?

A   It is a plant cell.

B   It is an animal cell.

C   It is a eukaryotic cell.

D   It is a prokaryotic cell.

2 A submarine uses sonar to **SPS9e** measure the distance between itself and other underwater objects. It sends out a sound wave, then records the echo that is reflected back by an underwater object. The speed of sound in water is about 1500 m/s. How far away is an object whose echo takes 5 seconds to return?

A   300 meters

B   7500 meters

C   3750 meters

D   15000 meters

3 Which would a breeder use to **SB5b** produce cows which give more milk?

A   natural selection

B   artificial selection

C   gene mutation

D   acquired characteristics

4 A beaker of water is boiling on a **SPS7d** hot plate. A thermometer measures the temperature of the liquid water as 100°C. If the hot plate is turned up, adding more heat to the water, what will happen?

A   The water temperature will rise above 100°C.

B   The water will remain at 100°C.

C   The water will melt.

D   The water will cool to below 100°C.

5 What is the effect of adding **SPS6e** bleach to a beaker of water?

A   The pH will increase.

B   The pH will decrease.

C   A flammable solution is made.

D   A heterogeneous solution is made.

Go On

6 During meiosis, only one chromosome from each homologue is passed on to the offspring. This helps increase   SB2b

A   genetic variation.

B   the chance of mitosis occurring.

C   the rate of fertilization.

D   the rate of evolution.

7 A free-living unicellular organism reproduces asexually through binary fission. If the parent cell contains 28 chromosomes, how many chromosomes are contained within the daughter cell?   SB2b

A   7

B   14

C   28

D   56

8 Lara navigates her kayak down a stretch of the Chattahoochee River in 15 minutes. Her rate of speed over the course of the trip is 8 km/hr. How far has she traveled?   SPS8a

A   0.12 km

B   1.2 km

C   2 km

D   120 km

9 Amino acids are linked by peptide bonds to make proteins. During what process does this occur?   SB1a

A   translation

B   transcription

C   replication

D   fertilization

10 Nuclear fission is a powerful energy source, used in both nuclear power plants and atomic bombs. Which statement is a possible description of the nuclear fission of an atom of U-235?   SPS3b

A   An atom of krypton-94, an atom of barium-139 and two neutrons join together to form an atom of U-235.

B   An atom of krypton-94, an atom of barium-139 and three neutrons join together to form an atom of U-235 plus a neutron.

C   U-235 absorbs one neutron and splits into an atom of krypton-94, an atom of barium-139 and three neutrons.

D   U-235 absorbs one neutron and splits into an atom of krypton-94, an atom of barium-139 and two neutrons.

11 A certain molecule is found on the surface of most cells and is responsible for communication between the cells. This molecule is made up of long chains of amino acids and is specific to each cell type. Identify the molecule.   SB1c

A   lipid

B   phosphate molecule

C   DNA

D   protein

Go On

12 How many protons does one atom of iron have in its nucleus?

SPS1a

26
Fe
Iron
55.847
2,8,14,2

A 56

B 30

C 2

D 26

13 Which of the following scenarios would make the box easiest to move?

SPS8e

FORCE
A 90N

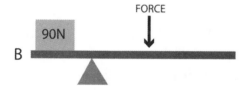

FORCE
B 90N

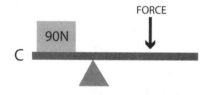

FORCE
C 90N

FORCE
D 90N

14 The circuit below represents the wiring in a power strip. Identify the way the circuit is wired and, if one device breaks, the effect on the other devices.

SPS10b

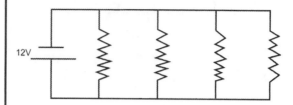

12V

A wired in parallel; other devices remain on

B wired in parallel; other devices turn off

C wired in series; other devices remain on

D wired in series; other devices turn off

Go On

Use the Punnett square to answer questions 15 and 16.

	BE	Be	bE	be
BE	BBEE	BBEe	BbEE	BbEe
Be	BBEe	BBee	BbEe	Bbee
bE	BbEE	BbEe	bbEE	bbEe
be	BbEe	Bbee	bbEe	bbee

15 Two rabbits that have the phenotype of brown fur and straight ears and the genotype (BbEe) were crossed. Use the completed Punnett square to determine the probability of offspring that have white fur and floppy ears.   SB2c

   A   1/16

   B   3/16

   C   4/16

   D   8/16

16 What are the possible genotypes for a rabbit with brown fur and floppy ears?   SB2c

   A   Bbee, BBee

   B   Bbee, BbEe, BBee and BBEe

   C   BBee and BBEE

   D   BbEe, BBEe, BbEE and BBEE

17 A horse breeder must confirm the lineage of a new foal in order to submit its pedigree. The diagram below shows DNA fingerprinting from the foal and its possible father, Steeplechase. Which conclusions can you draw?   SB2f

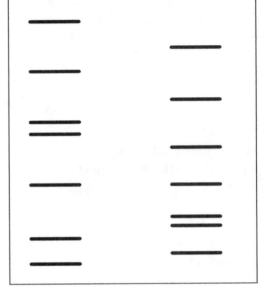

Foal's DNA   Steeplechase's DNA

   A   The foal was probably not sired by Steeplechase.

   B   The foal was definitely sired by Steeplechase.

   C   The foal was probably sired by Steeplechase.

   D   The lack of matches indicates that the test is corrupted.

18 Which of the following lists electromagnetic radiations from lowest to highest energies?   SPS9b

   A   microwaves, radio waves, visible light, X-rays

   B   radio waves, infrared radiation, visible light, ultraviolet radiation

   C   radio waves, microwaves, ultraviolet radiation, visible light

   D   infrared radiation, visible light, gamma radiation, X-rays

Go On

19 The parasitic yellow fly *SB4a, SB4f*
Ormia ochracea is attracted
to the song of the male cricket. She uses
the song to locate the male in order to
deposit her young on him. The larvae
promptly burrow into the cricket and
eat him. This is an example of

A mutualism.

B evolution.

C parasitism.

D commensalism.

20 Matter in the gas phase lacks a *SPS5b*
definite shape or volume.
Characterize particles in the gas phase.

A fast-moving and far apart

B slow-moving and far apart

C loosely packed into an ordered
structure

D tightly packed into an ordered
structure

21 A given radionuclide R_A has a *SPS3c*
half life of 100 years. Another
radionuclide R_B has a half life of 25
years. One thousand kilograms of each
material are placed in a hazardous
waste receptacle. How much of each will
be around after 100 years?

A 500 kg R_A and 62.5 kg R_B

B 500 kg R_A and 125 kg R_B

C 250 kg R_A and 250 kg R_B

D 250 kg R_A and 125 kg R_B

22 Red blood cells contain a high *SB1a*
concentration of solutes, including
salts and protein. When the cells are
placed in a hypotonic solution, water
rushes to the area of high solute
concentration, bursting the cell. This is
an example of

A diffusion.

B facilitated diffusion.

C osmosis.

D plasmolysis.

23 Look at the following block of *SPS4a*
elements from the Periodic
Table. List the elements in order of
increasing electronegativity.

6 C Carbon 12.011 2,4	7 N Nitrogen 14.0067 2,5	8 O Oxygen 15.9994 2,6	9 F Fluorine 18.998403 2,7	10 Ne Neon 20.179 2,8

A neon, carbon, nitrogen, oxygen,
fluorine

B carbon, nitrogen, oxygen, fluorine,
neon

C neon, fluorine, oxygen, nitrogen,
carbon

D carbon, neon, nitrogen, oxygen,
fluorine

Go On

Use the following diagram to answer question 24.

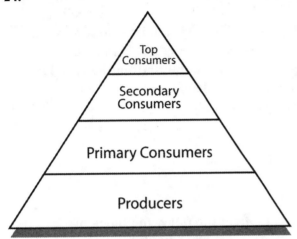

24 **Which of the following group contains organisms that belong in the first trophic level?** SB4b

A   Kingdom Fungi

B   Class Insecta

C   Class Mammalia

D   Kingdom Plantae

25 **Salt is added to a beaker of boiling water until no more will dissolve. As the solution cools** SPS6c

A   the concentration of salt in the water will increase until room temperature solubility is reached.

B   the concentration of salt in the water will decrease until room temperature solubility is reached.

C   the concentration of salt in the water will not change.

D   the concentration will go to zero as all of the salt crystallizes.

Go On

The green sea turtle lives in warm waters. This large turtle can weigh up to 200 pounds. It has a hard shell to protect its vital organs. The green sea turtle is so named because of the color of its body fat; its algae diet is responsible for the colored tissue.

The leatherback turtle spends most of its time in colder northern waters. The largest of all turtles, it can weigh up to 600 pounds. It has a black shell made of soft connective tissue, rather than the hard plates than most turtles have. The beak of the leatherback turtle is specially hooked to help it bite jellyfish and its throat has backward-facing barbs to help it swallow them

Green Sea Turtle

Leatherback Turtle

26 **What best explains the differences in appearance of these two turtle species?** SB4f, SB5d

   A   Over time, the two turtle species have adapted differences in appearance due to the differences in environment.

   B   Each baby turtle adapts its features to the specific food source of its habitat and thus grows distinct adult characteristics.

   C   Each turtle adapts a different appearance once it moves to a comfortable habitat.

   D   Over time, the two turtle species developed different breeding preferences, and came to look very different form each other.

Go On

27 A bowling ball with a mass of 5.44 kg and a soccer ball with a mass of 0.43 kg are dropped from a 15 m platform. Identify the correct description of the acceleration of the bowling ball and the force with which it hits the ground, with respect to the soccer ball. SPS8c

A The force of the bowling ball is greater, and its acceleration is greater.

B The force of the bowling ball is greater, and its acceleration is the same.

C The force of the bowling ball is the same, and its acceleration is greater.

D The force of the bowling ball is the same, and its acceleration is the same.

28 John removes his wool hat on a cold winter day. All of John's hair stands out. He throws the hat at his brother, Terry. Terry receives a small shock of static electricity. Based on this scenario, which of the following statements is NOT true? SPS10a

A Electrons rub off John's hair and onto his hat.

B Each of John's hairs is positively charged, and they repel each other.

C The hat is negatively charged before it hits Terry.

D The hat is positively charged after it hits Terry.

29 The loss or gain of which sub-atomic particle has the greatest effect on chemical reactivity? SPS1a

A electron

B proton

C neutron

D nucleon

Go On

30 What is the relationship between the caribou and the Dall sheep? SB4b

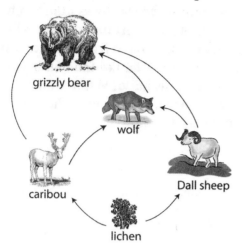

grizzly bear

wolf

caribou

Dall sheep

lichen

A   predator/prey

B   parasite

C   symbiotic

D   competitor

31 Lichens are negatively affected by pollution. An increase in the amount of pollution often causes the lichen population to decline. Which organisms shown in the food web would be affected by an increase in pollution amounts? SB4d

A   the caribou and the Dall sheep

B   the lichen only

C   the caribou, Dall sheep and wolf

D   the caribou, Dall sheep, wolf and grizzly bear

32 The iron handle of a cast iron skillet becomes very hot when it is heated on a stove. This is an example of heat transfer through SPS7b

A   convection.

B   radiation.

C   conduction.

D   friction.

33 UV light breaks apart the hydrogen bonds that hold the DNA strand together. Special enzymes act to correct the damage. As the organism ages, the corrective enzymes can no longer function at peak capacity. What will most likely happen to the DNA strand after intensive, repeated exposure to UV light? SB2d

A   evolution

B   mutation

C   translocation

D   crossing over

34 In an experiment, Julie determines that the leaves and stems of African violets always grow in the direction of a light source. What is the name of the phenomenon Julie has observed? SB4e

A   negative tropism

B   phototropism

C   geotropism

D   thigmotropism

35 Fission and fusion are two methods of producing nuclear energy. Which method is used in nuclear power reactors and why? SPS3c, 3d

A   Fusion, because it creates less waste.

B   Fission, because it produces more energy per atom of fuel.

C   Fusion, because it produces more energy per atom of fuel.

D   Fission, because fusion requires a large input of energy in order to occur.

Go On

36 Charles Darwin travelled extensively, collected a great deal of evidence and made many observations as he conceived of and refined his theory of evolution. Which of the following played NO role in the development of this theory? SB5a

A   Galapagos finches

B   circadian rhythms

C   fossil evidence

D   the ideas of other scientists

37 Francisco was heating soup in a metal pan on the stove. He noticed that the soup was about to boil over. He quickly grabbed the handle of the pan to remove it from the heat. Just as quickly, he let go of the pan because he burned his hand. What kind of heat transfer occurred through the metal handle of the pan? SPS7b

A   radiation

B   convection

C   conduction

D   chemical transfer

Go On

Study the following food chain & answer question 38.

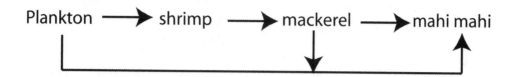

Plankton → shrimp → mackerel → mahi mahi

38 The mahi mahi (*Coryphaena hippurus*) is not a dolphin, but is sometimes called the dolphin fish. It has become a popular addition to many restaurant menus in recent years, largely due to the over-fishing of traditionally popular varieties of fish. What is the most likely result of the increase in mahi mahi fishing over the past decade? SB4b

A An increase in plankton population.

B An increase in plankton and mackerel populations.

C An decrease in mackerel and plankton populations.

D A decrease in mackerel, shrimp and plankton populations.

39 Which of the following statements is true concerning solubility? SPS6b, c

A Increased air pressure increases the solubility of solids and liquids.

B The more surface area of a solid solute that is exposed to a solvent, the less readily the solute will dissolve.

C Decreased air pressure increases the solubility of a gas.

D Increased temperature of a solvent increases the solubility of liquids and solids.

40 Noble gases are nonmetallic elements that do not readily react with other elements. What accounts for this non-reactivity? SPS4a, SPS4b

A Noble gases have an even number of protons and electrons.

B Noble gases have an even number of protons and neutrons.

C Noble gases have a full valence shell.

D Noble gases have an atomic number of eight.

41 Which chemical formula represents the compound silicon dioxide? SPS2c

A SiO_3

B SO_2

C SiO_2

D $2SiO$

42 When a machine is involved in doing work, a reduction in the effort force is generally accompanied by SPS8e

A a decrease in height.

B a decrease in the distance covered by the effort.

C an increase in the distance covered by the effort.

D no change in the distance.

Go On

43 Which of the following molecules features the MOST non- polar covalent bonding?   SPS1b

C_2H_6 $KMnO_4$ H_2SO_4 C_2H_3OH

- A C_2H_6
- B $KMnO_4$
- C H_2SO_4
- D C_2H_3OH

44 Solution G has a salt concentration of 2.36 g/mL and it is placed in one side of a U-shaped tube. Solution H has a salt concentration of 0.236 g/mL and is placed on the other side of the U-shaped tube. The semi-permeable membrane separating the two solutions will not allow passage of a solute. Predict the outcome of this experiment.   SB1a

- A   Water will not move through the membrane because both sides contain salt.
- B   Water will move through the membrane from solution H to solution G.
- C   Water will move through the membrane form solution G to solution H.
- D   Solute will accumulate at the membrane barrier and clog the passage of solvent.

45 Consider the line graph below. X, Y and Z each represent a different solute, and the curves represent solubility of the solute in water.   SPS6a

Which of the following statements is most likely to be correct?

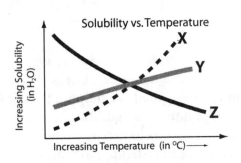

- A   X, Y and Z are gases
- B   X and Y are gases; Z is a solid
- C   X, Y and Z are solids
- D   X and Y are solids; Z is a gas

46 Opponents of genetic engineering argue that there is no way to accurately predict the consequences of crop alterations to the local habitat. Which of the following is a possible negative outcome of genetic modification (GM)?   SB2f

- A   Generally modified plants may cross-pollinate with unforeseen consequences.
- B   Weed-resistant plants may modify to attack other local crops.
- C   GM plants may cross-pollinate with similar plants and kill them.
- D   GM plants require more resources that non-GM plants to thrive.

Go On

47 Which of the following reactions is most likely to occur spontaneously? SPS2b

A $\quad F^{1-} + Cl^{1-} \longrightarrow FCl^{2-}$

B $\quad Ar_2 + Cl_2 \longrightarrow 2ArCl$

C $\quad K^{1+} + Cl^{1-} \longrightarrow KCl$

D $\quad Ne + Ar \longrightarrow NeAr$

48 Cephalosporins are a class of antibiotics that kill many different types of bacteria. These medications were used to treat bacterial infections during the late 1900s. Cephalosporin drugs were administered to many patients and used almost indiscriminately over many years. Soon, the development of second, third and forth generation cephalosporin drugs became necessary. Why do you suppose these drugs were developed? SB5e

A Bacteria developed resistance to the first generation cephalosporin drugs.

B The first generation Cephalosporins mutated into viruses.

C The first generation cephalosporin drugs never worked.

D Bacteria discovered how to use Cephalosporins as a food source.

49 In the experiment shown in the diagram below, a student is to record how much time elapses from the time the Bunsen burner is lit until the wax on the end of each rod begins to melt. Which of the following would be the best title for a laboratory report describing this experiment? SPS7b, c

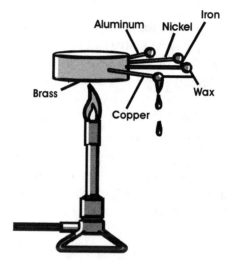

A Rate of Radiation of a Candle Flame

B Generation of Electric Currents in Various Metals

C Rate of Thermal Conduction in Various Metals

D Determining Specific Heat in Wax

50 Iron has a specific heat of 450 J/kg°C. How much heat is needed to raise the temperature of 10 grams of iron from 50°C to 250°C? SPS7c

A 1125

B 900

C 225

D 90000

Go On

51 Which of the following has the highest concentration of hydornium? SPS6d

A deuterium

B a strong acid

C a strong base

D ammonia

52 Which of the following types of energy is NOT transferred by the Sun to Earth? SPS3a, 9b

A infrared radiation

B gamma radiation

C beta radiation

D ultraviolet radiation

53 A non–water soluble molecule makes up a majority of the cell membrane. This molecule forms a double layer to regulate substances that flow into and out of the cell. This molecule is a SB1c

A lipid.

B carbohydrate.

C nucleic acid.

D protein.

54 When liquids of different densities are mixed together, they will sometimes separate and form layers. Based on the phases indicated below, what can you correctly infer about the density of these liquids? SPS2a

 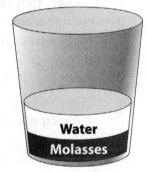

A Water is less dense than corn oil.

B Water is more dense than molasses.

C Corn oil is less dense than molasses.

D Corn syrup is more dense than molasses.

Go On

55 Ostriches and gazelles feed next to each other. They both watch for predators and alert each other to danger. The visual abilities of the two species are different, so that together they can identify threats that the individual animal would not readily see. What symbiotic relationship does this illustrate?   SB4f

   A   commensalism

   B   mutualism

   C   predation

   D   parasitism

56 The speed of an object increases 12 m/s over 3 seconds. What is its acceleration?   SPS8a

   A 9 m/s^2

   B 4 m/s^2

   C 3 m/s^2

   D 36 m/s^2

57 The atomic number for radon is 86, and the atomic mass is 222. How many neutrons does radon have?   SPS1a

   A   43

   B   86

   C   308

   D   136

58 An ion drive is a type of propulsion system commonly used by satellites in orbit to move around. Solar panels are used to capture radiant energy. This is transformed to a stream of electrons that are used to ionize a chamber of some noble gas, such as xenon or argon. The ionized gas is then accelerated by passing it through a series of charged grids. This acceleration produces a thrust when the gas is released from the rear engine chamber. The thrust pushes the satellite forward.   SPS7a

Trace the transformations of energy described in the passage.

   A   electromagnetic, electrical, mechanical

   B   electromagnetic, chemical

   C   electrical, thermal

   D   electrical, chemical

59 Identify the correct description of a saturated solution.   SPS6a

   A   a solution of an ionic solid in an ionic liquid

   B   a solution that is composed of multiple solutes and solvents

   C   a solid solution made by cooling a hot mixture of two liquid metals

   D   a solution in which no more solute can dissolve at the given temperature

Go On

60 Squirrels are an arboreal rodent found in most of the eastern United States. Natural predators of the squirrel include: hawks, eagles, owls, snakes and foxes. When a squirrel encounters any perceived threat, its instinct is to flee in an erratic way. The squirrel zigs and zags in several directions attempting to elude its pursuers. However, when a squirrel encounters a motor vehicle, its natural escape method often results in the death of the squirrel. If a squirrel population resided in a mostly urban area, with few natural predators, what do you think would most likely happen to the erratic escape trait after many generations?   SB5d

- **A** It would become less pronounced.
- **B** It would become more pronounced.
- **C** It would not change at all.
- **D** It would appear in field mice.

61 Which of the following BEST describes how a virus differs from a bacteria cell?   SB3d

- **A** A bacteria cell has no DNA, but a virus does.
- **B** A virus cell cannot metabolize food or reproduce without a host, so it is not alive.
- **C** A bacteria cell cannot metabolize food or reproduce without a host, so it is not alive.
- **D** A virus contains only RNA, whereas a bacteria cell contains DNA.

62 Within the human population, humans vary greatly in height. The height of a person cannot be directly related to any one other trait, and is not attributable to any one gene. What is the most likely inheritance pattern for height in humans?   SB2b, SB2c

- **A** co-dominant
- **B** polygenic trait
- **C** sex-linked
- **D** incomplete dominance

63 In the following concept map, some items are missing. Which of the following is an item that could appear as a non-metal?   SPS4a

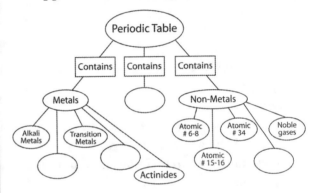

- **A** alkali earth metals
- **B** metalloids
- **C** halogens
- **D** lanthanides

Go On

64 Jill places a message in a bottle and drops it off the side of a mountain, into the ocean. When does the bottle have the greatest kinetic energy? *SPS8b*

- **A** when Jill holds the bottle in her hand, just before dropping it
- **B** just after Jill releases the bottle
- **C** just before the bottle hits the surface of the water
- **D** when it is floating on the water

65 Which of the following makes use of an electromagnetic wave? *SPS9c*

- **A** A seismograph detects the seismic waves caused by an earthquake.
- **B** A doctor uses ultrasound technology to see a developing fetus in a mother's womb.
- **C** An electric motor creates waves of water for the wave pool in a water park.
- **D** A family uses its microwave oven to pop popcorn.

66 Ammonia gas (NH_3) will burn in the presence of oxygen (O_2) to form nitrogen gas (N_2) and water (H_2O). Which of the following represents a balanced chemical equation for this reaction? *SPS2e*

- **A** $2NH_3 + O_2 \rightarrow 2N_2 + H_2O$
- **B** $4NH_3 + 3O_2 \rightarrow 2N_2 + 6H_2O$
- **C** $2NH_3 + O_2 \rightarrow N_2 + 2H_2O$
- **D** $2NH + 2H_2 + 2O_2 + O \rightarrow N_2 + 3H_2O$

67 When recovering from injury, blood platelets that cover the wound are slowly replaced by newly-formed skin cells. Old skin cells, with 46 chromosomes, divide to form new skin cells with 46 chromosomes. This is classified as what sort of reproductive process? *SB2e*

- **A** sexual
- **B** asexual
- **C** gestation
- **D** binary fission

68 A bird in the rain forest grows to sexual maturity. During his first mating season, he builds an elaborate nest with sticks and leaves. Then he performs an elaborate dance complete with specific calls and whistles. These behaviors are considered to be *SB4f*

- **A** learned behavior.
- **B** innate behavior.
- **C** diurnal behavior.
- **D** nocturnal behavior.

Go On

69 Two atoms of hydrogen may bond to form a   SPS1a, SPS1b

    A polar bonded molecule.

    B non-polar covalent molecule.

    C polar covalent compound.

    D non-polar ionic compound.

70 When a neutral metal sphere is charged by contact with a positively charged glass rod, the sphere   SPS10b

    A loses electrons.

    B loses protons.

    C gains electrons.

    D gains protons.

71 An environment has cold harsh winters with temperatures often far below freezing and cool summers with temperatures just above 45°F. This environment receives a moderate amount of precipitation. Which type of plant would most likely live in this environment?   SB4a

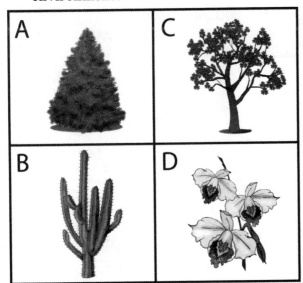

72 Why is the weight of an object less on the Moon than it is on the Earth?   SPS8d

    A The force of gravity is less on the Moon than on the Earth.

    B An object has less mass on the Moon than it does on the Earth.

    C The magnetic force of the Moon is less than the magnetic force on the Earth.

    D The force of gravity is less on the Earth than on the Moon.

Go On

Refer to the following passage and diagram (not to scale) to answer question 73.

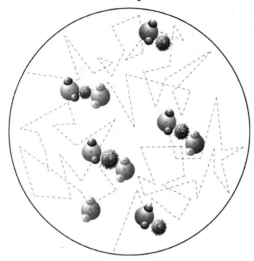

Robert Brown was an English botanist who studied pollen grains. In 1827, he made a remarkable discovery. While examining century old pollen grains suspended in water under the microscope, he noticed that the pollen seemed to move in a random fashion. He called this movement Brownian motion. This motion occurs because the pollen grains are assailed on all sides by the water molecules. As a result, the random motion of the water molecules is seen through the motion of the pollen grains. Einstein later described this motion in a mathematical model. Scientists now realize that all atoms, in all substances, exhibit this type of motion.

73 What would happen to the motion of the pollen grains if the water and pollen grain mixture were heated to a higher temperature?   SPS5a

   A   The motion would decrease.

   B   The motion would remain unchanged.

   C   The motion would increase.

   D   none of the above

74 Plants must use oxygen in the process of respiration. Based on this information, which of the following is a valid conclusion?   SB3a

   A   Plants are likely incapable of anaerobic respiration.

   B   Plants only engage in anaerobic respiration.

   C   Plants must use a synthetic respiration process.

   D   Plants do not respire, only animals.

Go On

75 The angle of the stirring rod in the beaker appears to change at the surface of the water. This phenomenon is explained by which property of light? `SPS9d`

   A scattering

   B diffraction

   C reflection

   D refraction

76 The process by which those organisms most suited for their environment survive and reproduce is known as `SB5d`

   A natural selection.

   B nondisjunction.

   C punctuated equilibrium.

   D classification.

77 Deuterium (^{2}H) is a common product of the fusion process. Which of the following could undergo fusion to become deuterium? `SPS3b`

   A uranium

   B helium and hydrogen

   C hydrogen and hydrogen

   D hydrogen and a neutron

78 In aspen trees, the allele for having round leaves (R) is dominant to the allele for having oval leaves (r). Use the Punnett square to determine the probability of parent trees of the following genotype having offspring with round leaves. `SB2c`

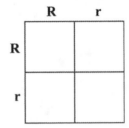

   A 75%

   B 25%

   C 50%

   D 0%

79 Sound waves cause molecules to vibrate and bump into one another. For sound to travel, there must be molecules which can be made to vibrate. The closer together the molecules are, the faster the sound is able to travel. This explains why `SPS9e`

   A sound travels faster in steel than in water.

   B sound travels faster in outer space than in air.

   C sound travels faster in air than in water.

   D sound travels faster in water than in steel.

80 Which of the following is NOT a heterotroph? `SB4a`

   A plants

   B animals

   C fungi

   D many bacteria

Go On

A

absorption 24, 280
acceleration 235, 236, 240, 241, 247
  gravity 247
acid 48, 216
  strong, weak 216
activation energy 47, 227
active transport 33
adaptation 23, 24, 101, 112
adenine 57, 58
adenosine triphosphate, ATP 46
aerobic respiration 51
alcoholic fermentation 52
algae 95
alkali metal 174, 176
alkaline 217
alkaline earth metal 174, 177
allele 75, 78
alpha particle 155
alternating current (AC) 271
amino acid monomer 42
ampere 262
amplitude 278, 284, 286
anaerobic respiration 51
anaphase 63
animal cell 26
anion 185
antibiotic 95
anticodon 59
aquatic 123
archaebacteria 92
Arrhenius theory 217
asexual reproduction 24, 63
atom 180
atomic mass 171
autotroph 94, 95
average rate 233

B

bacteria 26
bar magnet 268
base 48, 217
batteries 263
behavior 112
benthic zone 124
beta particle 155
Bethe, Hans 157
binary compound 184
binomial nomenclature 93
biodiversity 101
biome 121
  types of 122
biomolecule 39
biosphere 126
biotechnology 83
birth rate 132, 133
Bohr, Neils 161
boiling point 203
bond strength 45
bonding 174
bonds, covalent 45
bottlenecking 110
Bronsted-Lowry theory 217

C

Calvin cycle 50
carbohydrates 40
carbon 39
carbon cycle 140
carbon fixation reaction 51
carnivore 136, 137
carrier 80
catalyst 47, 227
cation 176, 185
cell 23, 24, 26
  animal, parts of 27
  cycle 62
  differentiation 67
  division 62, 63
  parts of 28
  plant, parts of 27
  reproductive 62
  somatic 62, 63
cell membrane 27, 28, 30
cell wall 27, 28
cellular biomolecule
  classes of 39
cellular respiration 28, 46, 53
centriole 27, 28, 63
centromere 63
chain reaction 162
chemical bond 45
chemical change 190
chemical equation 187
chemical formulas 183
chemical properties 190
chemical reaction 174, 187
chemotroph 94
Chernobyl 162
chlorophyll 50, 282
chloroplast 28, 50, 95
chromatin 62
chromosome 62, 64, 76
  types of 80
cilia 27, 28
circadian rhythm 113
circuit 263, 265
  diagram 264
  parallel 265
  series 263
  switch 264
citric acid cycle 51
class 91
classical conditioning 117
classification
  types of 93
cloning 85
clumped distribution 132
co-dominant 81
codon
  types of 59
coenzyme 47
cofactor 47
combustion 191
commensalism 129
compass 268
competition 108
  types of 129

compound 180, 181, 183, 198
compressible 207
compression waves 286
condensation point 203
conduction 226, 262
conductor 260
coniferous forest biome 122
consumer 48, 136
   types of 137, 138
control rod 161, 162
convection 226
corrosion 191
coulomb 262
Coulomb's law 259
covalent bond 39, 45, 180
covalent solids 208
critical point 203
crossing over process 64
cross-pollinate 76, 110
current (I) 262
cytokinesis 63
cytoplasm 28, 30
cytosine 57, 58

D

dalton 171
Darwin, Charles 104, 105
daughter (isotope) 160
daughter cell 63
death rate 132, 133
decay chain 160
deceleration 235
decibel 286
deciduous forest biome 123
decomposer 137, 141
deletion mutation 70
density 132, 202, 206
density-dependent factor 134
density-independent factor 134
deoxyribose 57
deposition 203
deserts 123
diffraction 280, 283
  light 283
diffusion 31
digestion 24
dihybrid cross 78
diploid 62, 63, 96
direct current (DC) 271
disaccharide 40
displacement 231
distance 231, 235, 236, 247
distortion 284
distribution
  types of 132
diurnal 116
diversity of life 69
DNA 43, 46, 57, 75, 105
DNA fingerprinting 83
dominance, principle of 77
dominant gene 75
Doppler effect 286
dormant 116

ductile 209

E

ecological balance 130
ecological succession 134
ecosystem 121, 126, 134, 136
  abiotic factors 126
  biotic factors 126
  types of 124
Einstein, Albert 161
electric field line 260
electric force 259
electrical conductivity 202
electromagnetic force 247, 271
electromagnetic induction 271
electromagnetic spectrum 288
electromagnetic waves 276, 288
electron 167, 180
electron configuration 168
electron transport 51
electronegativity 176
electrophoresis 84
electrostatic attraction 183
element 171, 198
  in living cells 39
embryo 67
embryonic development 102
emigration 132
endocytosis 34
endoplasmic reticulum 27, 28
endoskeleton 97
endothermic 191, 227
energy 24, 26, 28, 202
  kinds of 221
energy conversion 46
energy flow 136
energy pyramid, 138
environmental contamination 162
enzyme 45, 47, 58
equator 123
estivate 116
estuary 123, 124
ethology 115
eubacteria 92
eukaryote 92, 26
even distribution 132
evolution 101, 104
  evidence of 107
evolutionary relationship 101
excretion 24
exocytosis 33
exothermic 191, 226
exponential growth 132
extinction 101
extrinsic 206

F

facilitated diffusion 31
family 91
fermentation 52
Fermi, Enrico 157
fertilization 67

nuclear force 248
nucleic acid
    characteristics of 43
nucleolus 27, 28
nucleon 248
nucleotide 43
nucleus 26, 27, 28
nutrient cycle 140
nutrition 24

O

ohm 262, 263
Ohm's Law 263
oligosaccaride 40
omnivore 136, 137
operant conditioning 117
orbital 168
order 91
organelles 26
organic molecule 39, 140
organism 24
    characteristics of 23
Origin of Species 105, 108
osmosis 31, 32
oxygen 39

P

paramecium 27
parental generation 77
passive transport 31
pelagic zone 124
period (T) 277
Periodic Table 171, 190
pesticide 149
pH 48
phase changes 203
phase diagram 203
phases 202
phenotype 75, 76
phosphate group 57
phospholipid bilayer 30
phosphorous 39
phosphorous cycle 140, 142
photoperiodism 113
photosynthesis 24, 28, 50, 53, 123
phototropism 112
phylogeny 104
phylum 91, 97
physical adaptations 114
physical change 190
physical properties 206
pigment 50
pitch 286
plant cell 26
plasma 202, 207
plasmolysis 33
plastid 27, 28, 50
polar molecular solids 209
pollinate 76
polygenic traits 81
polypeptide 42
polysaccharide 40

population 127, 132
precipitate 143, 191
predation 130
prey 130
primary consumer 138
primary succession 134
producer 136
product 187
prokaryote 92, 26
propagate 275
properties of matter 206
prophase 63
protein 28
    types of 42
protein synthesis. 58
proton 167
protozoa 95
pulley 254
Punnett square 75, 80

Q

quantum mechanics 245

R

radiation 226, 228
radio waves 289
radioactive 155
radioactive decay 156
radioactive isotope 155
random distribution 132
rate 231
ray 280
    types of 281
reactant 187
reasoning or insight 117
recessive gene 75
recombinant DNA 84
reflection 280
reflection, law of 281
refraction 280, 281
    angle of 282
    index of 282
relativistic mechanics 245
released factor 60
replication 62
reproduction 23, 24
    types of 24
reproductive cell 62, 70
resistance 262
resistor 264
resource 129, 134
respiration 24
response 23, 24
ribose 40, 58
ribosome 28
RNA 43, 58
    types of 58, 59
rolling friction 240
Roy G Biv 289
rRNA 58, 59